D1095012

6.00

A First Course
in
CALCULUS

This book is in the

ADDISON-WESLEY SERIES IN MATHEMATICS

LYNN H. LOOMIS
Consulting Editor

A First Course
in
CALCULUS

SERGE LANG

Columbia University, New York, New York

Second Edition

ADDISON-WESLEY PUBLISHING COMPANY

Reading, Massachusetts · Menlo Park, California · London · Don Mills, Ontario

Second Printing—June 1969

Foreword

The purpose of a first course in Calculus is to teach the student the basic notions of derivative and integral, and the basic techniques and applications which accompany them.

At present in the United States, this material is covered during the first year of college. In fact, the material should be taught to students who are approximately fifteen years of age, and belongs properly in the secondary schools. (I have talked with several students of that age, and find them perfectly able to understand what it is all about.)

Irrespective of when it is taught, I believe that the presentation remains more or less invariant. The very talented student, with an obvious aptitude for mathematics, will rapidly require a course in functions of one real variable, more or less as it is understood by professional mathematicians. This book is not primarily addressed to him (although I hope he will be able to acquire from it a good introduction at an early age).

I have not written this course in the style I would use for an advanced monograph, on sophisticated topics. One writes an advanced monograph for oneself, because one wants to give permanent form to one's vision of some beautiful part of mathematics, not otherwise accessible, somewhat in the manner of a composer setting down his symphony in musical notation.

This book is written for the student, to give him an immediate, and pleasant, access to the subject. I hope that I have struck a proper compromise between dwelling too much on special details, and not giving enough technical exercises, necessary to acquire the desired familiarity with the subject. In any case, certain routine habits of sophisticated mathematicians are unsuitable for a first course.

This does not mean that so-called rigor has to be abandoned. The logical development of the mathematics of this course from the most basic axioms proceeds through the following stages:

> Set theory
> Integers (whole numbers)
> Rational numbers (fractions)
> Numbers (i.e. real numbers)
> Limits
> Derivatives
> and forward.

No one in his right mind suggests that one should begin a course with set theory. It happens that the most satisfactory place to jump into the subject is between limits and derivatives. In other words, any student is ready to accept as intuitively obvious the notions of numbers and limits and their basic properties. For some reason, it has become fashionable to hold that the best place to enter the subject is between numbers and limits. Experience shows that the students do *not* have the proper psychological background to accept this, and resist it tremendously.

In fact, it turns out that one can have the best of both ideas. The arguments which show how the properties of limits can be reduced to those of numbers form a self-contained whole. Logically, it belongs *before* the subject matter of our course. Nevertheless, we have inserted it as an appendix. If any student feels the need for it, he need but read it and visualize it as Chapter 0. In that case, everything that follows is as rigorous as any mathematician would wish it (so far as objects which receive an analytic definition are concerned). Not one word need be changed in any proof. I hope this takes care once and for all of possible controversies concerning so-called rigor.

Some objects receive a geometric definition, and there are applications to physical concepts. In that case, it is of course necessary to insert one step to bridge the physical notion and its mathematical counterpart. The major instances of this are the functions sine and cosine, and the area, as an integral.

For sine and cosine, we rely on the notions of plane geometry. If one accepts standard theorems concerning plane figures then our proofs satisfy the above-mentioned standards. An appendix shows how one can give purely analytic definitions and proofs for the basic properties.

For the integral, we first give a geometric argument. We then show, using the usual Riemann sums, how this geometric argument has a perfect counterpart when we require the rules of the game to reduce all definitions and proofs to numbers. This should satisfy everybody. Furthermore, the theory of the integral is so presented that only its existence depends either on a geometric argument or a slightly involved theoretical investigation (upper and lower sums). According to the level of ability of a class, the teacher may therefore dose the theory according to his judgement.

It is not generally recognized that some of the major difficulties in teaching mathematics are analogous to those in teaching a foreign language. (The secondary schools are responsible for this. Proper training in the secondary schools could entirely eliminate this difficulty.) Consequently, I have made great efforts to carry the student verbally, so to say, in using proper mathematical language. Some proofs are omitted. For instance, they would be of the following type. In the theory of maxima and minima, or increasing and decreasing functions, we carry out in full just one of the cases. The other is left as an exercise. The changes needed in the proof are slight, amounting mainly to the insertion of an occasional minus sign, but they force the student to understand the situation and train him in writing clearly. This is very valuable. Aside from that, such an omission allows the teacher to put greater emphasis on certain topics, if necessary, by carrying out the other proof himself. As in learning languages, repetition is one of the fundamental tools, and a certain amount of mechanical learning, as distinguished from logical thinking, is both healthy and necessary.

I have made no great innovations in the exposition of calculus. Since the subject was discovered some 300 years ago, it was out of the question. Rather, I have omitted some specialized topics which no longer belong in the curriculum. Stirling's formula is included only for reference, and can be skipped, or used to provide exercises. Taylor's formula is proved with the integral form of the remainder, which is then properly estimated. The proof with integration by parts is more natural than the other (differentiating some complicated expression pulled out of nowhere), and is the one which generalizes to the higher dimensional case. I have placed integration after differentiation, because otherwise one has no technique available to evaluate integrals. But on the whole, everything is fairly standard.

I have cut down the amount of analytic geometry to what is both necessary and sufficient for a general first course in this type of mathematics. For some applications, more is required, but these applications are fairly specialized. For instance, if one needs the special properties concerning the focus of a parabola in a course on optics, then that is the place to present them, not in a general course which is to serve mathematicians, physicists, chemists, biologists, and engineers, to mention but a few. I regard the tremendous emphasis on the analytic geometry of conics which has been the fashion for many years as an unfortunate historical accident. What is important is that the basic idea of representing a graph by a figure in the plane should be thoroughly understood, together with basic examples. The more abstruse properties of ellipses, parabolas, and hyperbolas should be skipped.

One other word—of a quite different nature. I disliked calculus and analysis when I was a student. I would have disliked the book I am writing now. It was only later in my life as a mathematician, that I began to appreciate the beauty of calculus. But I found out in the meantime that calculus and analysis are overemphasized at the expense of algebra, mostly through historical accidents. In fact, it is clear that elementary algebra courses (covering groups and vector spaces) should be available much earlier than they are. There are strong indications from physics, biology, and economics that they should receive greater attention at an elementary level than they have up to now. Since algebra is logically independent of calculus (at the early levels), has important applications, and to some minds, has a much greater appeal than calculus (it was like this for me) I would hope that the unbalance of the present programs will soon be changed. There is no reason why a student should be forced to take calculus before he takes an algebra course. This is particularly true at the moment for the more talented students.

An excess in this direction would be as disturbing as in the other. There is no point in replacing old specialized topics by new ones, and the attempts to replace old outdated and musty subjects by new outdated and musty subjects (like boolean algebra) are not to be recommended.

As for the question: Why write one more calculus book? I would answer: Because practically all existing ones are too long (500 to 600 pages) and one loses sight of the over-all ideas, sacrificed for the sake of topics which have hung on through habits, bad habits, I would say. I hope that the present arrangement of the chapters will give the reader a solid view of the subject.

To conclude, if I may be allowed another personal note here, I learned how to teach the present course from Artin, the year I wrote my Doctor's thesis. I could not have had a better introduction to the subject.

SERGE LANG
New York, 1963

To the Second Edition

I have transferred the section on complex numbers from the Second Course to this volume, and added a discussion of convexity and its relation to the second derivative. I have added many new exercises and examples because of complaints concerning the lack of them in the first edition. I have also rewritten a few passages to make them clearer, following public requests.

SERGE LANG
New York, 1968

Contents

CHAPTER X

Properties of the Integral

CHAPTER XI

Techniques of Integration

CHAPTER XII

Some Substantial Exercises

CHAPTER XIII

Applications of Integration

CHAPTER XIV

Taylor's Formula

Chapter XV

Series

Chapter XVI

Complex Numbers

Chapter I

Numbers and Functions

In starting the study of any sort of mathematics, we cannot prove everything. Every time that we introduce a new concept, we must define it in terms of a concept whose meaning is already known to us, and it is impossible to keep going backwards defining forever. Thus we must choose our starting place, what we assume to be known, and what we are willing to explain and prove in terms of these assumptions.

At the beginning of this chapter, we shall describe most of the things which we assume known for this course. Actually, this involves very little. Roughly speaking, we assume that you know about numbers, addition, subtraction, multiplication, and division (by numbers other than 0). We shall recall the properties of inequalities (when a number is greater than another). On a few occasions we shall take for granted certain properties of numbers which might not have occurred to you before and which will always be made precise. Proofs of these properties will be supplied in the appendix for those of you who are interested.

§1. INTEGERS, RATIONAL NUMBERS, AND REAL NUMBERS

The most common numbers are the numbers 1, 2, 3, ... which are called *positive integers*.

The numbers $-1, -2, -3, -4, \ldots$ are called *negative integers*. When we want to speak of the positive integers together with the negative integers and 0, we call them simply *integers*. Thus the integers are 0, 1, $-1, 2, -2, 3, -3, \ldots$.

The sum and product of two integers are again integers.

In addition to the integers we have *fractions*, like $\frac{3}{4}, \frac{5}{7}, -\frac{1}{8}, -\frac{101}{27}, \frac{8}{16}, \ldots$, which may be positive or negative, and which can be written as quotients m/n, where m, n are integers and n is not equal to 0. Such fractions are called *rational numbers*. Every integer m is a rational number, because it can be written as $m/1$, but of course it is not true that every rational number is an integer. We observe that the sum and product of two rational numbers are again rational numbers. If a/b and m/n are two rational numbers (a, b, m, n being integers and b, n unequal to 0), then their sum and product are given by the following formulas, which

1

you know from elementary school:

$$\frac{a}{b}\,\frac{m}{n} = \frac{am}{bn},$$

$$\frac{a}{b} + \frac{m}{n} = \frac{an + bm}{bn}.$$

In this second formula, we have simply put the two fractions over the common denominator bn.

We can represent the integers and rational numbers geometrically on a straight line. We first select a unit length. The integers are multiples of this unit, and the rational numbers are fractional parts of this unit. We have drawn a few rational numbers on the line below.

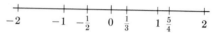

Observe that the negative integers and rational numbers occur to the left of zero.

Finally, we have the numbers which can be represented by infinite decimals, like $\sqrt{2} = 1.414...$ or $\pi = 3.14159...$, and which will be called *real numbers* or simply *numbers*.

Geometrically, the numbers are represented as the collection of all points on the above straight line, not only those which are a rational part of the unit length or a multiple of it.

We note that the sum and product of two numbers are numbers. If a is a number unequal to zero, then there is a unique number b such that $ab = ba = 1$, and we write

$$b = \frac{1}{a} \qquad \text{or} \qquad b = a^{-1}.$$

We say that b is the *inverse* of a, or "a inverse". We emphasize that the expression

$1/0$ or 0^{-1} is not defined.

In other words, we cannot divide by zero, and we do not attribute any meaning to the symbols $1/0$ or 0^{-1}.

However, if a is a number then the product $0 \cdot a$ is defined and is equal to 0. The product of any number and 0 is 0. Furthermore, if b is any number unequal to 0, then $0/b$ is defined and equal to 0. It can also be written $0 \cdot (1/b)$.

If a is a rational number $\neq 0$, then $1/a$ is also a rational number. Indeed, if we can write $a = m/n$, with integers m, n both different from 0, then

$$\frac{1}{a} = \frac{n}{m}$$

is also a rational number.

Not all numbers are rational numbers. *For instance, $\sqrt{2}$ is not a rational number*, and we shall now prove this fact.

We recall that the *even numbers* are the integers $\pm 2, \pm 4, \pm 6, \pm 8, \ldots$, which can be written in the form $2n$ for some integer n. An *odd* number is an integer like $\pm 1, \pm 3, \pm 5, \pm 7, \ldots$, which can be written in the form $2n + 1$ for some integer n. Thus $6 = 2 \cdot 3$ is even (we select $n = 3$) and

$$11 = 2 \cdot 5 + 1$$

is odd (we select $n = 5$).

We observe that the square of an even number is even. Indeed, if n is an integer and $2n$ is an even number, then

$$(2n)^2 = 4n^2$$

is an even number, which can be written $2(2n^2)$, the product of 2 and the integer $2n^2$.

The square of an odd number is odd. To prove this, let $2n + 1$ be an odd number (n being an integer). Then its square is

$$(2n + 1)^2 = 4n^2 + 4n + 1$$
$$= 2(2n^2 + 2n) + 1.$$

Since $2n^2 + 2n$ is an integer, we have written the square of our odd number in the form $2m + 1$ for some integer m, and thus have shown that our square is odd.

We are now ready to prove that the square root of 2 is not a rational number. Suppose it were. This would mean that we can find a rational number a such that $a^2 = 2$. We can write

$$a = \frac{m}{n},$$

where m, n are integers, and neither m nor n is 0. Furthermore, we can assume that not both m, n are even because we can put the fraction m/n in lowest form and cancel as many powers of 2 dividing both m and n as possible. Thus we can assume that at least one of the integers m or n is odd.

From our assumption that $a^2 = 2$ we get $(m/n)^2 = 2$ or

$$\frac{m^2}{n^2} = 2.$$

Multiplying both sides of this equation by n^2 yields

$$m^2 = 2n^2$$

and the right-hand side is even. By what we saw above, this means that m is even and we can therefore write $m = 2k$ for some integer k. Substituting, we obtain

$$(2k)^2 = 2n^2$$

or $4k^2 = 2n^2$. We cancel 2 and get $2k^2 = n^2$. This means that n^2 is even, and consequently, by what we saw above, that n is even. Thus we have reached the conclusion that both m, n are even, which contradicts the fact that we put our fraction in lowest form. We can therefore conclude that there was no fraction m/n whose square is 2.

It is usually very difficult to determine whether a given number is a rational number or not. For instance, the fact that π is not rational was discovered only at the end of the 18th century.

§2. INEQUALITIES

Aside from addition, multiplication, subtraction and division (by numbers other than 0), we shall now discuss another important feature of the real numbers.

We have the *positive numbers*, represented geometrically on the straight line by those numbers unequal to 0 and lying to the right of 0. If a is a positive number, we write $a > 0$. You have no doubt already worked with positive numbers, and with inequalities. The next two properties are the most basic ones, concerning positivity.

POS 1. *If a, b are positive, so is the product ab and the sum $a + b$.*

POS 2. *If a is a number, then either a is positive, or $a = 0$, or $-a$ is positive, and these possibilities are mutually exclusive.*

If a number is not positive and not 0, then we say that this number is *negative*. By POS 2, if a is negative then $-a$ is positive.

Although you know already that the number 1 is positive, it can in fact be *proved* from our two properties. It may interest you to see the proof, which runs as follows and is very simple. By POS 2, we know that either 1 or -1 is positive. If 1 is not positive, then -1 is positive. By POS 1, it must then follow that $(-1)(-1)$ is positive. But this product is equal to 1. Consequently, it must be 1 which is positive, and not -1. Using property POS 1, we could now conclude that $1 + 1 = 2$ is positive, that $2 + 1 = 3$ is positive, and so forth.

If $a > 0$ we shall also say that a is *greater than* 0. If we wish to say that a is positive or equal to 0, we write

$$a \geqq 0$$

and read this "a greater than or equal to zero".

Given two numbers a, b we shall say that a is *greater than* b and write $a > b$ if $a - b > 0$. We write $a < 0$ if $-a > 0$ and $a < b$ if $b > a$. Thus $3 > 2$ because $3 - 2 > 0$.

We shall write $a \geqq b$ when we want to say that a is *greater than or equal to b. Thus $3 \geqq 2$ and $3 \geqq 3$ are both true inequalities.

Using only our two properties POS 1 and POS 2 we shall now prove all the usual rules concerning inequalities. You probably know these already, but proving them systematically will both sharpen your wits and etch these rules more profoundly in your mind.

In what follows, let a, b, c be numbers.

Rule 1. If $a > b$ and $b > c$ then $a > c$.

Rule 2. If $a > b$ and $c > 0$ then $ac > bc$.

Rule 3. If $a > b$ and $c < 0$ then $ac < bc$.

Rule 2 expresses the fact that an inequality which is multiplied by a positive number is *preserved*. Rule 3 tells us that if we multiply both sides of an inequality by a negative number, then the inequality gets *reversed*. For instance, we have the inequality

$$1 < 3.$$

Since $2 > 0$ we also have $2 \cdot 1 < 2 \cdot 3$. But -2 is negative, and if we multiply both sides by -2 we get

$$-2 > -6.$$

In the geometric representation of the real numbers on the line, -2 lies to the right of -6. This gives us the geometric representation of the fact that -2 is greater than -6.

To prove Rule 1, suppose that $a > b$ and $b > c$. By definition, this means that $(a - b) > 0$ and $(b - c) > 0$. Using property POS 1, we conclude that

$$a - b + b - c > 0,$$

and canceling b gives us $(a - c) > 0$. By definition, this means $a > c$, as was to be shown.

To prove Rule 2, suppose that $a > b$ and $c > 0$. By definition,

$$a - b > 0.$$

Hence using the property of POS 1 concerning the product of positive numbers, we conclude that

$$(a - b)c > 0.$$

The left-hand side of this inequality is none other than $ac - bc$, which is therefore > 0. Again by definition, this gives us

$$ac > bc.$$

We leave the proof of Rule 3 as an exercise.

If a is a number, then we define the *absolute value* of a to be:

a itself if a is ≥ 0.

$-a$ if a is < 0.

In the second case, when a is negative, then $-a$ is positive. Thus the absolute value of a number is always a positive number, or 0. For instance, the absolute value of 3 is 3 itself. The absolute value of -3 is $-(-3) = 3$. The absolute value of $-\frac{1}{2}$ is $\frac{1}{2}$. The absolute value of $\sqrt{2}$ is $\sqrt{2}$ and the absolute value of $-\sqrt{2}$ is $\sqrt{2}$. We shall denote the absolute value of a number by two bars beside the number. Thus the absolute value of a number a is written $|a|$. For instance, $|3| = 3$ and $|-3| = 3$ also. We have by definition $|0| = 0$. In general, for any number x we have

$$|x| = |-x|.$$

Let a be a number > 0. Then there exists a number whose square is a. This is one of the facts which we take for granted about numbers. If $b^2 = a$ then we observe that

$$(-b)^2 = b^2$$

is also equal to a. Thus either b or $-b$ is positive. We agree to denote by $\sqrt{a}$ the *positive* square root and call it simply *the square root of a*. Thus $\sqrt{4}$ is equal to 2 and not -2, even though $(-2)^2 = 4$. This is the most practical convention about the use of the $\sqrt{\ }$ sign that we can make. Of course, the square root of 0 is 0 itself. A negative number does *not* have a square root.

Theorem 1. *If a is a number, then $|a|^2 = a^2$ and*

$$|a| = \sqrt{a^2}.$$

Proof. If a is positive then $|a| = a$ and our first assertion is clear. If a is negative, then $|a| = -a$ and

$$(-a)^2 = a^2,$$

so we again get $|a|^2 = a^2$. When $a = 0$ our first assertion simply means $0 = 0$. Finally, taking the (positive) square root, we get

$$|a| = \sqrt{a^2}.$$

Theorem 2. *If a, b are numbers, then*

$$|ab| = |a|\,|b|.$$

Proof. We have:

$$|ab| = \sqrt{(ab)^2} = \sqrt{a^2 b^2} = \sqrt{a^2}\,\sqrt{b^2} = |a|\,|b|.$$

As an example, we see that

$$|-6| = |(-3) \cdot 2| = |-3| \, |2| = 3 \cdot 2 = 6.$$

There is one final inequality which is extremely important.

Theorem 3. *If a, b are two numbers, then*

$$|a + b| \leq |a| + |b|.$$

Proof. We first observe that either ab is positive, or it is negative, or it is 0. In any case, we have

$$ab \leq |ab| = |a| \, |b|.$$

Hence, multiplying both sides by 2, we obtain the inequality

$$2ab \leq 2|a| \, |b|.$$

From this we get

$$\begin{aligned}
(a + b)^2 &= a^2 + 2ab + b^2 \\
&\leq a^2 + 2|a| \, |b| + b^2 \\
&= (|a| + |b|)^2.
\end{aligned}$$

We can take the square root of both sides and use Theorem 1 to conclude that

$$|a + b| \leq |a| + |b|,$$

thereby proving our theorem.

You will find plenty of exercises below to give you practice with inequalities. We shall work out some numerical examples to show you the way.

Example 1. Determine the numbers satisfying the equality

$$|x + 1| = 2.$$

This equality means that either $x + 1 = 2$ or $-(x + 1) = 2$, because the absolute value of $x + 1$ is either $(x + 1)$ itself or $-(x + 1)$. In the first case, solving for x gives us $x = 1$, and in the second case, we get $-x - 1 = 2$ or $x = -3$. Thus the answer is $x = 1$ or $x = -3$.

We shall also give an example showing how to determine numbers satisfying certain inequalities. For this we need some terminology. Let a, b be numbers, and assume $a < b$.

The collection of numbers x such that $a < x < b$ is called the *open interval* between a and b, and is sometimes denoted by (a, b).

The collection of numbers x such that $a \leq x \leq b$ is called the *closed interval* between a and b, and is sometimes denoted by $[a, b]$. A single point will also be called a closed interval.

In both above cases, the numbers a, b are called the *end-points* of the intervals. Sometimes we wish to include only one of them in an interval, and so we define the collection of numbers x such that $a \leq x < b$ to be a *half-closed interval*, and similarly for those numbers x such that $a < x \leq b$.

Finally, if a is a number, we call the collection of numbers $x > a$, or $x \geq a$, or $x < a$, or $x \leq a$ an *infinite interval*. Pictures of intervals are shown below.

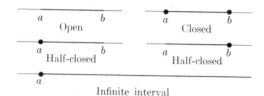

Open   Closed   Half-closed   Half-closed   Infinite interval

Example 2. Determine all intervals of numbers satisfying

$$|x| \leq 4.$$

We distinguish two cases. The first case is $x \geq 0$. Then $|x| = x$, and in this case, our inequality amounts to

$$0 \leq x \leq 4.$$

The second case is $x < 0$. In this case, $|x| = -x$, and our inequality amounts to $-x \leq 4$, or in other words, $-4 \leq x$. Thus in the second case, the numbers satisfying our inequality are precisely those in the interval

$$-4 \leq x < 0.$$

Considering now both cases together, we see that the interval of numbers satisfying our inequality $|x| \leq 4$ is the interval

$$-4 \leq x \leq 4.$$

Example 3. Determine all intervals of numbers satisfying the inequality

$$|x + 1| > 2.$$

We distinguish cases.

Case 1. $x + 1 \geq 0$. Then $|x + 1| = x + 1$, and in this case, we must find those x such that $x + 1 \geq 0$ and $x + 1 > 2$. The inequality $x + 1 > 2$ implies the inequality $x + 1 \geq 0$. Hence all x such that $x + 1 > 2$ will do, i.e. all x such that $x > 1$.

Case 2. $x + 1 < 0$. Then $|x + 1| = -(x + 1)$, and in this case we must find those numbers x such that $x + 1 < 0$ and $-x - 1 > 2$. These inequalities are equivalent with the inequalities $x < -1$ and $x < -3$.

The set of numbers x satisfying these inequalities is precisely the set of numbers x satisfying $x < -3$.

Putting our two cases together, we find that the required numbers x are those such that $x > 1$ or $x < -3$.

EXERCISES

Determine all intervals of numbers x satisfying the following inequalities.

1. $|x| < 3$
2. $|2x + 1| \leq 1$
3. $|x^2 - 2| \leq 1$
4. $|x - 5| < |x + 1|$
5. $(x + 1)(x - 2) < 0$
6. $(x - 1)(x + 1) > 0$
7. $(x - 5)(x + 5) < 0$
8. $x(x + 1) \leq 0$
9. $x^2(x - 1) \geq 0$
10. $(x - 5)^2(x + 10) \leq 0$
11. $(x - 5)^4(x + 10) \leq 0$
12. $(2x + 1)^6(x - 1) \geq 0$
13. $(4x + 7)^{20}(2x + 8) < 0$
14. $|x + 4| < 1$
15. $0 < |x + 2| < 1$
16. $|x| < 2$
17. $|x - 3| < 5$
18. $|x - 3| < 1$
19. $|x - 3| < 7$
20. Show that if x is a number and $|x| < 3$, then $-3 < x < 3$. Also prove the converse, that if x is a number satisfying this last inequality, then $|x| < 3$.
21. More generally, let a be a positive number. Show that a number x satisfies the inequality $|x| < a$ if and only if

$$-a < x < a.$$

Prove the following inequalities for all numbers x, y.

22. $|x + y| \geq |x| - |y|$ [*Hint:* Write $x = x + y - y$, and apply Theorem 3, together with the fact that $|-y| = |y|$.]
23. $|x - y| \geq |x| - |y|$
24. $|x - y| \leq |x| + |y|$
25. (a) Let a, b be positive numbers such that $a < b$. Show that $a^2 < b^2$.
    (b) If you have read the appendix on induction, prove that $a^n < b^n$ for all positive integers n.
26. Let a, b, c, d be numbers > 0, such that $a/b < c/d$. Show that

$$\frac{a}{b} < \frac{a + c}{b + d} < \frac{c}{d}.$$

27. Let a, b be numbers > 0. Show that

$$\sqrt{ab} \leq \frac{a + b}{2}.$$

§3. FUNCTIONS

A *function, defined for all numbers*, is an association which to any given number associates another number.

It is customary to denote a function by some letter, just as a letter "x" denotes a number. Thus if we denote a given function by f, and x is a number, then we denote by $f(x)$ the number associated with x by the function. This of course does not mean "f times x". There is no multiplication involved here. The symbols $f(x)$ are read "f of x". The association of the number $f(x)$ to the number x is sometimes denoted by a special arrow, namely

$$x \mapsto f(x).$$

For example, consider the function which associates to each number x the number x^2. If f denotes this function, then we have $f(x) = x^2$. In particular, the square of 2 is 4 and hence $f(2) = 4$. The square of 7 is 49 and thus $f(7) = 49$. The square of $\sqrt{2}$ is 2, and hence $f(\sqrt{2}) = 2$. The square of $(x + 1)$ is $x^2 + 2x + 1$ and thus $f(x + 1) = x^2 + 2x + 1$. If h is any number,

$$f(x + h) = x^2 + 2xh + h^2.$$

To take another example, let g be the function which to each number x associates the number $x + 1$. Then we may describe g by the symbols

$$x \mapsto x + 1$$

and write $g(x) = x + 1$. Therefore, $g(1) = 2$. Also $g(2) = 3$, $g(3) = 4$, $g(\sqrt{2}) = \sqrt{2} + 1$, and $g(x + 1) = x + 2$ for any number x.

We can view the *absolute value* as a function,

$$x \mapsto |x|$$

defined by the rule: Given any number a, we associate the number a itself if $a \geq 0$, and we associate the number $-a$ if $a < 0$. Let F denote the absolute value function. Then $F(x) = |x|$ for any number x. We have in particular $F(2) = 2$, and $F(-2) = 2$ also. The absolute value is not defined by means of a formula like x^2 or $x + 1$. We give you another example of such a function which is not defined by a formula.

We consider the function G described by the following rule:

$$G(x) = 0 \text{ if } x \text{ is a rational number.}$$

$$G(x) = 1 \text{ if } x \text{ is not a rational number.}$$

Then in particular, $G(2) = G(\tfrac{2}{3}) = G(-\tfrac{3}{4}) = 0$ but

$$G(\sqrt{2}) = 1.$$

You must be aware that you can construct a function just by prescribing arbitrarily the rule associating a number to a given one.

If f is a function and x a number, then $f(x)$ is called the *value* of the function at x. Thus if f is the function

$$x \mapsto x^2$$

the value of f at 2 is 4 and the value of f at $\frac{1}{2}$ is $\frac{1}{4}$.

In order to describe a function, we need simply to give its value at any number x. That is the reason why we use the notation $x \mapsto f(x)$. Sometimes, for brevity, we speak of a function $f(x)$, meaning by that the function f whose value at x is $f(x)$. For instance, we would say "Let $f(x)$ be the function $x^3 + 5$" instead of saying "Let f be the function which to each number x associates $x^3 + 5$". Using the special arrow $\mapsto$, we could say also "Let f be the function $x \mapsto x^3 + 5$".

We would also like to be able to define a function for some numbers and leave it undefined for others. For instance we would like to say that $\sqrt{x}$ is a function (the square root function, whose value at a number x is the square root of that number), but we observe that a negative number does not have a square root. Hence it is desirable to make the notion of function somewhat more general by stating explicitly for what numbers it is defined. For instance, the square root function is defined only for numbers ≥ 0. This function is denoted by $\sqrt{x}$. The value $\sqrt{x}$ is the unique number ≥ 0 whose square is x.

Thus in general, let S be a collection of numbers. By a *function, defined on S*, we mean an association, which to each number x in S associates a number. We call S the *domain of definition* of the function. For example, the domain of definition of the square root function is the collection of all numbers ≥ 0.

Let us give another example of a function which is not defined for all numbers. Let S be the collection of all numbers $\neq 0$. The function

$$f(x) = \frac{1}{x}$$

is defined for numbers $x \neq 0$, and is thus defined on the domain S. For this particular function, we have $f(1) = 1, f(2) = \frac{1}{2}, f(\frac{1}{2}) = 2$ and

$$f(\sqrt{2}) = \frac{1}{\sqrt{2}} .$$

One final word before we pass to the exercises: There is no magic reason why we should always use the letter x to describe a function $f(x)$. Thus instead of speaking of the function $f(x) = 1/x$ we could just as well say $f(y) = 1/y$ or $f(q) = 1/q$. Unfortunately, the most neutral way of writing would be $f(\text{blank}) = 1/\text{blank}$, and this is really not convenient.

EXERCISES

1. Let $f(x) = 1/x$. What is $f(\frac{3}{4})$, $f(-\frac{2}{3})$?

2. Let $f(x) = 1/x$ again. What is $f(2x + 1)$ (for any number x such that $x \neq -\frac{1}{2}$)?

3. Let $g(x) = |x| - x$. What is $g(1)$, $g(-1)$, $g(-54)$?

4. Let $f(y) = 2y - y^2$. What is $f(z)$, $f(w)$?

5. For what numbers could you define a function $f(x)$ by the formula

$$f(x) = \frac{1}{x^2 - 2} ?$$

What is the value of this function for $x = 5$?

6. For what numbers could you define a function $f(x)$ by the formula $f(x) = \sqrt[3]{x}$ (cube root of x)? What is $f(27)$?

7. Let $f(x) = x/|x|$, defined for $x \neq 0$. What is:

  (a) $f(1)$ (b) $f(2)$ (c) $f(-3)$ (d) $f(-\frac{4}{3})$

8. Let $f(x) = x + |x|$. What is:

  (a) $f(\frac{1}{2})$ (b) $f(2)$ (c) $f(-4)$ (d) $f(-5)$

9. Let $f(x) = 2x + x^2 - 5$. What is:

  (a) $f(1)$ (b) $f(-1)$ (c) $f(x + 1)$

10. For what numbers could you define a function $f(x)$ by the formula $f(x) = \sqrt[4]{x}$ (fourth root of x)? What is $f(16)$?

11. A function (defined for all numbers) is said to be an *even* function if $f(x) = f(-x)$ for all x. It is said to be an *odd* function if $f(x) = -f(-x)$ for all x. Determine which of the following functions are odd or even.

  (a) $f(x) = x$ (b) $f(x) = x^2$ (c) $f(x) = x^3$
  (d) $f(x) = 1/x$ if $x \neq 0$, and $f(0) = 0$.

12. Let f be any function defined for all numbers. Show that the function $g(x) = f(x) + f(-x)$ is even. What about the function   odd

$$h(x) = f(x) - f(-x),$$

is it even, odd, or neither?

13. Show that any function defined for all numbers can be written as a sum of an even function and an odd function.

§4. POWERS

In this section we just summarize some elementary arithmetic.

Let n be an integer ≥ 1 and let a be any number. Then a^n is the product of a with itself n times. For example, let $a = 3$. If $n = 2$, then $a^2 = 9$. If $n = 3$, then $a^3 = 27$. Thus we obtain a function which is called the n-th *power*. If f denotes this function, then $f(x) = x^n$.

We recall the rule

$$x^{m+n} = x^m x^n$$

for any number x and integers $m, n \geq 1$.

Again, let n be an integer ≥ 1, and let a be a positive number. We define $a^{1/n}$ to be the unique positive number b such that $b^n = a$. (That there exists such a unique number b is taken for granted as part of the properties of numbers.) We get a function called the n-th *root*. Thus if f is the 4-th root, then $f(16) = 2$ and $f(81) = 3$.

The n-th root function can also be defined at 0, the n-th root of 0 being 0 itself.

Question: If n is an odd integer like 1, 3, 5, 7, . . . , can you define an n-th root function for all numbers?

If a, b are two numbers ≥ 0 and n is an integer ≥ 1 then

$$(ab)^{1/n} = a^{1/n} b^{1/n}.$$

There is another useful and elementary rule. Let m, n be integers ≥ 1 and let a be a number ≥ 0. We define $a^{m/n}$ to be $(a^{1/n})^m$ which is also equal to $(a^m)^{1/n}$. This allows us to define fractional powers, and gives us a function

$$f(x) = x^{m/n}$$

defined for $x \geq 0$.

We now come to powers with negative numbers or 0. We want to define x^a when a is a negative rational number or 0 and $x > 0$. We want the fundamental rule

$$x^{a+b} = x^a x^b$$

to be true. This means that we must define x^0 to be 1. For instance, since

$$2^3 = 2^{3+0} = 2^3 2^0,$$

we see from this example that the only way in which this equation holds is if $2^0 = 1$. Similarly, in general, if the relation

$$x^a = x^{a+0} = x^a x^0$$

is true, then x^0 must be equal to 1.

Suppose finally that a is a positive rational number, and let x be a number > 0. We define x^{-a} to be

$$\frac{1}{x^a}.$$

Thus

$$2^{-3} = \frac{1}{2^3} = \frac{1}{8}, \quad \text{and} \quad 4^{-2/3} = \frac{1}{4^{2/3}}.$$

We observe that in this special case,

$$(4^{-2/3})(4^{2/3}) = 4^0 = 1.$$

In general, $x^a x^{-a} = x^0 = 1$.

We are tempted to define x^a even when a is not a rational number. This is more subtle. For instance, it is absolutely meaningless to say that $2^{\sqrt{2}}$ is the product of 2 square root of 2 times itself. The problem of defining 2^a (or x^a) when a is not rational will be postponed to a later chapter. Until that chapter, when we deal with such a power, we shall assume that there is a function, written x^a, described as we have done above for rational numbers, and satisfying the fundamental relation

$$x^{a+b} = x^a x^b, \qquad x^0 = 1.$$

Example. We have a function $f(x) = x^{\sqrt{2}}$ defined for all $x > 0$. It is actually hard to describe its values for special numbers, like $2^{\sqrt{2}}$. It was unknown for a very long time whether $2^{\sqrt{2}}$ is a rational number or not. The solution (*it is not*) was found only in 1927 by the mathematician Gelfond, who became famous for solving a problem that was known to be very hard.

Warning. Do not confuse a function like x^2 and a function like 2^x. Given a number $c > 0$, we can view c^x as a function defined for all x. (It will be discussed in detail in Chapter VIII.) This function is called an *exponential function.* Thus 2^x and 10^x are exponential functions. We shall select a number

$$e = 2.718...$$

and the exponential function e^x as having special properties which make it better than any other exponential function. The meaning of our use of the word "better" will be explained in Chapter VIII.

EXERCISES

Find a^x and x^a for the following values of x and a.

1. $a = 2$ and $x = 3$
2. $a = 5$ and $x = -1$
3. $a = \frac{1}{2}$ and $x = 4$
4. $a = \frac{1}{3}$ and $x = 2$
5. $a = -\frac{1}{2}$ and $x = 4$
6. $a = 3$ and $x = 2$
7. $a = -3$ and $x = -1$
8. $a = -2$ and $x = -2$
9. $a = -1$ and $x = -4$
10. $a = -\frac{1}{2}$ and $x = 9$

11. Determine whether $2^{\sqrt{2}} + 3^{\sqrt{3}}$ is a rational number. (This is actually a major research problem whose answer is not known today. Later in this course we shall deal with numbers e and π. Although it is known that neither e nor π is rational, it is not known whether $e\pi$ or $e + \pi$ is rational.)

Chapter II

Graphs and Curves

The ideas contained in this chapter allow us to translate certain statements backwards and forwards between the language of numbers and the language of geometry.

It is extremely basic for what follows, because we can use our geometric intuition to help us solve problems concerning numbers and functions, and conversely, we can use theorems concerning numbers and functions to yield results about geometry.

§1. COORDINATES

Once a unit length is selected, we can represent numbers as points on a line. We shall now extend this procedure to the plane, and to pairs of numbers.

We visualize a horizontal line and a vertical line intersecting at an origin O.

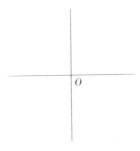

These lines will be called *coordinate axes* or simply *axes*.

We select a unit length and cut the horizontal line into segments of lengths 1, 2, 3, . . . to the left and to the right, and do the same to the vertical line, but up and down, as indicated in the next figure.

On the vertical line we visualize the points going below 0 as corresponding to the negative integers, just as we visualized points on the left of the horizontal line as corresponding to negative integers. We follow the same idea as that used in grading a thermometer, where the numbers below zero are regarded as negative. See figure on page 16.

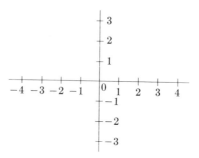

We can now cut the plane into squares whose sides have length 1.

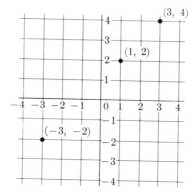

We can describe each point where two lines intersect by a pair of integers. Suppose that we are given a pair of integers like (1, 2). We go to the right of the origin 1 unit and vertically up 2 units to get the point (1, 2) which has been indicated above. We have also indicated the point (3, 4). The diagram is just like a map.

Furthermore, we could also use negative numbers. For instance to describe the point $(-3, -2)$ we go to the left of the origin 3 units and vertically downwards 2 units.

There is actually no reason why we should limit ourselves to points which are described by integers. For instance we can also have the point $(\frac{1}{2}, -1)$ and the point $(-\sqrt{2}, 3)$ as on the figure below.

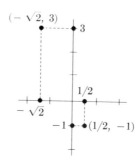

We have not drawn all the squares on the plane. We have drawn only the relevant lines to find our two points.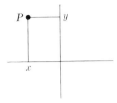

In general, if we take any point P in the plane and draw the perpendicular lines to the horizontal axis and to the vertical axis, we obtain two numbers x, y as in the figure at the right.

The perpendicular line from P to the horizontal axis determines a number x which is negative in the figure because it lies to the left of the origin. The number y determined by the perpendicular from P to the vertical axis is positive because it lies above the origin. The two numbers x, y are called the *coordinates* of the point P, and we can write $P = (x, y)$.

Every pair of numbers (x, y) determines a point of the plane. We find the point by going a distance x from the origin 0 in the horizontal direction and then a distance y in the vertical direction. If x is positive we go to the right of 0. If x is negative, we go to the left of 0. If y is positive we go vertically upwards, and if y is negative we go vertically downwards. The coordinates of the origin are $(0, 0)$. We usually call the horizontal axis the *x-axis* and the vertical axis the *y-axis*. If a point P is described by two numbers, say $(5, -10)$, it is customary to call the first number its x-coordinate and the second number its y-coordinate. Thus 5 is the x-coordinate, and -10 the y-coordinate of our point. Of course, we could use other letters besides x and y, for instance t and s, or u and v.

Our two axes separate the plane into four quadrants which are numbered as indicated in the figure:

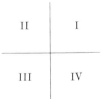

If (x, y) is a point in the first quadrant, then both x and y are > 0. If (x, y) is a point in the fourth quadrant, then $x > 0$ but $y < 0$.

EXERCISES

1. Plot the following points: $(-1, 1)$, $(0, 5)$, $(-5, -2)$, $(1, 0)$.

2. Plot the following points: $(\frac{1}{2}, 3)$, $(-\frac{1}{3}, -\frac{1}{2})$, $(\frac{4}{3}, -2)$, $(-\frac{1}{4}, -\frac{1}{2})$.

3. Let (x, y) be the coordinates of a point in the second quadrant. Is x positive or negative? Is y positive or negative?

4. Let (x, y) be the coordinates of a point in the third quadrant. Is x positive or negative? Is y positive or negative?

5. Plot the following points: $(1.2, -2.3)$, $(1.7, 3)$.

6. Plot the following points: $(-2.5, \frac{1}{3})$, $(-3.5, \frac{5}{4})$.

7. Plot the following points: $(1.5, -1)$, $(-1.5, -1)$.

§2. GRAPHS

Let f be a function. We define the *graph* of f to be the collection of all pairs of numbers $(x, f(x))$ whose first coordinate is any number for which f is defined and whose second coordinate is the value of the function at the first coordinate.

For example, the graph of the function $f(x) = x^2$ consists of all pairs (x, y) such that $y = x^2$. In other words, it is the collection of all pairs (x, x^2), like $(1, 1)$, $(2, 4)$, $(-1, 1)$, $(-3, 9)$, etc.

Since each pair of numbers corresponds to a point on the plane (once a system of axes and a unit length have been selected), we can view the graph of f as a collection of points in the plane. The graph of the function $f(x) = x^2$ has been drawn in the figure below, together with the points which we gave above as examples.

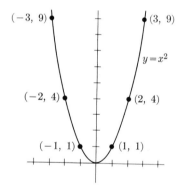

To determine the graph, we plot a lot of points making a table giving the x- and y-coordinates.

x	$f(x)$		x	$f(x)$
1	1		-1	1
2	4		-2	4
3	9		-3	9
$\frac{1}{2}$	$\frac{1}{4}$		$-\frac{1}{2}$	$\frac{1}{4}$

At this stage of the game there is no other way for you to determine the graph of a function other than this trial and error method. Later, we shall develop techniques which give you greater efficiency in doing it.

We shall now give several examples of graphs of functions which occur very frequently in the sequel.

Example 1. Consider the function $f(x) = x$. The points on its graph are of type (x, x). The first coordinate must be equal to the second. Thus $f(1) = 1, f(-\sqrt{2}) = -\sqrt{2}$, etc. The graph looks like this:

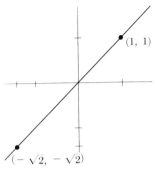

Example 2. Let $f(x) = -x$. Its graph looks like this:

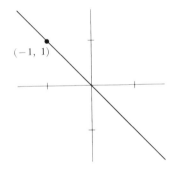

Observe that the graphs of the preceding two functions are straight lines. We shall study the general case of a straight line later.

Example 3. Let $f(x) = |x|$. When $x \geqq 0$, we know that $f(x) = x$. When $x \leqq 0$, we know that $f(x) = -x$. Hence the graph of $|x|$ is obtained by combining the preceding two, and looks like this:

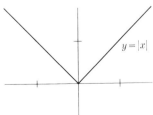

All values of y are $\geqq 0$, whether x is positive or negative.

Example 4. There is an even simpler type of function than the ones we have just looked at, namely the constant functions. For instance, we can define a function f such that $f(x) = 2$ for all numbers x. In other words, we associate the number 2 to any number x. It is a very simple association, and the graph of this function is a horizontal line, intersecting the vertical axis at the point $(0, 2)$.

$$f(x) = 2$$

$(0,\ 2)$

If we took the function $f(x) = -1$, then the graph would be a horizontal line intersecting the vertical axis at the point $(0, -1)$.

In general, let c be a fixed number. The graph of the function $f(x) = c$ is the horizontal line intersecting the vertical axis at the point $(0, c)$. The function $f(x) = c$ is called a *constant* function.

Example 5. The last of our examples is the function $f(x) = 1/x$ (defined for $x \neq 0$). By plotting a few points of the graph, you will see that it looks like this:

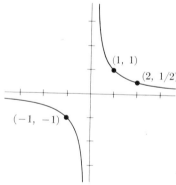

$(1,\ 1)$

$(2,\ 1/2)$

$(-1,\ -1)$

For instance, you can plot the following points:

x	$1/x$		x	$1/x$
1	1		1	1
2	$\frac{1}{2}$		-2	$-\frac{1}{2}$
3	$\frac{1}{3}$		-3	$-\frac{1}{3}$
$\frac{1}{2}$	2		$-\frac{1}{2}$	-2
$\frac{1}{3}$	3		$-\frac{1}{3}$	3

As x becomes very large positive, $1/x$ becomes very small. As x approaches 0 from the right, $1/x$ becomes very large. A similar phenomenon occurs when x approaches 0 from the left; then x is negative and $1/x$ is negative also. Hence in that case, $1/x$ is very large negative.

In trying to determine how the graph of a function looks, you can already watch for the following:

The points at which the graph intersects the two coordinate axes. What happens when x becomes very large positive and very large negative.

On the whole, however, in working out the exercises, your main technique is just to plot a lot of points until it becomes clear to you what the graph looks like.

EXERCISES

Sketch the graphs of the following functions and plot at least three points on each graph. In each case we give the value of the function at x.

1. $x + 1$ 2. $2x$ 3. $3x$

4. $4x$ 5. $2x + 1$ 6. $5x + \frac{1}{2}$

7. $\dfrac{x}{2} + 3$ 8. $-3x + 2$ 9. $2x^2 - 1$

10. $-3x^2 + 1$ 11. x^3 12. x^4

13. $\sqrt{x}$ 14. $x^{-1/2}$ 15. $2x$

16. $x + 1$ 17. $|x| + x$ 18. $|x| + 2x$

19. $-|x|$ 20. $-|x| + x$ 21. $\dfrac{1}{x + 2}$

22. $\dfrac{1}{x - 2}$ 23. $\dfrac{1}{x + 3}$ 24. $\dfrac{1}{x - 3}$

25. $\dfrac{2}{x - 2}$ 26. $\dfrac{2}{x + 2}$ 27. $\dfrac{2}{x}$

28. $\dfrac{-2}{x + 5}$ 29. $\dfrac{3}{x + 1}$ 30. $\dfrac{x}{|x|}$

(In Exercises 13, 14, and 21 through 30, the functions are not defined for all values of x.)

31. Sketch the graph of the function $f(x)$ such that:

$f(x) = 0$ if $x \leqq 0$. $f(x) = 1$ if $x > 0$.

32. Sketch the graph of the function $f(x)$ such that:

$f(x) = x$ if $x < 0$. $f(0) = 2$. $f(x) = x$ if $x > 0$.

33. Sketch the graph of the function $f(x)$ such that:

$f(x) = x^2$ if $x < 0$. $f(x) = x$ if $x \geq 0$.

34. Sketch the graph of the function $f(x)$ such that:

$f(x) = |x| + x$ if $-1 \leq x \leq 1$.

$f(x) = 3$ if $x > 1$. [$f(x)$ is not defined for other values of x.]

35. Sketch the graph of the function $f(x)$ such that:

$f(x) = x^3$ if $x \leq 0$. $f(x) = 1$ if $0 < x < 2$.

$f(x) = x^2$ if $x \geq 2$.

36. Sketch the graph of the function $f(x)$ such that:

$f(x) = x$ if $0 < x \leq 1$. $f(x) = x - 1$ if $1 < x \leq 2$.

$f(x) = x - 2$ if $2 < x \leq 3$. $f(x) = x - 3$ if $3 < x \leq 4$.

[We leave $f(x)$ undefined for other values of x, but try to define it yourself in such a way as to preserve the symmetry of the graph.]

§3. THE STRAIGHT LINE

One of the most basic types of functions is the type whose graph represents a straight line. We have already seen that the graph of the function $f(x) = x$ is a straight line. If we take $f(x) = 2x$, then the line slants up much more steeply, and even more so for $f(x) = 3x$. The graph of the function $f(x) = 10,000x$ would look almost vertical. In general, let a be a positive number $\neq 0$. Then the graph of the function

$$f(x) = ax$$

represents a straight line. The point $(2, 2a)$ lies on the line because $f(2) = 2a$. The point $(\sqrt{2}, \sqrt{2}\,a)$ also lies on the line, and if c is any number, the point (c, ca) lies on the line. The (x, y) coordinates of these points are obtained by making a similarity transformation, starting with the coordinates $(1, a)$ and multiplying them by some number c.

We can visualize this procedure by means of similar triangles. In the figure below, we have a straight line. If we select a point (x, y) on the line and drop the perpendicular from this point to the x-axis, we obtain a right triangle.

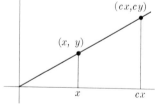

If x is the length of the base of the smaller triangle in the figure, and y its height, and if cx is the length of the base of the bigger triangle, then cy is the height of the bigger triangle: The smaller triangle is similar to the bigger one.

If a is a number < 0, then the graph of the function $f(x) = ax$ is also a straight line, which slants to the left. For instance, the graphs of $f(x) = -x$ or $f(x) = -2x$.

Let a, b be two numbers. The graph of the function $g(x) = ax + b$ is also a straight line, which is parallel to the line determined by the function $f(x) = ax$. In order to convince you of this, we observe the following. When $x = 0$ we see that $g(x) = b$. Let $y' = y - b$. The equation $y' = ax$ is of the type discussed above. If we have a point (x, y') on the straight line $y' = ax$, then we get a point $(x, y' + b)$ on the straight line $y = ax + b$, by simply adding b to the second coordinate. This means that the graph of the function $g(x) = ax + b$ is the straight line parallel to the line determined by the function $f(x) = ax$ and passing through the point $(0, b)$.

Example 1. Let $g(x) = 2x + 1$. When $x = 0$, then $g(x) = 1$. When $g(x) = 0$, then $x = -\frac{1}{2}$. The graph looks like this:

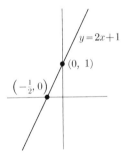

Example 2. Let $g(x) = -2x - 5$. When $x = 0$, then $g(x) = -5$. When $g(x) = 0$, then $x = -\frac{5}{2}$. The graph looks like this:

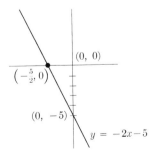

We shall frequently speak of a function $f(x) = ax + b$ as a straight line (although of course, it is its graph which is a straight line).

The number a which is the coefficient of x is called the *slope* of the line. It determines how much the line is slanted. As we have already seen in many examples, when the slope is positive, the line is slanted to the right, and when the slope is negative, the line is slanted to the left. The relationship $y = ax + b$ is also called the *equation* of the line. It gives us the relation between the x- and y-coordinates of a point on the line.

Let $f(x) = ax + b$ be a straight line, and let (x_1, y_1) and (x_2, y_2) be two points of the line. It is easy to find the slope of the line in terms of the coordinates of these two points. By definition, we know that

$$y_1 = ax_1 + b$$

and

$$y_2 = ax_2 + b.$$

Subtracting, we get

$$y_2 - y_1 = ax_2 - ax_1 = a(x_2 - x_1).$$

Consequently, if the two points are distinct, $x_2 \neq x_1$, then we can divide by $x_2 - x_1$ and obtain

$$a = \frac{y_2 - y_1}{x_2 - x_1}.$$

This formula gives us the slope in terms of the coordinates of two distinct points on the line.

Example 3. Look at the line $f(x) = 2x + 5$. Letting $x = 1$, we have $f(x) = 7$ and letting $x = -1$, we get $f(x) = 3$. Thus the points $(1, 7)$ and $(-1, 3)$ are on the line. The slope is 2, and is equal to

$$\frac{7 - 3}{1 - (-1)}$$

as it should be.

Geometrically, our quotient

$$\frac{y_2 - y_1}{x_2 - x_1}$$

is simply the ratio of the vertical side and horizontal side of the triangle in the next diagram:

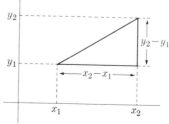

Conversely, given two points in the plane, it is easy to determine the equation of the line passing through them.

Example 4. Let (1, 2) and (2, −1) be the two points. What is the slope of the line between them? What is the equation of the line?

We first find the slope. It must be the quotient

$$\frac{y_2 - y_1}{x_2 - x_1}$$

which is equal to

$$\frac{-1 - 2}{2 - 1} = -3.$$

Thus we know that our line is given by the equation

$$y = -3x + b$$

for some number b. Furthermore, we know also that the line must pass through the point (1, 2). If $f(x) = -3x + b$, then we must have $f(1) = 2$. From this we can solve for b, namely

$$2 = -3 \cdot 1 + b$$

yields $b = 2 + 3 = 5$. Thus the equation of the line is

$$f(x) = -3x + 5.$$

Observe that it does not matter which point we call (x_1, y_1) and which we call (x_2, y_2). We would get the same answer for the slope.

Knowing two points on a line, we first determine the slope and then solve for the constant b, using the coordinates of one of the points.

We can also determine the equation of a line provided we know the slope and one point.

Example 5. Find the equation of the line having slope −7 and passing through the point (−1, 2).

The equation must be of type

$$y = -7x + b$$

for some number b. Furthermore, when $x = -1$, we must have $y = 2$. Thus

$$2 = (-7)(-1) + b$$

and $b = -5$. Hence the equation of the line is

$$y = -7x - 5.$$

Example 6. In general, let a be a number, and (x_1, y_1) some point. *We wish to find the equation of the line having slope equal to a, and passing through the point* (x_1, y_1). The condition that a point (x, y) with $x \neq x_1$ be on this line is equivalent with the condition that

$$\frac{y - y_1}{x - x_1} = a.$$

Thus the equation of the desired line is

$$y - y_1 = a(x - x_1).$$

Point-slope equation.

In Example 5, we could also work it out using the present description, obtaining

$$y - 2 = -7(x - (-1)),$$

from which we also find

$$y = -7x - 5.$$

Example 7. In general, let (x_1, y_1) and (x_2, y_2) be two distinct points with $x_1 \neq x_2$. We wish to find the equation of the line passing through these two points. Its slope must then be equal to

$$\frac{y_2 - y_1}{x_2 - x_1}.$$

From the preceding example, we find that the equation of the line can be expressed by the formula

$$\frac{y - y_1}{x - x_1} = \frac{y_2 - y_1}{x_2 - x_1}$$

for all points (x, y) such that $x \neq x_1$.

Finally, we should mention vertical lines. These cannot be represented by equations of type $y = ax + b$. Suppose that we have a vertical line intersecting the x-axis at the point $(2, 0)$. The y-coordinate of any point on the line can be arbitrary. Thus the equation of the line is simple $x = 2$. In general, the equation of the vertical line intersecting the x-axis at the point $(c, 0)$ is $x = c$.

EXERCISES

Sketch the graphs of the following lines:

1. $y = -2x + 5$

2. $y = 5x - 3$

3. $y = \dfrac{x}{2} + 7$

4. $y = -\dfrac{x}{3} + 1$

What is the equation of the line passing through the following points?

5. $(-1, 1)$ and $(2, -7)$

6. $(3, \frac{1}{2})$ and $(4, -1)$

7. $(\sqrt{2}, -1)$ and $(\sqrt{2}, 1)$

8. $(-3, -5)$ and $(\sqrt{3}, 4)$

What is the equation of the line having the given slope and passing through the given point?

9. slope 4 and point $(1, 1)$

10. slope -2 and point $(\frac{1}{2}, 1)$

11. slope $-\frac{1}{2}$ and point $(\sqrt{2}, 3)$

12. slope $\sqrt{3}$ and point $(-1, 5)$

Sketch the graphs of the following lines:

13. $x = 5$

14. $x = -1$

15. $x = -3$

16. $y = -4$

17. $y = 2$

18. $y = 0.$

What is the slope of the line passing through the following points?

19. $(1, \frac{1}{2})$ and $(-1, 1)$

20. $(\frac{1}{4}, 1)$ and $(\frac{1}{2}, -1)$

21. $(2, 3)$ and $(\sqrt{2}, 1)$

22. $(\sqrt{3}, 1)$ and $(3, 2)$

What is the equation of the line passing through the following points?

23. $(\pi, 1)$ and $(\sqrt{2}, 3)$

24. $(\sqrt{2}, 2)$ and $(1, \pi)$

25. $(-1, 2)$ and $(\sqrt{2}, -1)$

26. $(-1, \sqrt{2})$ and $(-2, -3)$

27. Sketch the graphs of the following lines:

   (a) $y = 2x$ (b) $y = 2x + 1$ (c) $y = 2x + 5$

   (d) $y = 2x - 1$ (e) $y = 2x - 5$

28. Two straight lines are said to be *parallel* if they have the same slope. Let $y = ax + b$ and $y = cx + d$ be the equations of two straight lines with $b \neq d$. (a) If they are parallel, show that they have no point in common. (b) If they are not parallel, show that they have exactly one point in common.

29. Find the common point of the following pairs of lines:

   (a) $y = 3x + 5$ and $y = 2x + 1$ (b) $y = 3x - 2$ and $y = -x + 4$

   (c) $y = 2x + 3$ and $y = -x + 2$ (d) $y = x + 1$ and $y = 2x + 7$

§4. DISTANCE BETWEEN TWO POINTS

Let (x_1, y_1) and (x_2, y_2) be two points in the plane, for instance as in the following diagrams.

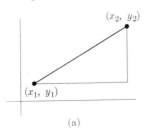

(a)

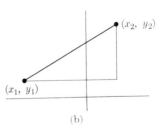

(b)

We can then make up a right triangle. By the Pythagoras theorem, the length of the line segment joining our two points can be determined from the lengths of the two sides. The square of the bottom side is $(x_2 - x_1)^2$, which is also equal to $(x_1 - x_2)^2$. This is clear in part (a) of the figure. It is also true in part (b) (convince yourself by working out an example, as for instance in Example 2 below). The length of the vertical side is $(y_2 - y_1)^2$, which is equal to $(y_1 - y_2)^2$. If L denotes the length of the line segment, then

$$L^2 = (x_1 - x_2)^2 + (y_1 - y_2)^2$$

and consequently,

$$L = \sqrt{(x_2 - x_1)^2 + (y_2 - y_1)^2}.$$

Example 1. Let the two points be $(1, 2)$ and $(1, 3)$. Then the length of the line segment between them is

$$\sqrt{(1 - 1)^2 + (3 - 2)^2} = 1.$$

The length L is also called the *distance* between the two points.

Example 2. Find the distance between the points $(-1, 5)$ and $(4, -3)$.

The distance is

$$\sqrt{(4 - (-1))^2 + (-3 - 5)^2} = \sqrt{89}.$$

(You should plot these points, and convince yourself that the minus signs do not affect the validity of our formula for the length of the line segment between the two points.)

EXERCISES

Find the distance between the following points:

1. The points $(-3, -5)$ and $(1, 4)$
2. The points $(1, 1)$ and $(0, 2)$
3. The points $(-1, 4)$ and $(3, -2)$
4. The points $(1, -1)$ and $(-1, 2)$
5. The points $(\frac{1}{2}, 2)$ and $(1, 1)$
6. Find the coordinates of the fourth corner of a rectangle, three of whose corners are $(-1, 2)$, $(4, 2)$, $(-1, -3)$.
7. What are the lengths of the sides of the rectangle in Exercise 6?
8. Find the coordinates of the fourth corner of a rectangle, three of whose corners are $(-2, -2)$, $(3, -2)$, $(3, 5)$.

9. What are the lengths of the sides of the rectangle in Exercise 8?

10. If x, y are numbers, define the distance between these two numbers to be $|x - y|$. Show that this is the same as the distance between the points $(x, 0)$ and $(y, 0)$ in the plane.

11. Denote by $d(x, y)$ the distance between two numbers x and y. Show that if x, y, z are numbers, then

$$d(x, z) \leqq d(x, y) + d(y, z)$$
$$d(x, y) = d(y, x).$$

§5. CURVES AND EQUATIONS

Let $F(x, y)$ be an expression involving a pair of numbers (x, y). Let c be a number. We consider the equation

$$F(x, y) = c.$$

The collection of points (a, b) in the plane satisfying this equation, i.e. such that

$$F(a, b) = c,$$

is called the *graph* of the equation. This graph is also known as a curve, and we will usually not make a distinction between the equation

$$F(x, y) = c$$

and the curve which represents the equation.

For example,

$$x + y = 2$$

is the equation of a straight line, and its graph is the straight line. We shall study below important examples of equations which arise frequently.

If f is a function, then we can form the expression $y - f(x)$, and the graph of the *equation*

$$y - f(x) = 0$$

is none other than the graph of the *function f* as we discussed it in §2.

You should observe that there are equations of type

$$F(x, y) = c$$

which are not obtained from a function $y = f(x)$. For instance, the equation $x^2 + y^2 = 1$ is such an equation.

We shall now study important examples of graphs of equations

$$F(x, y) = 0 \qquad \text{or} \qquad F(x, y) = c.$$

§6. THE CIRCLE

The expression $F(x, y) = x^2 + y^2$ has a simple geometric interpretation. It is the square of the distance of the point (x, y) from the origin $(0, 0)$. Thus the points (x, y) satisfying the equation

$$x^2 + y^2 = 1^2 = 1$$

are simply those points whose distance from the origin is 1. It is the circle of radius 1, with center at the origin.

Similarly, the points (x, y) satisfying the equation

$$x^2 + y^2 = 4$$

are those points whose distance from the origin is 2. They constitute the circle of radius 2. In general, if c is any number > 0, then the graph of the equation

$$x^2 + y^2 = c^2$$

is the circle of radius c, with center at the origin.

We have already remarked that the *equation*

$$x^2 + y^2 = 1$$

or $x^2 + y^2 - 1 = 0$ is not of the type $y - f(x) = 0$, i.e. does not come from a function $y = f(x)$. However, we can write our equation in the form

$$y^2 = 1 - x^2.$$

For any value of x between -1 and $+1$, we can solve for y and get

$$y = \sqrt{1 - x^2} \quad \text{or} \quad y = -\sqrt{1 - x^2}.$$

If $x \neq 1$ or $x \neq -1$, then we get two values of y for each value of x. Geometrically, these two values correspond to the points indicated on the following diagram.

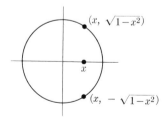

There is a function, defined for $-1 \leq x \leq 1$, such that

$$f(x) = \sqrt{1 - x^2},$$

and the graph of this function is the upper half of our circle. Similarly, there is another function

$$g(x) = -\sqrt{1 - x^2},$$

also defined for $-1 \leq x \leq 1$, whose graph is the lower half of the circle. Neither of these functions is defined for other values of x.

We now ask for the equation of the circle whose center is $(1, 2)$ and whose radius has length 3. It consists of the points (x, y) whose distance from $(1, 2)$ is 3. These are the points satisfying the equation

$$(x - 1)^2 + (y - 2)^2 = 9.$$

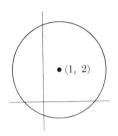

The graph of this equation has been drawn above.

To pick another example, we wish to determine those points at a distance 2 from the point $(-1, -3)$. They are the points (x, y) satisfying the equation

$$(x - (-1))^2 + (y - (-3))^2 = 4$$

or, in other words,

$$(x + 1)^2 + (y + 3)^2 = 4.$$

(Observe carefully the cancellation of minus signs!) Thus the graph of this equation is the circle of radius 2 and center $(-1, -3)$.

In general, let a, b be two numbers and r a number > 0. Then the circle of radius r and center (a, b) is the graph of the equation

$$(x - a)^2 + (y - b)^2 = r^2.$$

In our last example, we have

$$r = 2, \quad a = -1, \quad b = -3.$$

Example 1. Suppose that we have a quadratic expression like

$$x^2 + 2x.$$

We can complete the square and write it as

$$x^2 + 2x = (x + 1)^2 - 1.$$

Similarly, given the expression $y^2 - 3y$, we can write it

$$y^2 - 3y = (y - \tfrac{3}{2})^2 - \tfrac{9}{4}.$$

Given an equation

$$x^2 + y^2 + 2x - 3y - 5 = 0,$$

we can use the trick of completing the square to see what its graph looks like. Our equation can be written in the form

$$(x + 1)^2 + (y - \tfrac{3}{2})^2 = 5 + \tfrac{9}{4} + 1 = \tfrac{33}{4}.$$

Thus our equation is a circle of center $(-1, \tfrac{3}{2})$ and radius $\sqrt{33/4}$.

EXERCISES

Sketch the graph of the following equations:

1. (a) $(x - 2)^2 + (y + 1)^2 = 25$ (b) $(x - 2)^2 + (y + 1)^2 = 4$
   (c) $(x - 2)^2 + (y + 1)^2 = 1$ (d) $(x - 2)^2 + (y + 1)^2 = 9$

2. (a) $x^2 + (y - 1)^2 = 9$ (b) $x^2 + (y - 1)^2 = 4$
   (c) $x^2 + (y - 1)^2 = 25$ (d) $x^2 + (y - 1)^2 = 1$

3. (a) $(x + 1)^2 + y^2 = 1$ (b) $(x + 1)^2 + y^2 = 4$
   (c) $(x + 1)^2 + y^2 = 9$ (d) $(x + 1)^2 + y^2 = 25$

4. $\dfrac{x^2}{9} + \dfrac{y^2}{16} = 1$ 5. $\dfrac{x^2}{4} + \dfrac{y^2}{9} = 1$

6. $\dfrac{x^2}{5} + \dfrac{y^2}{16} = 1$ 7. $\dfrac{x^2}{4} + \dfrac{y^2}{25} = 1$

8. $\dfrac{(x - 1)^2}{9} + \dfrac{(y + 2)^2}{16} = 1$ 9. $4x^2 + 25y^2 = 100$

10. $\dfrac{(x + 1)^2}{3} + \dfrac{(y + 2)^2}{4} = 1$ 11. $25x^2 + 16y^2 = 400$

12. $(x - 1)^2 + \dfrac{(y + 3)^2}{4} = 1$

(In Exercises 4 through 12, the graph of the equation is called an *ellipse*. It is a stretched-out circle. Investigate for yourself the effect of changing the coefficients of x^2 and y^2 in these equations.)

§7. THE PARABOLA. CHANGES OF COORDINATES

We have seen what the graph of the equation $y = x^2$ looks like. Suppose that we graph the equation $y = (x - 1)^2$. We shall find that it looks exactly the same, but as if the origin were placed at the point $(1, 0)$.

Similarly, the curve $y - 2 = (x - 4)^2$ looks again like $y = x^2$ except that the whole curve has been moved as if the origin were the point $(4, 2)$. The graphs of these equations have been drawn on the next diagram.

We can formalize these remarks as follows. Suppose that in our given coordinate system we pick a point (a, b) as a new origin. We let new coordinates be $x' = x - a$ and $y' = y - b$. Thus when $x = a$ we have $x' = 0$ and when $y = b$ we have $y' = 0$. If we have a curve

$$y' = x'^2$$

in the new coordinate system whose origin is at the point (a, b), then it gives rise to the equation

$$(y - b) = (x - a)^2$$

in terms of the old coordinate system. This type of curve is known as a *parabola*.

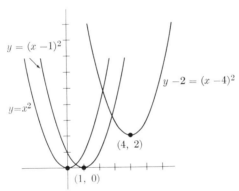

We can apply the same technique of completing the square that we did for the circle.

Example. What is the graph of the equation

$$2y - x^2 - 4x + 6 = 0?$$

Completing the square, we can write

$$x^2 + 4x = (x + 2)^2 - 4.$$

Thus our equation can be rewritten

$$2y = (x + 2)^2 - 10$$

or

$$2(y + 5) = (x + 2)^2.$$

We choose a new coordinate system

$$x' = x + 2 \quad \text{and} \quad y' = y + 5$$

so that our equation becomes

$$2y' = x'^2$$

or $y' = \frac{1}{2}x'^2$. This is a function whose graph you already know, and whose sketch we leave to you.

Finally, we remark that if we have an equation

$$x - y^2 = 0$$

or

$$x = y^2,$$

then we get a parabola which is tilted horizontally.

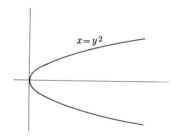

We can then apply the technique of changing the coordinate system to see what the graph of a more general equation is like, for instance the graph of

$$x - y^2 + 2y + 5 = 0.$$

We can write this equation in the form

$$(x + 6) = (y - 1)^2$$

and hence its graph looks like this:

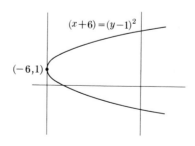

EXERCISES

Sketch the graph of the following equations:

1. $y = -x + 2$ 2. $y = 2x^2 + x - 3$

3. $x - 4y^2 = 0$ 4. $x - y^2 + y + 1 = 0$

Complete the square in the following equations and change the coordinate system to put them into the form

$$x'^2 + y'^2 = r^2 \qquad \text{or} \qquad y' = cx'^2 \qquad \text{or} \qquad x' = cy'^2$$

with a suitable constant c.

5. $x^2 + y^2 - 4x + 2y - 20 = 0$ 6. $x^2 + y^2 - 2y - 8 = 0$

7. $x^2 + y^2 + 2x - 2 = 0$ 8. $y - 2x^2 - x + 3 = 0$

9. $y - x^2 - 4x - 5 = 0$ 10. $y - x^2 + 2x + 3 = 0$

11. $x^2 + y^2 + 2x - 4y = -3$ 12. $x^2 + y^2 - 4x - 2y = -3$

13. $x - 2y^2 - y + 3 = 0$ 14. $x - y^2 - 4y = 5$

§8. THE HYPERBOLA

We have already seen what the graph of the equation

$$xy = 1$$

looks like. It is of course the same as the graph of the function $f(x) = 1/x$ (defined for $x \neq 0$). If we pick a coordinate system whose origin is at the point (a, b), the equation

$$y - b = \frac{1}{x - a}$$

is known as a *hyperbola*. In terms of the new coordinate system $x' = x - a$ and $y' = y - b$, our hyperbola has the old type of equation

$$x'y' = 1.$$

If we are given an equation like

$$xy - 2x + 3y + 4 = 5,$$

we can factor the left-hand side and rewrite the equation as

$$(x + 3)(y - 2) + 6 + 4 = 5$$

or

$$(x + 3)(y - 2) = -5.$$

In terms of the coordinate system $x' = x + 3$ and $y' = y - 2$, we get the equation

$$x'y' = -5.$$

The graph of this equation has been drawn on the following diagram.

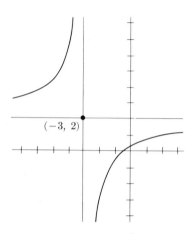

$(-3, 2)$

EXERCISES

Sketch the graphs of the following curves:

1. $(x - 1)(y - 2) = 2$

2. $x(y + 1) = 3$

3. $xy - 4 = 0$

4. $y = \dfrac{2}{1 - x}$

5. $y = \dfrac{1}{x + 1}$

6. $(x + 2)(y - 1) = 1$

7. $(x - 1)(y - 1) = 2$

8. $(x - 1)(y - 1) = 1$

9. $y = \dfrac{1}{x - 2} + 4$

10. $y = \dfrac{1}{x + 1} - 2$

11. $y = \dfrac{4x - 7}{x - 2}$

12. $y = \dfrac{-2x - 1}{x + 1}$

13. $y = \dfrac{x + 1}{x - 1}$

14. $y = \dfrac{x - 1}{x + 1}$

Chapter III

The Derivative

The two fundamental notions of this course are those of the derivative and the integral. We take up the first one in this chapter.

The derivative will give us the slope of a curve at a point. It has also applications to physics, where it can be interpreted as the rate of change.

We shall develop some basic techniques which will allow you to compute the derivative in all the standard situations which you are likely to encounter in practice.

§1. THE SLOPE OF A CURVE

Consider a curve, and take a point P on the curve. We wish to define the notions of slope of the curve at that point, and tangent line to the curve at that point. Sometimes the statement is made that the tangent to the curve at the point is the line which touches the curve only at that point. This is pure nonsense, as the subsequent pictures will convince you.

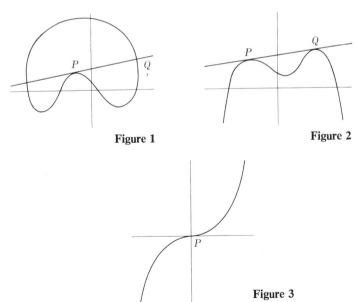

Figure 1

Figure 2

Figure 3

In Figs. 1, 2, and 3, we look at the tangent line to the curve at the point P. In Fig. 1 the line cuts the curve at the other point Q. In Fig. 2 the line is also tangent to the curve at the point Q. In Fig. 3 the curve is supposed to be very flat near the point P, and the horizontal line cuts the curve at P, but we would like to say that it is tangent to the curve at P if the curve is very flat. The vertical line cuts the curve only at P, but is not tangent.

Observe also that you cannot get out of the difficulties by trying to distinguish a line "cutting" the curve, or "touching the curve", or by saying that the line should lie on one side of the curve (cf. Fig. 1).

We therefore have to give up the idea of touching the curve only at one point, and look for another idea.

We have to face two problems. One of them is to give the correct geometric idea which allows us to define the tangent to the curve, and the other is to test whether this idea allows us to compute effectively this tangent line when the curve is given by a simple equation with numerical coefficients. It is a remarkable thing that our solution of the first problem will in fact give us a solution to the second.

In the first chapter, we have seen that knowing the slope of a straight line and one point on the straight line allows us to determine the equation of the line. We shall therefore define the slope of a curve at a point and then get its tangent afterward by using the method of Chapter II.

Our examples show us that to define the slope of the curve at P, we should not consider what happens at a point Q which is far removed from P. Rather, it is what happens near P which is important.

Let us therefore take any point Q on the given curve $y = f(x)$, and assume that $Q \neq P$. Then the two points P, Q determine a straight line with a certain slope which depends on P, Q and which we shall write as $S(P, Q)$. Suppose that the point Q approaches the point P on the curve (but stays distinct from P). Then, as Q comes near P, the slope $S(P, Q)$ of the line passing through P and Q should approach the (unknown) slope of the (unknown) tangent line to the curve at P. In the following diagram, we have drawn the tangent line to the curve at P and two lines between P and another point on the curve close to P (Fig. 4). The point Q_2 is closer to P on the curve and so the slope of the line between P and Q_2 is closer to the slope of the tangent line than is the slope of the line between P and Q_1.

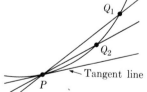

Figure 4

If the limit of the slope $S(P, Q)$ exists as Q approaches P, then it should be regarded as the slope of the curve itself at P. This is the basic idea

behind our definition of the slope of the curve at P. We take it as a definition, perhaps the most important definition in this book. To repeat:

Given a curve $y = f(x)$, let P be a point on the curve. The *slope* of
the curve at P is the limit of the slope of lines between P and another
point Q on the curve, as Q approaches P.

The idea of defining the slope in this manner was discovered in the
seventeenth century by Newton and Leibnitz. We shall see that this
definition allows us to determine the slope effectively in practice.

First we observe that when $y = ax + b$ is a straight line, then the slope
of the line between any two distinct points on the curve is always the
same, and is the slope of the line as we defined it in the preceding chapter.

Let us now look at the next simplest example,

$$y = f(x) = x^2.$$

We wish to determine the slope of this curve at the point $(1, 1)$.

We look at a point near $(1, 1)$, for instance a point whose x-coordinate
is 1.1. Then $f(1.1) = (1.1)^2 = 1.21$. Thus the point $(1.1, 1.21)$ lies on
the curve. The slope of the line between two points (x_1, y_1) and (x_2, y_2) is

$$\frac{y_2 - y_1}{x_2 - x_1}.$$

Therefore the slope of the line between $(1, 1)$ and $(1.1, 1.21)$ is

$$\frac{1.21 - 1}{1.1 - 1} = \frac{0.21}{0.1} = 2.1.$$

In general, the x-coordinate of a point near $(1, 1)$ can be written $1 + h$,
where h is some small number, positive or negative, but $h \neq 0$. We have

$$f(1 + h) = (1 + h)^2 = 1 + 2h + h^2.$$

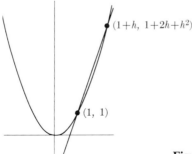

$(1+h, \; 1+2h+h^2)$

$(1, 1)$

Figure 5

Thus the point $(1 + h, 1 + 2h + h^2)$ lies on the curve. When h is positive, the line between our two points would look like that in Fig. 5.

When h is negative, then $1 + h$ is smaller than 1 and the line would look like this:

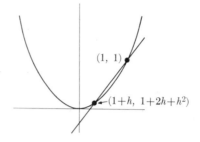

Figure 6

For instance, h could be -0.1 and $1 + h = 0.9$.

The slope of the line between our two points is therefore the quotient

$$\frac{(1 + 2h + h^2) - 1}{(1 + h) - 1},$$

which is equal to

$$\frac{2h + h^2}{h} = 2 + h.$$

When the point whose x-coordinate is $1 + h$ approaches our point $(1, 1)$, the number h approaches 0. As h approaches 0, the slope of the line between our two points approaches 2, which is therefore the slope of the curve at the point $(1, 1)$ by definition.

You will appreciate how simple the computation turns out to be, and how easy it was to get this slope!

Let us take another example. We wish to find the slope of the same curve $f(x) = x^2$ at the point $(-2, 4)$. Again we take a nearby point whose x-coordinate is $-2 + h$ for small $h \neq 0$. The y-coordinate of this nearby point is

$$f(-2 + h) = (-2 + h)^2 = 4 - 4h + h^2.$$

The slope of the line between the two points is therefore

$$\frac{4 - 4h + h^2 - 4}{-2 + h - (-2)} = \frac{-4h + h^2}{h} = -4 + h.$$

As h approaches 0, the nearby point approaches the point $(-2, 4)$ and we see that the slope approaches -4.

EXERCISES

Find the slopes of the following curves at the indicated points:

1. $y = 2x^2$ at the point $(1, 2)$ 2. $y = x^2 + 1$ at the point $(-1, 2)$

3. $y = 2x - 7$ at the point $(2, -3)$ 4. $y = x^3$ at the point $(\frac{1}{2}, \frac{1}{8})$

5. $y = 1/x$ at the point $(2, \frac{1}{2})$ 6. $y = x^2 + 2x$ at the point $(-1, -1)$

7. $y = x^2$ at the point $(2, 4)$ 8. $y = x^2$ at the point $(3, 9)$

9. $y = x^3$ at the point $(1, 1)$ 10. $y = x^3$ at the point $(2, 8)$

11. $y = 2x + 3$ at the point whose x-coordinate is 2.

12. $y = 3x - 5$ at the point whose x-coordinate is 1.

13. $y = ax + b$ at an arbitrary point.

(In Exercises 11, 12, 13 use the h-method, and verify that this method gives the same answer for the slope as that stated in Chapter II, §3.)

§2. THE DERIVATIVE

We continue to consider the function $y = x^2$. Instead of picking a definite numerical value for the x-coordinate of a point, we could work at an arbitrary point on the curve. Its coordinates are then (x, x^2). We write the x-coordinate of a point nearby as $x + h$ for some small number h, positive or negative, but $h \neq 0$. The y-coordinate of this nearby point is

$$(x + h)^2 = x^2 + 2xh + h^2.$$

Hence the slope of the line between them is

$$\frac{(x + h)^2 - x^2}{(x + h) - x} = \frac{x^2 + 2xh + h^2 - x^2}{x + h - x}$$

$$= \frac{2xh + h^2}{h}$$

$$= 2x + h.$$

As h approaches 0, $2x + h$ approaches $2x$. Consequently, the slope of the curve $y = x^2$ at an arbitrary point (x, y) is $2x$. In particular, when $x = 1$ the slope is 2 and when $x = -2$ the slope is -4, as we found out before by the explicit computation using the special x-coordinates 1 and -2.

This time, however, we have found out a general formula giving us the slope for any point on the curve. Thus when $x = 3$ the slope is 6 and when $x = -10$ the slope is -20.

The example we have just worked out gives us the procedure for treating more general functions.

Given a function $f(x)$, we form the quotient

$$\frac{f(x + h) - f(x)}{x + h - x} = \frac{f(x + h) - f(x)}{h}.$$

This quotient is the slope of the line between the points

$$(x, f(x)) \quad \text{and} \quad (x + h, f(x + h)).$$

We shall call it the *Newton quotient*. If it approaches a limit as h approaches 0, then this limit is called the *derivative* of f at x, and we say that f is *differentiable* at x. The limit will be written in an abbreviated fashion,

$$\lim_{h \to 0} \frac{f(x + h) - f(x)}{h}.$$

The derivative will be written $f'(x)$, and we thus have

$$f'(x) = \lim_{h \to 0} \frac{f(x + h) - f(x)}{h}.$$

The derivative may thus be viewed as a function f', which is defined at all numbers x such that the Newton quotient approaches a limit as h tends to 0.

We say that f is *differentiable* if it is differentiable at all points for which it is defined. For instance the function $f(x) = x^2$ is differentiable and its derivative is $2x$.

It will also be convenient to use another notation for the derivative, namely

$$f'(x) = \frac{df}{dx}$$

(or df/dx). Thus the two expressions $f'(x)$ and df/dx mean the same thing. We emphasize however that in the expression df/dx we do not multiply f or x by d or divide df by dx. The expression is to be read *as a whole*. We shall find out later that the expression, under certain circumstances, behaves *as if* we were dividing, and it is for this reason that we adopt this classical way of writing the derivative.

We work out some examples before giving you exercises on this section.

Example 1. Let $f(x) = 2x + 1$. Find the derivative $f'(x)$.

We form the Newton quotient. We have $f(x + h) = 2(x + h) + 1$. Thus

$$\frac{f(x + h) - f(x)}{h} = \frac{2x + 2h + 1 - (2x + 1)}{h} = \frac{2h}{h} = 2.$$

As h approaches 0 (which we write also $h \to 0$), this number is equal to 2 and hence the limit is 2. Thus

$$f'(x) = 2$$

for all values of x. The derivative is constant.

Example 2. Find the slope of the graph of the function $f(x) = 2x^2$ at the point whose x-coordinate is 3.

We may just as well find the slope at an arbitrary point on the graph. It is the derivative $f'(x)$. We have

$$f(x + h) = 2(x + h)^2 = 2(x^2 + 2xh + h^2).$$

The Newton quotient is

$= 2(x+h)^2$

$$\frac{f(x + h) - f(x)}{h} = \frac{2(x^2 + 2xh + h^2) - 2x^2}{h}$$

$$= \frac{4xh + 2h^2}{h}$$

$$= 4x + 2h.$$

As $h \to 0$ the limit is $4x$. Hence $f'(x) = 4x$. At the point $x = 3$ we get $f'(3) = 12$, which is the desired slope.

Example 3. Find the equation of the tangent line to the curve $y = 2x^2$ at the point whose x-coordinate is -2.

In the preceding example we have computed the general formula for the slope of the tangent line. It is

$$f'(x) = 4x.$$

At the point $x = -2$ the slope is therefore -8. The tangent line has an equation

$$y = -8x + b$$

for some number b. The y-coordinate of our point is $2(-2)^2 = 8$. Hence we must have

$$8 = -8(-2) + b$$

and solving for b yields

$$b = -8.$$

Thus the equation of the tangent line is

$$y = -8x - 8.$$

In defining the Newton quotient, we can take h positive or negative. It is sometimes convenient when taking the limit to look only at values of h which are positive. In this manner we get what is called the *right derivative*. If in taking the limit of the Newton quotient we took only negative values for h, we would get the *left derivative*.

Example 4. Let $f(x) = |x|$. Find its right derivative and its left derivative when $x = 0$.

The right derivative is the limit

$$\lim_{\substack{h \to 0 \\ h > 0}} \frac{f(0 + h) - f(0)}{h}.$$

When $h > 0$, we have $f(0 + h) = f(h) = h$, and $f(0) = 0$. Thus

$$\frac{f(0 + h) - f(0)}{h} = \frac{h}{h} = 1.$$

The limit as $h \to 0$ and $h > 0$ is therefore 1.

The left derivative is the limit

$$\lim_{\substack{h \to 0 \\ h < 0}} \frac{f(0 + h) - f(0)}{h}.$$

When $h < 0$ we have

$$f(0 + h) = f(h) = -h.$$

Hence

$$\frac{f(0 + h) - f(0)}{h} = \frac{-h}{h} = -1.$$

The limit as $h \to 0$ and $h < 0$ is therefore -1.

We see that the right derivative at 0 is 1 and the left derivative is -1. They are not equal. We would of course expect this from the graph of our function $f(x) = |x|$, which looks like that in Fig. 7.

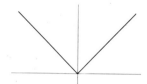

Figure 7

Both the right derivative of f and the left derivative of f exist but they are not equal.

We would rephrase our definition of the derivative and say that the derivative of a function $f(x)$ is defined when the right derivative and the left derivative exist and they are equal, in which case this common value is simply called the *derivative*.

Example 5. Let $f(x)$ be equal to x if $0 < x \leq 1$ and $x - 1$ if $1 < x \leq 2$. We do not define f for other values of x. Then the graph of f looks like this:

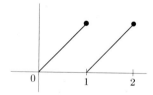

Figure 8

The left derivative of f at 1 exists and is equal to 1, but the right derivative of f at 1 does not exist. We leave the verification of the first assertion to you. To verify the second assertion, we must see whether the limit

$$\lim_{\substack{h \to 0 \\ h > 0}} \frac{f(1 + h) - f(1)}{h}$$

exists. Since $1 + h > 1$ we have

$$f(1 + h) = 1 + h - 1 = h.$$

Also $f(1) = 1$. Thus the Newton quotient is

$$\frac{f(1 + h) - f(1)}{h} = \frac{h - 1}{h} = 1 - \frac{1}{h}.$$

As h approaches 0 the quotient $1/h$ has no limit since it becomes arbitrarily large. Thus the Newton quotient has no limit for $h > 0$ and the function does not have a right derivative when $x = 1$.

EXERCISES

Find the derivatives of the following functions:

1. $x^2 + 1$ 2. x^3

3. $2x^3$ 4. $3x^2$

5. $x^2 - 5$ 6. $2x^2 + x$

7. $2x^2 - 3x$ 8. $\frac{1}{2}x^3 + 2x$

9. $\dfrac{1}{x + 1}$ 10. $\dfrac{2}{x + 1}$

11. In Exercises 1 through 10, find the slope of the graph at the point whose x-coordinate is 2, and find the equation of the tangent line at that point.

12. Let $f(x)$ be defined as follows:

$$f(x) = -x \quad \text{if} \quad x \leq 0 \qquad f(x) = 2 \quad \text{if} \quad x > 0.$$

Find $f'(x)$ when $x = -1$. Find the right and left derivatives of f at $x = 0$, if they exist.

13. Let $f(x) = |x| + x$. Does $f'(0)$ exist? Does $f'(x)$ exist for values of x other than 0?

14. Let $f(x) = 0$ if $x \leq 1$ and $f(x) = x$ if $x > 1$. Sketch the graph. Find the right and left derivatives of f when $x = 1$. Find $f'(x)$ for all other values of x.

15. Determine whether the following functions have a derivative at 0, and if so, what is the derivative.

(a) $f(x) = x|x|$ (b) $f(x) = x^2|x|$ (c) $f(x) = x^3|x|$

§3. LIMITS

In defining the slope of a curve at a point, or the derivative, we used the notion of limit, which we regarded as intuitively clear. It is indeed. You can see in the Appendix how one may define limits using only properties of numbers, but we do not worry about this here. However, we shall make a list of the properties of limits which will be used in the sequel, just to be sure of what we assume about them, and also to give you a technique for computing limits.

First, we note that if F is a constant function, $F(x) = c$ for all x, then

$$\lim_{h \to 0} F(h) = c$$

is the constant itself.

If $F(h) = h$, then

$$\lim_{h \to 0} F(h) = 0.$$

The next properties relate limits with addition, subtraction, multiplication, division, and inequalities.

Suppose that we have two functions $F(x)$ and $G(x)$ which are defined for the same numbers. Then we can form the sum of the two functions $F + G$, whose value at a point x is $F(x) + G(x)$. Thus when $F(x) = x^4$ and $G(x) = 5x^{3/2}$ we have

$$F(x) + G(x) = x^4 + 5x^{3/2}.$$

The value $F(x) + G(x)$ is also written $(F + G)(x)$. The first property of limits concerns the sum of two functions.

Property 1. Suppose that we have two functions F and G defined for small values of h, and assume that the limits

$$\lim_{h \to 0} F(h) \qquad \text{and} \qquad \lim_{h \to 0} G(h)$$

exist. Then

$$\lim_{h \to 0} [F(h) + G(h)]$$

exists and

$$\lim_{h \to 0} (F + G)(h) = \lim_{h \to 0} F(h) + \lim_{h \to 0} G(h).$$

In other words the limit of a sum is equal to the sum of the limits.

A similar statement holds for the difference $F - G$, namely

$$\lim_{h \to 0} \big(F(h) - G(h)\big) = \lim_{h \to 0} F(h) - \lim_{h \to 0} G(h)$$

After the sum we discuss the product. Suppose we have two functions F and G defined for the same numbers. Then we can form their product

FG whose value at a number x is

$$(FG)(x) = F(x)G(x).$$

For instance if $F(x) = 2x^2 - 2^x$ and $G(x) = x^2 + 5x$, then the product is

$$(FG)(x) = (2x^2 - 2^x)(x^2 + 5x).$$

Property 2. Let F, G be two functions defined for small values of h, and assume that

$$\lim_{h \to 0} F(h) \quad \text{and} \quad \lim_{h \to 0} G(h)$$

exist. Then the limit of the product exists and we have

$$\lim_{h \to 0} (FG)(h) = \lim_{h \to 0} [F(h)G(h)]$$
$$= \lim_{h \to 0} F(h) \cdot \lim_{h \to 0} G(h).$$

In words, we can say that the product of the limits is equal to the limit of the product.

As a special case, suppose that $F(x)$ is the constant function $F(x) = c$. Then we can form the function cG, product of the constant by G, and we have

$$\lim_{h \to 0} cG(h) = c \cdot \lim_{h \to 0} G(h).$$

Thirdly, we come to quotients. Let F, G be as before, but assume that $G(x) \neq 0$ for any x. Then we can form the quotient function F/G whose value at x is

$$\frac{F}{G}(x) = \frac{F(x)}{G(x)}.$$

Property 3. Assume that the limits

$$\lim_{h \to 0} F(h) \quad \text{and} \quad \lim_{h \to 0} G(h)$$

exist, and that

$$\lim_{h \to 0} G(h) \neq 0.$$

Then the limit of the quotient exists and we have

$$\lim_{h \to 0} \frac{F(h)}{G(h)} = \frac{\lim F(h)}{\lim G(h)}.$$

In words, the quotient of the limits is equal to the limit of the quotient.

As we have done above, we shall sometimes omit writing $h \to 0$ for the sake of simplicity.

Property 4. Let F, G be two functions defined for small values of h, and assume that $G(h) \leq F(h)$. Assume also that

$$\lim_{h \to 0} F(h) \quad \text{and} \quad \lim_{h \to 0} G(h)$$

exist. Then

$$\lim_{h \to 0} G(h) \leq \lim_{h \to 0} F(h).$$

Property 5. Let the assumptions be as in Property 4, and in addition, assume that

$$\lim_{h \to 0} G(h) = \lim_{h \to 0} F(h).$$

Let E be another function defined for the same numbers as F, G such that

$$G(h) \leq E(h) \leq F(h)$$

for all small values of h. Then

$$\lim_{h \to 0} E(h)$$

exists and is equal to the limits of F and G.

Property 5 is known as the squeezing process. You will find many applications of it in the sequel.

Example 1. Find the limit

$$\lim_{h \to 0} \frac{2xh + 3}{x^2 - 4h}$$

when $x \neq 0$.

The numerator of our quotient approaches 3 when $h \to 0$ and the denominator approaches x^2. Thus the quotient approaches $3/x^2$. We can justify these steps more formally by applying our three properties. For instance:

$$\begin{aligned}
\lim_{h \to 0} (2xh + 3) &= \lim_{h \to 0} (2xh) + \lim_{h \to 0} 3 \\
&= \lim (2x) \lim (h) + \lim 3 \\
&= 2x \cdot 0 + 3 \\
&= 3.
\end{aligned}$$

For the denominator, we have

$$\begin{aligned}
\lim (x^2 - 4h) &= \lim x^2 + \lim (-4h) \\
&= x^2 + \lim (-4) \lim (h) \\
&= x^2 + (-4) \cdot 0 \\
&= x^2.
\end{aligned}$$

Using the rule for the quotient, we get $3/x^2$.

The properties of limits which we have stated above will allow you to compute limits in determining derivatives. We illustrate this by an example.

Example 2. Let $f(x) = 1/x$ (defined for $x \neq 0$). Find the derivative df/dx.

The Newton quotient is

$$\frac{f(x + h) - f(x)}{h} = \frac{\dfrac{1}{x + h} - \dfrac{1}{x}}{h}.$$

We put everything over a common denominator $(x + h)xh$. The Newton quotient is equal to

$$\frac{x - (x + h)}{(x + h)xh} = \frac{-h}{(x + h)xh} = \frac{-1}{(x + h)x}.$$

Thus we have to determine the limit of a quotient as h approaches 0. Using the property of a product, we have

$$\lim (x + h)x = \lim (x + h) \lim x$$
$$= x^2.$$

Using the property of quotients, we see that the Newton quotient for the function $1/x$ approaches $-1/x^2$. Thus

$$\frac{df}{dx} = \lim_{h \to 0} \frac{f(x + h) - f(x)}{h} = \frac{-1}{x^2}.$$

EXERCISES

Find the derivatives of the following functions, justifying the steps in taking limits by means of the first three properties:

1. $f(x) = 2x^2 + 3x$

2. $f(x) = \dfrac{1}{2x + 1}$

3. $f(x) = \dfrac{x}{x + 1}$

4. $f(x) = x(x + 1)$

5. $f(x) = \dfrac{x}{2x - 1}$

6. $f(x) = 3x^3$

7. $f(x) = x^4$

8. $f(x) = x^5$

9. $f(x) = 2x^3$

10. $f(x) = \frac{1}{2}x^3 + x$

§4. POWERS

We have seen that the derivative of the function x^2 is $2x$.

Let us consider the function $f(x) = x^3$ and find its derivative. We have

$$f(x + h) = (x + h)^3 = x^3 + 3x^2h + 3xh^2 + h^3.$$

Hence the Newton quotient is

$$\frac{f(x + h) - f(x)}{h} = \frac{x^3 + 3x^2h + 3xh^2 + h^3 - x^3}{h}$$
$$= 3x^2 + 3xh + h^2.$$

Using the properties of limits of sums and products, we see that $3x^2$ remains equal to itself as h approaches 0, that $3xh$ and h^3 both approach 0. Hence

$$f'(x) = \lim_{h \to 0} \frac{f(x + h) - f(x)}{h} = 3x^2.$$

This suggests that in general, whenever $f(x) = x^n$ for some positive integer n, the derivative $f'(x)$ should be nx^{n-1}. This is indeed the case, and we state it as a theorem.

Theorem 1. *Let n be an integer ≥ 1 and let $f(x) = x^n$. Then*

$$\frac{df}{dx} = nx^{n-1}.$$

Proof. We have

$$f(x + h) = (x + h)^n = (x + h)(x + h) \cdots (x + h),$$

the product being taken n times. Selecting x from each factor gives us a term x^n. If we take x from all but one factor and h from the remaining factor, we get hx^{n-1} taken n times. This gives us a term $nx^{n-1}h$. All other terms will involve selecting h from at least two factors, and the corresponding term will be divisible by h^2. Thus we get

$$f(x + h) = (x + h)^n = x^n + nx^{n-1}h + h^2g(x, h),$$

where $g(x, h)$ is simply some expression involving powers of x and h with numerical coefficients which it is unnecessary for us to determine. However, using the rules for limits of sums and products we can conclude that

$$\lim_{h \to 0} g(x, h)$$

will be some number which it is unnecessary for us to determine. The Newton quotient is therefore

$$\frac{f(x + h) - f(x)}{h} = \frac{x^n + nx^{n-1}h + h^2g(x, h) - x^n}{h}.$$

We can cancel x^n and are left with

$$\frac{nx^{n-1}h + h^2g(x, h)}{h}.$$

We can now divide numerator and denominator by h, thereby giving us

$$nx^{n-1} + hg(x, h).$$

As h approaches 0, the term nx^{n-1} remains unchanged. The limit of h as h tends to 0 is 0, and hence by the product rule, the term $hg(x, h)$ approaches 0 when h tends to 0. Thus finally

$$\lim_{h \to 0} \frac{f(x + h) - f(x)}{h} = nx^{n-1},$$

which proves our theorem.

Theorem 2. *Let a be any number and let* $f(x) = x^a$ *(defined for $x > 0$). Then $f(x)$ has a derivative, which is*

$$f'(x) = ax^{a-1}.$$

It would not be difficult to prove Theorem 2 when a is a negative integer. It is best however to wait until we have a rule giving us the derivative of a quotient before doing it. We could also give a proof when a is a rational number. However, we shall prove the general result in a later chapter, and thus we prefer to wait until then, when we have more techniques available.

Examples. If $f(x) = x^{10}$ then $f'(x) = 10x^9$.

If $f(x) = x^{3/2}$ (for $x > 0$) then $f'(x) = \frac{3}{2}x^{1/2}$.

If $f(x) = x^{-5/4}$ then $f'(x) = -\frac{5}{4}x^{-9/4}$.

If $f(x) = x^{\sqrt{2}}$ then $f'(x) = \sqrt{2}\,x^{\sqrt{2}-1}$.

Note especially the special case when $f(x) = x$. Then $f'(x) = 1$.

EXERCISES

1. Write out the expansion of $(x + h)^4$ in terms of powers of x and h.

2. Find the derivative of the function x^4 directly, using the Newton quotient.

3. What are the derivatives of the following functions?

    (a) $x^{2/3}$ (b) $x^{-3/2}$ (c) $x^{7/6}$

4. What is the equation of the tangent line to the curve $y = x^9$ at the point $(1, 1)$?

5. What is the slope of the curve $y = x^{2/3}$ at the point $(8, 4)$? What is the equation of the tangent line at that point?

6. Give the slope and equation of the tangent line to the curve $y = x^{-3/4}$ at the point whose x-coordinate is 16.

7. Give the slope and equation of the tangent line to the curve $y = \sqrt{x}$ at the point whose x-coordinate is 3.

8. Give the derivatives of the following functions at the indicated points:

(a) $f(x) = x^{1/4}$ at $x = 5$ (b) $f(x) = x^{-1/4}$ at $x = 7$

(c) $f(x) = x^{\sqrt{2}}$ at $x = 10$ (d) $f(x) = x^{\pi}$ at $x = 7$

§5. SUMS, PRODUCTS, AND QUOTIENTS

In this section we shall derive several rules which allow you to find the derivatives for sums, products, and quotients of functions when you know the derivative of each factor.

Before stating and proving these rules, we make one remark concerning the derivative.

Let $f(x)$ be a function having a derivative $f'(x)$. Since the quotient

$$\frac{f(x + h) - f(x)}{h}$$

approaches a limit as h approaches 0, and since

$$f(x + h) = f(x) + h\frac{f(x + h) - f(x)}{h},$$

using the rules for sums and products of limits, we conclude that

$$\lim_{h \to 0} f(x + h) = f(x),$$

and that $f(x + h) - f(x)$ approaches 0 as h approaches 0.

Of course, we can never substitute $h = 0$ in our quotient, because then it becomes $0/0$, which is meaningless. Geometrically, letting $h = 0$ amounts to taking the two points on the curve equal to each other. It is then impossible to have a unique straight line through one point. Our procedure of taking the limit of the Newton quotient is meaningful only if $h \neq 0$.

Let c be a number and $f(x)$ a function which has a derivative $f'(x)$ for all values of x for which it is defined. We can multiply f by the constant c to get another function cf whose value at x is $cf(x)$.

The derivative of cf is then given by the formula

$$(cf)'(x) = c \cdot f'(x);$$

in other words, the derivative of a constant times a function is the constant times the derivative of the function.

To prove this rule, we use the definition of derivative. The Newton quotient for the function cf is

$$\frac{(cf)(x + h) - (cf)(x)}{h} = \frac{cf(x + h) - cf(x)}{h} = c\frac{f(x + h) - f(x)}{h}.$$

Let us take the limit as h approaches 0. Then c remains fixed, and

$$\frac{f(x + h) - f(x)}{h}$$

approaches $f'(x)$. According to the rule for the product of limits, we see that our Newton quotient approaches $cf'(x)$, as was to be proved.

For example, let $f(x) = 3x^2$. Then $f'(x) = 6x$. If $f(x) = 17x^{1/2}$, then $f'(x) = \frac{17}{2}x^{-1/2}$. If $f(x) = 10x^a$, then $f'(x) = 10ax^{a-1}$.

Next we look at the sum of two functions.

Let $f(x)$ and $g(x)$ be two functions which have derivatives $f'(x)$ and $g'(x)$, respectively. Then the sum $f(x) + g(x)$ has a derivative, and

$$(f + g)'(x) = f'(x) + g'(x).$$

The derivative of a sum is equal to the sum of the derivatives.

To prove this, we have by definition

$$(f + g)(x + h) = f(x + h) + g(x + h)$$
$$(f + g)(x) = f(x) + g(x).$$

Therefore the Newton quotient for $f + g$ is

$$\frac{(f + g)(x + h) - (f + g)(x)}{h} = \frac{f(x + h) + g(x + h) - f(x) - g(x)}{h}.$$

Collecting terms and separating the fraction, we see that this expression is equal to

$$\frac{f(x + h) - f(x) + g(x + h) - g(x)}{h}$$
$$= \frac{f(x + h) - f(x)}{h} + \frac{g(x + h) - g(x)}{h}.$$

Taking the limit as h approaches 0 and using the rule for the limit of a sum, we see that this last sum approaches $f'(x) + g'(x)$ as h approaches 0. This proves what we wanted.

For example, the derivative of the function $x^3 + x^2$ is $3x^2 + 2x$. The derivative of the function $4x^{1/2} + 5x^{-10}$ is

$$2x^{-1/2} - 50x^{-11}.$$

Carried away by our enthusiasm at determining so easily the derivative of functions built up from others by means of constants and sums, we might now be tempted to state the rule that the derivative of a product is the product of the derivatives. Unfortunately, this is false. To see that the rule is false, we look at an example.

Let $f(x) = x$ and $g(x) = x^2$. Then $f'(x) = 1$ and $g'(x) = 2x$. Therefore $f'(x)g'(x) = 2x$. However, the derivative of the product $(fg)(x) = x^3$ is $3x^2$, which is certainly not equal to $2x$. Thus the product of the derivatives is not equal to the derivative of the product.

Through trial and error the correct rule was discovered. It can be stated as follows:

Let $f(x)$ and $g(x)$ be two functions having derivatives $f'(x)$ and $g'(x)$. Then the product function $f(x)g(x)$ has a derivative, which is given by the formula

$$(fg)'(x) = f'(x)g(x) + f(x)g'(x).$$

In words, the derivative of the product is equal to the derivative of the first times the second, plus the first times the derivative of the second.

The proof is not very much more difficult than the proofs we have already encountered. By definition, we have

$$(fg)(x + h) = f(x + h)g(x + h)$$
$$(fg)(x) = f(x)g(x).$$

Consequently the Newton quotient for the product function fg is

$$\frac{(fg)(x + h) - (fg)(x)}{h} = \frac{f(x + h)g(x + h) - f(x)g(x)}{h}.$$

At this point, it looks a little hopeless to transform this quotient in such a way that we see easily what limit it approaches as h tends to 0. But we rewrite our quotient by inserting

$$-f(x)g(x + h) + f(x)g(x + h)$$

in the numerator. This certainly does not change the value of our quotient, which now looks like

$$\frac{f(x + h)g(x + h) - f(x)g(x + h) + f(x)g(x + h) - f(x)g(x)}{h}.$$

We can split this fraction into a sum of two fractions:

$$\frac{f(x + h)g(x + h) - f(x)g(x + h)}{h} + \frac{f(x)g(x + h) - f(x)g(x)}{h}.$$

We can factor $g(x + h)$ in the first term, and $f(x)$ in the second term, to obtain

$$\frac{f(x + h) - f(x)}{h} g(x + h) + f(x) \frac{g(x + h) - g(x)}{h}.$$

The situation is now well under control. As h tends to 0, $g(x + h)$ tends to $g(x)$, and the two quotients in the expression we have just written tend to $f'(x)$ and $g'(x)$ respectively. Thus the Newton quotient for fg tends to

$$f'(x)g(x) + f(x)g'(x),$$

thereby proving our assertion.

To illustrate the rules for products, let us find the derivative of

$$(x + 1)(3x^2).$$

Applying the rule, we see that it is equal to

$$1 \cdot (3x^2) + (x + 1)6x.$$

Similarly, let $f(x) = 2x^5 + 5x^4$ and $g(x) = 2x^{1/2} + x^{-1}$. Then the derivative of $f(x)g(x)$ is

$$(10x^4 + 20x^3)(2x^{1/2} + x^{-1}) + (2x^5 + 5x^4)\left(x^{-1/2} - \frac{1}{x^2}\right),$$

which you may and should leave just like that without attempting to simplify the expression.

The last rule of this section concerns the derivative of a quotient. We begin with a special case.

Let $g(x)$ be a function having a derivative $g'(x)$, and such that $g(x) \neq 0$. Then the derivative of the quotient $1/g(x)$ exists, and is equal to

$$\frac{-1}{g(x)^2}\, g'(x).$$

To prove this, we look at the Newton quotient

$$\frac{\dfrac{1}{g(x + h)} - \dfrac{1}{g(x)}}{h}$$

which is equal to

$$\frac{g(x) - g(x + h)}{g(x + h)g(x)h} = -\frac{1}{g(x + h)g(x)}\, \frac{g(x + h) - g(x)}{h}.$$

Letting h approach 0 we see immediately that our expression approaches

$$\frac{-1}{g(x)^2}\, g'(x)$$

as desired.

The general case of the rule for quotients can now be easily stated and proved.

Let $f(x)$ and $g(x)$ be two functions having derivatives $f'(x)$ and $g'(x)$ respectively, and such that $g(x) \neq 0$. Then the derivative of the quotient

$f(x)/g(x)$ exists, and is equal to

$$\frac{g(x)f'(x) - f(x)g'(x)}{g(x)^2}.$$

Putting this into words yields: *The bottom times the derivative of the top, minus the top times the derivative of the bottom, over the bottom squared* (which you can memorize like a poem).

To prove this rule, we write our quotient in the form

$$\frac{f(x)}{g(x)} = f(x)\frac{1}{g(x)}$$

and use the rule for the derivative of a product, together with the special case we have just proved. We obtain

$$f'(x)\frac{1}{g(x)} + f(x)\frac{-1}{g(x)^2}g'(x).$$

Putting this expression over the common denominator $g(x)^2$ yields

$$\frac{g(x)f'(x) - f(x)g'(x)}{g(x)^2},$$

which is the desired derivative.

We work out some examples.

Let $f(x) = x^2 + 1$ and $g(x) = 3x^4 - 2x$. Then the derivative of $f(x)/g(x)$ is

$$\frac{(3x^4 - 2x)2x - (x^2 + 1)(12x^3 - 2)}{(3x^4 - 2x)^2}.$$

Still another: The derivative of $2x/(x + 4)$ is

$$\frac{(x + 4)\cdot 2 - 2x\cdot 1}{(x + 4)^2}.$$

For future reference, we write the various rules which we have proved into the df/dx notation. The first one:

$$\frac{d(cf)}{dx} = c\cdot\frac{df}{dx}.$$

The sum: $$\frac{d(f + g)}{dx} = \frac{df}{dx} + \frac{dg}{dx}.$$

The product: $$\frac{d(fg)}{dx} = \frac{df}{dx}g(x) + f(x)\frac{dg}{dx}.$$

The quotient: $$\frac{d(f/g)}{dx} = \frac{g\dfrac{df}{dx} - f\dfrac{dg}{dx}}{g(x)^2}.$$

EXERCISES

Find the derivatives of the following functions:

1. $2x^{1/3}$

2. $5x^{11}$

3. $\frac{1}{2}x^{-3/4}$

4. $7x^3 + 4x^2$

5. $25x^{-1} + 12x^{1/2}$

6. $\frac{3}{5}x^2 - 2x^8$

7. $(x^3 + x)(x - 1)$

8. $(2x^2 - 1)(x^4 + 1)$

9. $(x + 1)(x^2 + 5x^{3/2})$

10. $(2x - 5)(3x^4 + 5x + 2)$

11. $(x^{-2/3} + x^2)\left(x^3 + \dfrac{1}{x}\right)$

12. $(2x + 3)\left(\dfrac{1}{x^2} + \dfrac{1}{x}\right)$

13. $\dfrac{2x + 1}{x + 5}$

14. $\dfrac{2x}{x^2 + 3x + 1}$

To break the monotony of the letter x, let us use another.

15. $f(t) = \dfrac{t^2 + 2t - 1}{(t + 1)(t - 1)}$

16. $\dfrac{t^{-5/4}}{t^2 + t - 1}$

17. What is the slope of the curve

$$(f'(t))$$

$$y = \frac{t}{t + 5}$$

$$\frac{v \cdot du - u \cdot dv}{v^2} : \frac{(t+5)(1) - (t)(1)}{(t+5)^2}$$

at the point $t = 2$? What is the equation of the tangent line at this point?

$$\frac{5}{(t+5)^2}$$

18. What is the slope of the curve

$$= \frac{5}{49}.$$

$$y = \frac{t^2}{t^2 + 1}$$

at $t = 1$? What is the equation of the tangent line?

§6. THE CHAIN RULE

We know how to build up new functions from old ones by means of sums, products, and quotients. There is one other important way of building up new functions. We shall first give examples of this new way.

Consider the function $(x + 2)^{10}$. We can say that this function is made up of the 10-th power function, and the function $x + 2$. Namely, given a number x, we first add 2 to it, and then take the 10-th power. Let

$$g(x) = x + 2$$

and let f be the 10-th power function. Then we can take the value of f at $x + 2$, namely

$$f(x + 2) = (x + 2)^{10}$$

and we can also write it as

$$f(x + 2) = f(g(x)).$$

Another example: Consider the function $(3x^4 - 1)^{1/2}$. If we let $g(x) = 3x^4 - 1$ and f be the square root function, then

$$f(g(x)) = \sqrt{3x^4 - 1} = (3x^4 - 1)^{1/2}.$$

In order not to get confused by the letter x, which cannot serve us any more in all contexts, we use another letter to denote the values of g. Thus we may write $f(u) = u^{1/2}$.

Similarly, let $f(u)$ be the function $u + 5$ and $g(x) = 2x$. Then

$$f(g(x)) = f(2x) = 2x + 5.$$

One more example of the same type: Let

$$f(u) = \frac{1}{u + 2}$$

and

$$g(x) = x^{10}.$$

Then

$$f(g(x)) = \frac{1}{x^{10} + 2}.$$

In order to give you sufficient practice with many types of functions, we now mention several of them whose definitions will be given later. These will be sin and cos (which we read sine and cosine), log (which we read logarithm or simply log), and the exponential function exp. We shall select a special number e (whose value is approximately 2.718...), such that the function exp is given by

$$\exp(x) = e^x.$$

We now see how we make new functions out of these.

Let $f(u) = \sin u$ and $g(x) = x^2$. Then

$$f(g(x)) = \sin(x^2).$$

Let $f(u) = e^u$ and $g(x) = \cos x$. Then

$$f(g(x)) = e^{\cos x}.$$

Let $f(v) = \log v$ and $g(t) = t^3 - 1$. Then

$$f(g(t)) = \log(t^3 - 1).$$

Let $g(w) = w^{10}$ and $f(z) = \log z + \sin z$. Then

$$g(f(z)) = (\log z + \sin z)^{10}.$$

You should practice with part (a) of the exercises, in order to assimilate properly the terminology and mechanisms of these combined functions.

Whenever we have two functions f and g such that f is defined for all numbers which are values of g, then we can build a new function denoted by $f \circ g$ whose value at a number x is

$$(f \circ g)(x) = f(g(x)).$$

The rule defining this new function is: Take the number x, find the number $g(x)$, and then take the value of f at $g(x)$. This is the value of $f \circ g$ at x. The function $f \circ g$ is called the *composite function* of f and g. We say that g is the *inner* function and that f is the *outer* function.

It is important to keep in mind that we can compose two functions only when the outer function is defined at all values of the inner function. For instance, let $f(u) = u^{1/2}$ and $g(x) = -x^2$. Then we cannot form the composite function $f \circ g$ because f is defined only for positive numbers (or 0) and the values of g are all negative, or 0. Thus $(-x^2)^{1/2}$ does not make sense.

However, for the moment you are asked to learn the mechanism of composite functions just the way you learned the multiplication table, in order to acquire efficient conditioned reflexes when you meet composite functions. Hence for the drills given by the exercises at the end of the section, you should forget for a while the meaning of the symbols and operate with them formally, just to learn the formal rules properly.

We come to the problem of taking the derivative of a composite function.

We start with an example. Suppose we want to find the derivative of the function $(x + 1)^{10}$. The Newton quotient would be a very long expression, which it would be essentially hopeless to disentangle by brute force, the way we have up to now. It is therefore a pleasant surprise that there will be an easy way of finding the derivative. We tell you the answer right away: The derivative of this function is $10(x + 1)^9$. This looks very much related to the derivative of powers.

Before proving and stating the general theorem, we give you other examples. The derivative of $(x^2 + 2x)^{3/2}$ is $\frac{3}{2}(x^2 + 2x)^{1/2}(2x + 2)$. Observe carefully the extra term $2x + 2$, which is the derivative of the expression $x^2 + 2x$.

The derivative of $(x^2 + x)^{10}$ is $10(x^2 + x)^9(2x + 1)$. Observe again the presence of the term $2x + 1$, which is the derivative of $x^2 + x$.

Can you guess the general rule from the preceding assertions? The general rule was also discovered by trial and error, but we profit from three centuries of experience, and thus we are able to state it and prove it very simply, as follows.

Let f and g be two functions having derivatives, and such that f is defined at all numbers which are values of g. Then the composite function $f \circ g$ has *a derivative, given by the formula*

$$(f \circ g)'(x) = f'(g(x))g'(x).$$

This can be expressed in words by saying that we take the *derivative of the outer function times the derivative of the inner function* (or the derivative of what's inside).

The preceding assertion is known as the *chain rule*, and we shall now prove it. We shall use a property of composite limits proved in the Appendix 1.

We must consider the Newton quotient of the composite function $f \circ g$. By definition, it is

$$\frac{f((gx + h)) - f(g(x))}{h}.$$

Put $u = g(x)$, and let

$$k = g(x + h) - g(x).$$

Then k depends on h, and tends to 0 as h approaches 0. Our Newton quotient is equal to

$$\frac{f(u + k) - f(u)}{h}.$$

Suppose that k is unequal to 0 for all small values of h. Then we can multiply and divide this quotient by k, and obtain

$$\frac{f(u + k) - f(u)}{k} \frac{k}{h} = \frac{f(u + k) - f(u)}{k} \frac{g(x + h) - g(x)}{h}.$$

If we let h approach 0 and use the rule for the limit of a product, we see that our Newton quotient approaches

$$f'(u)g'(x),$$

and this would prove our chain rule, under the assumption that k is not 0.

It does not happen very often that $k = 0$ for arbitrarily small values of h, but when it does happen, the preceding argument breaks down. For those of you who are interested, we shall show you how the argument can be slightly modified so as to be valid in all cases. The uninterested reader can just skip it.

We go back to the definition of the derivative of f. Given a number u such that $f(u)$ is defined, we know that

$$\lim_{k \to 0} \frac{f(u + k) - f(u)}{k} = f'(u).$$

Therefore, the limit of the expression

$$\varphi(k) = \frac{f(u + k) - f(u)}{k} - f'(u)$$

as k approaches 0 is equal to 0. In symbols:

$$\lim_{k \to 0} \varphi(k) = 0.$$

Multiplying by k we obtain

$$k\varphi(k) = f(u + k) - f(u) - kf'(u)$$

or

$$f(u + k) - f(u) = k \cdot f'(u) + k \cdot \varphi(k).$$

So far, this is valid only when k is not 0. But if we define $\varphi(0)$ to be 0, then we note that the relationship we have just derived is still valid when $k = 0$ because k does not appear in the denominator. Substituting $k = 0$ just yields

$$f(u) - f(u) = 0,$$

which is certainly true.

Now let $u = g(x)$ and let $k = g(x + h) - g(x)$. As h approaches zero, so does k.

The Newton quotient for the composite function $f \circ g$ is

$$\frac{f\big(g(x + h)\big) - f\big(g(x)\big)}{h} = \frac{f(u + k) - f(u)}{h},$$

which, by the expression we have just derived, is equal to

$$\frac{k \cdot f'(u) + k \cdot \varphi(k)}{h},$$

or substituting the value for k, is equal to

$$\frac{g(x + h) - g(x)}{h} f'(u) + \frac{g(x + h) - g(x)}{h} \varphi(k).$$

Taking the limit as h approaches 0, we see that the first term approaches $g'(x)f'(u)$. So far as the second term is concerned, taking the limit, we get

$$\lim_{h \to 0} \frac{g(x + h) - g(x)}{h} \varphi(k) = g'(x) \cdot 0 = 0$$

because the limit of $\varphi(k)$ as h or k goes to 0 is 0. This proves that the Newton quotient of $f \circ g$ approaches

$$f'(u)g'(x)$$

and concludes the proof of the chain rule in general.

We are in a position to see the reason for the notation dg/dx. The chain rule in this notation can be expressed by the formula

$$\frac{d(f \circ g)}{dx} = \frac{df}{du} \frac{du}{dx}$$

if $u = g(x)$ is a function of x. Thus the derivative behaves *as if* we could cancel the du. As long as we have proved this result, there is nothing wrong with working like a machine in computing derivatives of composite functions, and we shall give you several examples before the exercises.

Let $f(u) = u^{10}$ and $u = g(x) = x^2 + 1$. Then $f'(u) = 10u^9$ and $g'(x) = 2x$. Thus

$$\frac{d(f \circ g)}{dx} = 10u^9 \cdot 2x = 10(x^2 + 1)^9 2x.$$

Let $f(u) = 2u^{1/2}$ and $g(x) = 5x + 1$. Then $f'(u) = u^{-1/2}$ and $g'(x) = 5$. Thus

$$\frac{d(f \circ g)}{dx} = (5x + 1)^{-1/2} \cdot 5.$$

(Pay attention to the constant 5, which is the derivative of $5x + 1$. You are very likely to forget it.)

In order to give you more extensive drilling than would be afforded by the functions we have considered, like powers, we summarize the derivatives of the elementary functions which are to be considered later.

$$\frac{d(\sin x)}{dx} = \cos x. \qquad \frac{d(\cos x)}{dx} = -\sin x.$$

$$\frac{d(e^x)}{dx} = e^x \text{ (yes, } e^x, \text{ the same as the function!).}$$

$$\frac{d(\log x)}{dx} = \frac{1}{x}.$$

In view of these, and the chain rule, we see that the derivative of $(\sin x)^7$ is $7(\sin x)^6(\cos x)$. (Here again we emphasize the appearance of $\cos x$, which is the derivative of what's inside our composite function.)

The derivative of $(\log x)^{1/2}$ is $\dfrac{1}{2} (\log x)^{-1/2} \cdot \dfrac{1}{x}$.

The derivative of $e^{\sin x}$ is $e^{\sin x} (\cos x)$.

The derivative of $\cos (2x^2)$ is $-\sin (2x^2) \cdot 4x$. (The $4x$ is the derivative of $2x^2$.)

EXERCISES

(a) In each case, find two functions $f(u)$ and $g(x)$ such that the indicated function is of type $f(g(x))$.

(b) Find the derivative of the indicated function. Do not attempt to simplify your answers.

1. $(x + 1)^8$

2. $(2x - 5)^{1/2}$

3. $(\sin x)^3$

4. $(\log x)^5$

5. $\sin 2x$

6. $\log (x^2 + 1)$

7. $e^{\cos x}$

8. $\log (e^x + \sin x)$

9. $\sin \left(\log x + \dfrac{1}{x} \right)$

10. $\dfrac{x + 1}{\sin 2x}$

11. $(2x^2 + 3)^3$

12. $\cos (\sin 5x)$

13. $\log (\cos 2x)$

14. $\sin [(2x + 5)^2]$

15. $\sin [\cos (x + 1)]$

16. $\sin (e^x)$

17. $\dfrac{1}{(3x - 1)^4}$

18. $\dfrac{1}{(4x)^3}$

19. $\dfrac{1}{(\sin 2x)^2}$

20. $\dfrac{1}{(\cos 2x)^2}$

21. $\dfrac{1}{\sin 3x}$

22. $(\sin x)(\cos x)$

23. $(x^2 + 1)e^x$

24. $(x^3 + 2x)(\sin 3x)$

25. $\dfrac{1}{\sin x + \cos x}$

26. $\dfrac{\sin 2x}{e^x}$

27. $\dfrac{\log x}{x^2 + 3}$

28. $\dfrac{x + 1}{\cos 2x}$

29. $(2x - 3)(e^x + x)$

30. $(x^3 - 1)(e^{3x} + 5x)$

31. $\dfrac{x^3 + 1}{x - 1}$

32. $\dfrac{x^2 - 1}{2x + 3}$

33. $(x^{4/3} - e^x)(2x + 1)$

34. $(\sin 3x)(x^{1/4} - 1)$

35. $\sin (x^2 + 5x)$

36. $e^{3x^2 + 8}$

37. $\dfrac{1}{\log (x^4 + 1)}$

38. $\dfrac{1}{\log (x^{1/2} + 2x)}$

39. $\dfrac{2x}{e^x}$

40. Relax.

§7. HIGHER DERIVATIVES

Given a differentiable function f defined on an interval, its derivative f' is also a function on this interval. If it turns out to be also differentiable (this being usually the case), then its derivative is called the *second derivative* of f and is denoted by $f''(x)$. For instance, the first derivative of $(x^2 + 1)^2$ is $2(x^2 + 1)2x = 4x^3 + 4x$, and the second derivative $f''(x)$ is $12x^2 + 4$.

There is no reason to stop at the second derivative, and one can of course continue with the third, fourth, etc. provided they exist.

Example. The third derivative of the function $f(x) = x^3$ is the constant function 6.

Since it is notationally inconvenient to pile up primes after f to denote successive derivatives, one writes

$$f^{(n)}$$

for the n-th derivative of f. Thus f'' is also written $f^{(2)}$.

EXERCISES

Find the second derivatives of the following functions:

1. $3x^3 + 5x + 1$ 2. $(x^2 + 1)^5$
3. Find the 80-th derivative of $x^7 + 5x - 1$.
4. Find the 7-th derivative of $x^7 + 5x - 1$.
5. Find the third derivative of $x^2 + 1$.
6. Find the third derivative of $x^3 + 2x - 5$.
7. Find the third derivative of the function $f(x) = \sin x$.
8. Find the fourth derivative of the function $g(x) = \cos x$.
9. Find the 10th derivative of $\sin x$.   10. Find the 10th derivative of $\cos x$.
11. Find the 100th derivative of $\sin x$.
12. Find the 100th derivative of $\cos x$.

§8. RATE OF CHANGE

The derivative has an interesting physical interpretation, which was very closely connected with it in its historical development, and is worth mentioning.

Suppose that a particle moves along some straight line a certain distance depending on time t. Then the distance s is a function of t, which we write $s = f(t)$.

For two values of the time, t_1 and t_2, the quotient

$$\frac{f(t_2) - f(t_1)}{t_2 - t_1}$$

can be regarded as a sort of average velocity of the particle. At a given time t_0, it is therefore reasonable to regard the limit

$$\lim_{t \to t_0} \frac{f(t) - f(t_0)}{t - t_0}$$

as the rate of change of s with respect to t. This is none other than the derivative $f'(t)$.

For instance if the particle is an object dropping under the influence of gravity, then experimental data show that

$$s = \tfrac{1}{2}gt^2,$$

where g is the gravitational constant. In that case,

$$\frac{ds}{dt} = gt$$

is its velocity.

The rate of change of the velocity is the acceleration. In the case of gravity, we take the derivative of the speed and we get simply the constant g.

In general, given a function $y = f(x)$, the derivative $f'(x)$ is interpreted as the rate of change of y with respect to x. Thus f' is also a function. If x is given as some function of time, say, $x = g(t)$, then we can determine both the rate of change of y with respect to x, namely dy/dx, but also the rate of change of y with respect to t, namely

$$\frac{dy}{dt} = \frac{dy}{dx}\frac{dx}{dt}$$

by the chain rule.

Example 1. A particle is moving so that at time t the distance traveled is given by the function

$$s(t) = t^2 + 1.$$

The derivative $s'(t)$ is equal to $2t$. Thus the velocity of the particle is equal to 0 at time $t = 0$. Its velocity is equal to 4 at time $t = 2$.

Example 2. A square is expanding in such a way that its edge is changing at a rate of 2 in./sec. When its edge is 6 in. long, find the rate of change of its area.

The area of a square as a function of its side is given by the function

$$f(x) = x^2.$$

If the side x is given as a function of time t, say $x = x(t)$, then the rate of change of the area with respect to time is by definition

$$\frac{d(f(x(t)))}{dt}.$$

Thus we use the chain rule, and if we denote the area by A, we find

$$\frac{dA}{dt} = 2x(t)x'(t).$$

We know that $x'(t)$ is the constant 2. Thus when $x(t) = 6$, we find that

$$\frac{dA}{dt} = 2 \cdot 6 \cdot 2 = 24 \text{ in./sec.}$$

Example 3. A point moves along the graph of $y = x^3$ so that its x-coordinate changes at the rate of 2 units per second. What is the rate of change of its y-coordinate when $x = 3$?

We have by the chain rule,

$$\frac{dy}{dt} = 3x^2 \frac{dx}{dt}.$$

Thus when $x = 3$, we have $dy/dt = 3 \cdot 9 \cdot 2 = 54$ units per second.

EXERCISES

1. A particle is moving so that at time t, the distance is given by $s(t) = t^3 - 2t$. At what time is the acceleration equal to
   (a) 1   (b) 0   (c) -5?

2. A particle is moving so that at time t, the distance is given by the function $s(t) = 2t^4 + t^2$. At what time is the velocity equal to 0?

3. An object travels on a straight line with velocity given by the function $v(t) = 4t^5$. Find the acceleration at time $t = 2$.

4. A particle is moving so that at time t, the distance traveled is given by $s(t) = t^3 - 2t + 1$. At what time is the acceleration equal to 0?

5. A cube is expanding in such a way that its edge is changing at a rate of 5 in./sec. When its edge is 4 in. long, find the rate of change of its volume.

6. A sphere is increasing so that its radius increases at the rate of 1 in./sec. How fast is its volume changing when its radius is 3 in.? (The volume of a sphere is $4\pi r^3/3$.)

7. What is the rate of change of the area of a circle with respect to its radius, diameter, circumference? (You may assume that the area of the circle is given by the formula πr^2, where r is the radius, and its circumference is given by the formula $2\pi r$.)

8. A point moves along the graph of $y = 1/(x^2 + 4)$ so that its x-coordinate changes at the rate of 3 units per second. What is the rate of change of its y-coordinate when $x = 2$?

Supplementary Exercises

SUMS, PRODUCTS, AND QUOTIENTS

Find the derivatives of the following functions. Do not simplify your answers!

1. $3x^3 - 4x + 5$

2. $x^2 + 2x + 27$

3. $x^2 + x - 1$

4. $x^{1/2} - 8x^4 + x^{-1}$

5. $x^{5/2} + x^{-5/2}$

6. $x^7 + 15x^{-1/5}$

7. $(x^2 - 1)(x + 5)$

8. $\left(x^5 + \dfrac{1}{x}\right)(x^5 + 1)$

9. $(x^{3/2} + x^2)(x^4 - 99)$

10. $(x^2 + x + 1)(x^5 - x - 25)$

11. $(2x^2 + 1)\left(\dfrac{1}{x^2} + 4x + 8\right)$

12. $(x^4 - x^2)(x^2 - 1)$

13. $(x + 1)(x + 2)(x + 3)$

14. $5(x - 1)(x + 2)(x^2 + 1)$

15. $x^3(x^2 + 1)(x + 1)$

16. $(x^4 + 1)(x + 5)(2x + 7)$

17. $\dfrac{1}{2x + 3}$

18. $\dfrac{1}{7x + 27}$

19. $\dfrac{-5}{x^3 + 2x^2}$

20. $\dfrac{3}{2x4 + x^{3/2}}$

21. $\dfrac{-2x}{x + 1}$

22. $\dfrac{x + 1}{x - 5}$

23. $\dfrac{3x^{1/2}}{(x + 1)(x - 1)}$

24. $\dfrac{2x^{1/2} + x^{3/4}}{(x + 1)x^3}$

25. $\dfrac{x^5 + 1}{(x^2 + 1)(x + 7)}$

26. $\dfrac{(x + 1)(x + 5)}{x - 4}$

27. $\dfrac{x^3}{1 - x^2}$

28. $\dfrac{x^5}{x^{3/2} + x}$

29. $\dfrac{x^2 - x}{x^2 + 1}$

30. $\dfrac{x^2 + 2x + 7}{8x}$

31. $\dfrac{2x + 1}{x^2 + x - 4}$

32. $\dfrac{x^5}{x^2 + 3}$

33. $\dfrac{4x - x^3}{x^2 + 2}$

34. $\dfrac{x^3}{x^2 - 5x + 7}$

35. $\dfrac{1 - 5x}{x}$

36. $\dfrac{1 + 6x + x^{3/4}}{7x - 2}$

37. $\dfrac{x^2}{(x + 1)(x - 2)}$

38. $\dfrac{x^{1/2} - x^{-1/2}}{x^{3/4}}$

39. $\dfrac{3x^4 + x^{5/4}}{4x^3 - x^5 + 1}$

40. $\dfrac{x - 1}{(x - 2)(x - 3)}$

Find the equations of the tangent lines to the following curves at the given point.

41. $y = x^{1/4} + 2x^{3/4}$ at $x = 16$

42. $y = 2x^3 + 3$ at $x = \frac{1}{2}$

43. $y = (x - 1)(x - 3)(x - 4)$ at $x = 0$

44. $y = 2x^2 + 5x - 1$ at $x = 2$

45. $y = (x^2 + 1)(2x + 3)$ at $x = 1$

46. $y = \dfrac{x-1}{x+5}$ at $x = 2$ 47. $y = \dfrac{x^2}{x^3+1}$ at $x = 2$

48. $y = \dfrac{x^2+1}{x^3+1}$ at $x = 2$ 49. $y = \dfrac{x^2}{x^2-1}$ at $x = 2$

50. $y = \dfrac{x-1}{x^2+1}$ at $x = 1$

51. Show that the line $y = -x$ is tangent to the curve given by the equation $y = x^3 - 6x^2 + 8x$. Find the point of tangency.

52. Show that the line $y = 9x - 15$ is tangent to the curve $y = x^3 - 3x + 1$. Find the point of tangency.

53. Show that the graphs of the equations

$$y = 3x^2 \quad \text{and} \quad y = 2x^3 + 1$$

have a common tangent line at the point $(1, 3)$. Sketch the graphs.

54. Show that there are exactly two tangent lines to the graph of $y = (x + 1)^2$ which pass through the origin, and find their equations.

55. Find all the points (x_0, y_0) on the curve

$$y = 4x^4 - 8x^2 + 16x + 7$$

such that the tangent line to the curve at (x_0, y_0) is parallel to the line

$$16x - y + 5 = 0.$$

Find the tangent line to the curve at each of these points.

CHAIN RULE

Find the derivatives of the following functions.

1. $(2x + 1)^2$ 2. $(2x + 5)^3$

3. $(5x + 3)^7$ 4. $(7x - 2)^{81}$

5. $(2x^2 + x - 5)^3$ 6. $(2x^3 - 3x)^4$

7. $(3x + 1)^{1/2}$ 8. $(2x - 5)^{5/4}$

9. $(x^2 + x - 1)^{-2}$ 10. $(x^4 + 5x + 6)^{-1}$

11. $(x + 5)^{-5/3}$ 12. $(x^3 + 2x + 1)^3$

13. $(x - 1)(x - 5)^3$ 14. $(2x^2 + 1)^2(x^2 + 3x)$

15. $(x^3 + x^2 - 2x - 1)^4$ 16. $(x^2 + 1)^3(2x + 5)^2$

17. $\dfrac{(x + 1)^{3/4}}{(x - 1)^{1/2}}$ 18. $\dfrac{(2x + 1)^{1/2}}{(x + 5)^5}$

19. $\dfrac{(2x^2 + x - 1)^{5/2}}{(3x + 2)^9}$ 20. $\dfrac{(x^2 + 1)(3x - 7)^8}{(x^2 + 5x - 4)^3}$

21. $\sqrt{2x + 1}$ 22. $\sqrt{x + 3}$

23. $\sqrt{x^2 + x + 5}$

24. $\sqrt{2x^3 - x + 1}$

In the following exercises, we may assume that there are functions sin u, cos u, log u, and e^u whose derivatives are given by the following formulas:

$$\frac{d\sin u}{du} = \cos u, \qquad \frac{d\cos u}{du} = -\sin u,$$

$$\frac{d(e^u)}{du} = e^u, \qquad \frac{d\log u}{du} = \frac{1}{u}.$$

Find the derivative of each function (with respect to x):

25. $\sin (x^3 + 1)$ 26. $\cos (x^3 + 1)$ 27. e^{x^3+1}

28. $\log (x^3 + 1)$ 29. $\sin (\cos x)$ 30. $\cos (\sin x)$

31. $e^{\sin(x^3+1)}$ 32. $\log [\sin (x^3 + 1)]$ 33. $\sin [(x + 1)(x^2 + 2)]$

34. $\log (2x^2 + 3x + 5)$ 35. $e^{(x+1)(x-3)}$ 36. e^{2x+1}

37. $\sin (2x + 5)$ 38. $\cos (7x + 1)$ 39. $\log (2x + 1)$

40. $\log \dfrac{2x + 1}{x + 3}$ 41. $\sin \dfrac{x - 5}{2x + 4}$ 42. $\cos \dfrac{2x - 1}{x + 3}$

43. e^{2x^2+3x+1} 44. $\log (4x^3 - 2x)$ 45. $\sin [\log (2x + 1)]$

46. $\cos (e^{2x})$ 47. $\cos (3x^2 - 2x + 1)$ 48. $\sin \left(\dfrac{x^2 - 1}{2x^3 + 1}\right)$

49. $(2x + 1)^{80}$ 50. $(\sin x)^{50}$ 51. $(\log x)^{49}$

52. $(\sin 2x)^4$ 53. $(e^{2x+1} - x)^5$ 54. $(\log x)^{20}$

55. $(3 \log (x^2 + 1) - x^3)^{1/2}$ 56. $(\log (2x + 3))^{4/3}$

57. $\dfrac{\sin 2x}{\cos 3x}$ 58. $\dfrac{\sin (2x + 5)}{\cos (x^2 - 1)}$ 59. $\dfrac{\log 2x^2}{\sin x^3}$

60. $\dfrac{e^{x^3}}{x^2 - 1}$ 61. $\dfrac{x^4 + 4}{\cos 2x}$ 62. $\dfrac{\sin (x^3 - 2)}{\sin 2x}$

63. $\dfrac{(2x^2 + 1)^4}{(\cos x^3)}$ 64. $\dfrac{e^{-x}}{\cos 2x}$ 65. e^{-3x}

66. e^{-x^2} 67. e^{-4x^2+x} 68. $\sqrt{e^x + 1}$

69. $\dfrac{\log (x^2 + 2)}{e^{-x}}$ 70. $\dfrac{\log (2x + 1)}{\sin (4x + 5)}$

RATE OF CHANGE

do rates of change P.66...

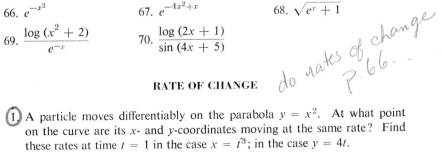

1. A particle moves differentiably on the parabola $y = x^2$. At what point on the curve are its x- and y-coordinates moving at the same rate? Find these rates at time $t = 1$ in the case $x = t^3$; in the case $y = 4t$.

2. One side of a right triangle decreases 1 in./min and the other side increases 2 in./min. At some time the first side is 8 in. and the second side is 6 in. long. At what rate is the area increasing after 2 min?

3. The length of the side of a square is increasing at the rate of 3 in. per second. Find the rate at which the area is increasing when the side is 15 in. long.

4. A ladder 17 ft long leans against a vertical wall. If the lower end of the ladder is being moved away from the foot of the wall at the rate of 3 ft/sec, how fast is the top descending when the lower end is 8 ft from the wall?

5. A swimming pool is 25 ft wide, 40 ft long, 3 ft deep at one end and 9 ft deep at the other, the bottom being an inclined plane. If water is pumped into the pool at the rate of 10 ft^3/min, how fast is the water level rising when it is 4 ft deep at the deep end?

6. A reservoir has the shape of a cone, vertex down, 10 ft high. The radius of the top is 4 ft. Water is poured into the reservoir at the rate of 5 ft^3/min. How fast is the water rising when the depth of the water is 5 ft? (The volume of a cone whose base has radius r and of height h is $\pi r^2 h/3$.)

7. A particle is moving so that at time t the distance traveled is given by $s(t) = 2t^2 - t$. At what time is the velocity equal to 0? What is the acceleration of the particle?

8. A point moves on the parabola with equation $y = x^2 - 6x$. Find the point on the curve at which the rate of change of the y-coordinate is four times the rate of change of the x-coordinate.

9. Water is flowing into a tank in the form of a hemisphere of radius 10 ft with flat side up at the rate of 4 ft^3/min. Let h be the depth of the water, r the radius of the surface of the water, and V the volume of the water in the tank. Assume that $dV/dt = \pi r^2 \, dh/dt$. Find how fast the water level is rising when $h = 5$ ft.

10. A train leaves a station at a certain time and travels north at the rate of 50 mi/hr. A second train leaves the same station 2 hr after the first train leaves, and goes east at the rate of 60 mi/hr. Find the rate at which the two trains are separating 1.5 hr after the second train leaves the station.

11. Sand is falling on a pile, always having the shape of a cone, at the rate of 3 ft^3/min. Assume that the diameter at the base of the pile is always three times the altitude. At what rate is the altitude increasing when the altitude is 4 ft?

Chapter IV

Sine and Cosine

From the sine of an angle and the cosine of an angle, we shall define functions of numbers, and determine their derivatives.

It is convenient to recall all the facts about trigonometry which we need in the sequel, especially the formula giving us the sine and cosine of the sum of two angles. Thus our treatment of the trigonometric functions is self-contained—you do not need to know anything about sine and cosine before starting to read this chapter. However, most of the proofs of statements in §1 come from plane geometry and will be left to you.

§1. THE SINE AND COSINE FUNCTIONS

Suppose that we have given coordinate axes, and a certain angle, as shown on the figure.

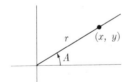

We select a point (x, y) (not the origin) on the line determining our angle A. We let $r = \sqrt{x^2 + y^2}$. Then r is the distance from $(0, 0)$ to the point (x, y). We define

$$\text{sine } A = \frac{y}{r} = \frac{y}{\sqrt{x^2 + y^2}}$$

$$\text{cosine } A = \frac{x}{r} = \frac{x}{\sqrt{x^2 + y^2}}.$$

If we select another point (x_1, y_1) on the line determining our angle A and use its coordinates to get the sine and cosine, then we shall obtain the same values as with (x, y). Indeed, there is a positive number c such that

$$x_1 = cx \quad \text{and} \quad y_1 = cy.$$

Thus

$$\frac{y_1}{\sqrt{x_1^2 + x_1^2}} = \frac{cy}{\sqrt{c^2x^2 + c^2y^2}}.$$

We can factor c from the denominator, and then cancel c in both the numerator and denominator to get

$$\frac{y}{\sqrt{x^2 + y^2}}.$$

In this way we see that sine A does not depend on the choice of coordinates (x, y).

The geometric interpretation of the above argument simply states that the triangles in the following diagram are similar.

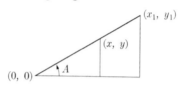

The angle A can go all the way around. For instance, we could have an angle determined by a point (x, y) in the second or third quadrant.

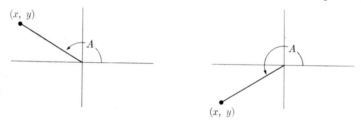

When the angle A is in the first quadrant, then its sine and cosine are positive because both coordinates x, y are positive. When the angle A is in the second quadrant, its sine is positive because y is positive, but its cosine is negative because x is negative.

When A is in the third quadrant, sine A is negative and cosine A is negative also.

In order to define the sine of a *number*, we select a unit for measuring angles. We let π be the area of the circle of radius 1. We then choose a unit angle such that the flat angle is equal to π times the unit angle. (See the following figures.) The right angle has measure $\pi/2$. The full angle going once around is then 2π.

The unit of measurement for which the flat angle is π is called the *radian*. Thus the right angle has $\pi/2$ radians.

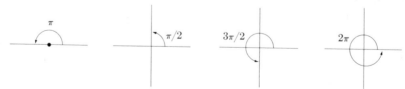

There is another current unit of measurement for which the flat angle is 180. This unit is called the *degree*. Thus the flat angle has 180 degrees, and the right angle has 90 degrees. We also have

$$360 \text{ degrees} = 2\pi \text{ radians}$$
$$60 \text{ degrees} = \pi/3 \text{ radians}$$
$$45 \text{ degrees} = \pi/4 \text{ radians}$$
$$30 \text{ degrees} = \pi/6 \text{ radians.}$$

We make a table of the sines and cosines of these angles.

Angle	Sine	Cosine	Angle (°)
$\pi/6$	$1/2$	$\sqrt{3}/2$	$30°$
$\pi/4$	$1/\sqrt{2}$	$+1/\sqrt{2}$	$45°$
$\pi/3$	$\sqrt{3}/2$	$1/2$	$60°$
$\pi/2$	1	0	$90°$
π	0	-1	$180°$
2π	0	1	$360°$

Unless otherwise specified, we *always use the radian measure*, and our table is given for this measure.

The values of this table are easily determined, using properties of similar triangles and plane geometry. For instance, we get the sine of the angle $\pi/4$ radians from a right triangle with two equal sides:

We can determine the sine of $\pi/4$ by means of the point $(1, 1)$. Then $r = \sqrt{2}$ and sine $\pi/4$ radians is $1/\sqrt{2}$. Similarly for the cosine.

The following is an important rule relating the sine and cosine.

Theorem 1. *For any angle A we have*

$$\text{cosine } A = \text{sine}\left(A + \frac{\pi}{2}\right) \quad \text{or} \quad \text{sine } A = \text{cosine}\left(A - \frac{\pi}{2}\right).$$

Proof. You can use theorems of plane geometry to prove our theorem. We leave this to you.

We define a function of numbers, which will also be called the *sine*, by the association:

> For any number x we associate to it the number which is the sine of x radians.

This function is denoted by sin x and is defined for all x. Thus sin $\pi = 0$, sin $\pi/2 = 1$, sin $2\pi = 0$, sin $0 = 0$.

Similarly, we have the *cosine function*, which is defined for all numbers x by the rule:

cos x is the number which is the cosine of the angle x radians.

Thus cos $0 = 1$ and cos $\pi = -1$.

We can also define the tangent function, tan x, which is the quotient

$$\tan x = \frac{\sin x}{\cos x}$$

and is defined for all numbers x such that cos $x \neq 0$. These are the numbers x which are unequal to

$$\frac{\pi}{2}, \quad \frac{3\pi}{2}, \quad \frac{5\pi}{2}, \quad \cdots;$$

in general $x \neq (2n + 1)\pi/2$ for some integer n.

If we had used the measure of angles in degrees we would obtain *another* sine function which is not equal to the sine function which we defined in terms of radians. Suppose we call this other sine function sin*. Then

$$\sin* (180) = \sin \pi,$$

and in general

$$\sin* (180x) = \sin \pi x$$

for any number x. Thus

$$\sin^* x = \sin \left(\frac{\pi}{180} x \right)$$

is the formula relating our two sine functions. It will become clear later why we always pick the radian measure instead of any other.

At present we have no means of computing values for the sine and cosine other than the very special cases listed above (and similar ones, based on simple symmetries of right triangles). It will be only in Chapter XIV that we shall develop a method which will allow us to find sin x and cos x for any value of x, up to any degree of accuracy that you wish.

EXERCISES

Find the following values of the sin function and cos function:

1. sin $3\pi/4$ 2. sin $2\pi/6$ 3. sin $\dfrac{2\pi}{3}$ 4. sin $\left(\pi - \dfrac{\pi}{6} \right)$

5. cos $\left(\pi + \dfrac{\pi}{6} \right)$ 6. cos $\left(\pi + \dfrac{2\pi}{6} \right)$ 7. cos $\left(2\pi - \dfrac{\pi}{6} \right)$ 8. cos $\dfrac{5\pi}{4}$

Find the following values:

9. $\tan \dfrac{\pi}{4}$ 10. $\tan \dfrac{2\pi}{6}$ 11. $\tan \dfrac{5\pi}{4}$ 12. $\tan \left(2\pi - \dfrac{\pi}{4}\right)$

13. Prove by plane geometry that $\sin (\pi - x) = \sin x$.

14. Prove by plane geometry that $\cos (\pi - x) = -\cos x$.

15. Prove by plane geometry that $\sin (2\pi - x) = -\sin x$.

16. Prove by plane geometry that $\sin (-x) = -\sin x$.

17. Prove by plane geometry that $\cos (-x) = \cos x$.

18. Let a be a given number. Determine all numbers x such that $\sin x = \sin a$. (You may suppose that $0 \leq a < 2\pi$, and distinguish the cases $a = \pi/2$, $a = -\pi/2$ and $a \neq \pm\pi/2$.)

§2. THE GRAPHS

We wish to sketch the graph of the sine function.

We know that $\sin 0 = 0$. As x goes from 0 to $\pi/2$, the sine of x increases until x reaches $\pi/2$, at which point the sine is equal to 1.

As x ranges from $\pi/2$ to π, the sine decreases until it becomes $\sin \pi = 0$.

As x ranges from π to $3\pi/2$ the sine becomes negative, but otherwise behaves in a similar way to the first quadrant, until it reaches

$$\sin 3\pi/2 = -1.$$

Finally, as x goes from $3\pi/2$ to 2π, the sine of x goes from -1 to 0, and we are ready to start all over again.

The graph looks like this:

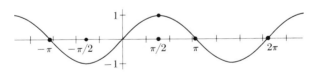

The graph of the cosine will look like that of the sine, but it starts with $\cos 0 = 1$. In the next picture the scale used on the vertical axis is different from that on the horizontal axis so that we will have more room for the arches of the graph.

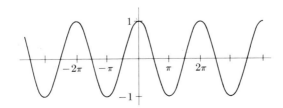

If we go once around by 2π, both the sine and cosine take on the same values, in other words

$$\sin (x + 2\pi) = \sin x$$
$$\cos (x + 2\pi) = \cos x$$

for all x. This holds whether x is positive or negative, and the same would be true if we took $x - 2\pi$ instead of $x + 2\pi$.

You might legitimately ask why one arch of the sine (or cosine) curve looks the way we have drawn it, and not the following way:

In the next section, we shall find the slope of the curve $y = \sin x$. It is equal to $\cos x$. Thus when $x = 0$, the slope is $\cos 0 = 1$. Furthermore, when $x = \pi/2$, we have $\cos \pi/2 = 0$ and hence the slope is 0. This means that the curve becomes horizontal, and cannot have a peak the way we have drawn it above.

At present we have no means for computing more values of $\sin x$ and $\cos x$. However, using the few that we know and the derivative, we can convince ourselves that the graphs look as we have drawn them.

Example. Sketch the graph of $y = \sin (x - \pi)$.

Let $x' = x - \pi$, $y' = y$. We know how to draw the graph of $y = x'$ relative to (x', y)-axes. When $x = 0$, we have $x' = -\pi$. Thus the graph of $y = \sin (x - \pi)$ looks like this.

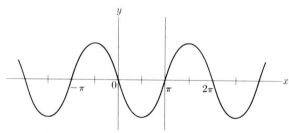

The values $-\pi$, 0, π, 2π indicated are those corresponding to the x-coordinate.

EXERCISES

1. Draw the graph of $\tan x$.

2. Let $\sec x = 1/\cos x$ be defined when $\cos x \neq 0$. Draw the graph of $\sec x$.

3. Let $\cot x = 1/\tan x$. Draw the graph of $\cot x$.
   (Sec and cot are abbreviations for the secant and cotangent.)

4. Draw the graph of the function $\sin(1/x)$ for $0 < x \leqq \pi$.

5. Draw the graph of the function $x \sin(1/x)$ for $0 < x \leqq \pi$.

6. Draw the graph of the function $x^2 \sin(1/x)$ for $0 < x \leqq \pi$.
   (In Exercises 4, 5, 6 the function is not defined for $x = 0$.)

7. Let $f(x) = x^2 \sin(1/x)$ when $x \neq 0$ and let $f(0) = 0$. Using the Newton quotient, show that f has a derivative at 0 and that $f'(0) = 0$.

8. Let $f(x) = x \sin(1/x)$ when $x \neq 0$ and let $f(0) = 0$. Show that f does not have a derivative at 0. Look at small values of x like

$$h = \frac{2}{n\pi},$$

n being a large integer. Try $n = 1, 2, 3, 4$, etc. and see what happens to the values of $f(x)$ and the Newton quotient

$$\frac{f(h) - f(0)}{h}.$$

9. Sketch the graphs of the following functions:

   (a) $y = \sin 2x$ (b) $y = \sin 3x$

   (c) $y = \cos 2x$ (d) $y = \cos 3x$

   (e) $y = \tan 2x$ (f) $y = \sin\left(x + \frac{\pi}{4}\right)$

   (g) $y = \tan\left(x + \frac{\pi}{6}\right)$ (h) $y = \tan\left(x - \frac{\pi}{6}\right)$

   (i) $y = \sin \frac{1}{2}x$ (j) $y = \cos \frac{1}{2}x$

10. Sketch the graphs of the following functions:

   (a) $y = 1 + \sin x$ (b) $y = 1 + \sin 2x$

   (c) $y = -2 + \cos(x - 1)$ (d) $y = -\cos \frac{2}{3}\pi x$

   (e) $y = \sin\left(2x - \frac{\pi}{3}\right)$ (f) $y = 5 \sin \frac{1}{2}\pi x$

   (g) $y = 4 \cos \frac{1}{2}\pi x$ (h) $y = -\cos 2x$

§3. ADDITION FORMULA

In this section we shall state and prove the most important formulas about sine and cosine.

To begin with, using the Pythagoras theorem, we observe that

$$(\sin x)^2 + (\cos x)^2 = 1$$

for all x. Indeed, if we have an angle A and we determine its sine and cosine from the right triangle, as in the following figure, then we have

$$a^2 + b^2 = r^2.$$

Dividing by r^2 yields

$$\left(\frac{a}{r}\right)^2 + \left(\frac{b}{r}\right)^2 = 1.$$

The same argument works when A is greater than $\pi/2$, by means of a triangle like this one:

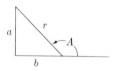

In both cases, we have sine $A = a/r$ and cosine $A = b/r$, so that we have the relation

$$(\text{sine } A)^2 + (\text{cosine } A)^2 = 1.$$

It is customary to write the square of the sine and cosine as $\sin^2 A$ and $\cos^2 A$. In the second case note that b is negative.

Our main result is the *addition formula*.

Theorem 2. *For any angles A and B, we have*

$$\sin (A + B) = \sin A \cos B + \cos A \sin B$$
$$\cos (A + B) = \cos A \cos B - \sin A \sin B.$$

Proof. We shall prove the second formula first.

We consider two angles A, B and their sum:

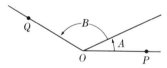

We take two points P, Q as indicated, at a distance 1 from the origin O. We shall now compute the distance from P to Q, using two different coordinate systems.

First, we take a coordinate system as usual:

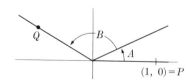

Then the coordinates of P are $(1, 0)$ and those of Q are

$$\big(\cos (A + B), \sin (A + B)\big).$$

The square of the distance between P and Q is

$$\sin^2 (A + B) + \big(\cos (A + B) - 1\big)^2,$$

which is equal to

$$-2 \cos (A + B) + 2.$$

Next we place the coordinate system as shown in the figure below.

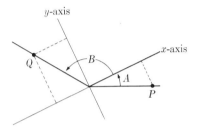

Then the coordinates of P become

$$\big(\cos A, \sin (-A)\big) = (\cos A, -\sin A).$$

Those of Q are simply $(\cos B, \sin B)$. The square of the distance between P and Q is

$$(\sin B + \sin A)^2 + (\cos B - \cos A)^2,$$

which is equal to

$$\sin^2 B + 2 \sin B \sin A + \sin^2 A + \cos^2 B - 2 \cos B \cos A + \cos^2 A$$
$$= 2 + 2 \sin A \sin B - 2 \cos A \cos B.$$

If we set the squares of the two distances equal to each other, we get our formula.

The addition formula for the sine can be obtained by the following device:

$$\sin (A + B) = \cos \left(A + B - \frac{\pi}{2} \right)$$
$$= \cos A \cos \left(B - \frac{\pi}{2} \right) - \sin A \sin \left(B - \frac{\pi}{2} \right)$$
$$= \cos A \sin B + \sin A \sin \left(\frac{\pi}{2} - B \right)$$
$$= \cos A \sin B + \sin A \cos B,$$

thereby proving our formula.

Example. Find $\sin(\pi/12)$.
We write

$$\frac{\pi}{12} = \frac{\pi}{3} - \frac{\pi}{4}.$$

Then $\sin(\pi/12) = \sin(\pi/3)\cos(\pi/4) - \cos(\pi/3)\sin(\pi/4)$, and substituting the known values we find

$$\sin(\pi/12) = \frac{\sqrt{3} - 1}{2\sqrt{2}}.$$

EXERCISES

1. Find $\sin 7\pi/12$. [*Hint:* Write $7\pi/12 = 4\pi/12 + 3\pi/12$.]

2. Find $\cos 7\pi/12$.

3. Find the following values:
   (a) $\sin \pi/12$ (b) $\cos \pi/12$
   (c) $\sin 5\pi/12$ (d) $\cos 5\pi/12$
   (e) $\sin 11\pi/12$ (f) $\cos 11\pi/12$
   (g) $\sin 10\pi/12$ (h) $\cos 10\pi/12$

4. Prove the following formulas.
   (a) $\sin 2x = 2 \sin x \cos x$ (b) $\cos 2x = \cos^2 x - \sin^2 x$
   (c) $\cos^2 x = \dfrac{1 + \cos 2x}{2}$ (d) $\sin^2 x = \dfrac{1 - \cos 2x}{2}$

5. Find a formula for $\sin 3x$ in terms of $\sin x$ and $\cos x$. Similarly for $\sin 4x$, and $\sin 5x$.

6. Prove by induction that for any positive integer n, $\sin nx$ can be expressed as a sum of terms

$$\sum a_{ij}(\sin x)^i(\cos x)^j$$

where a_{ij} are integers.

7. Express $\sin^3 x$ as a sum of terms $a_n \cos nx$ and $b_n \sin nx$ where a_n, b_n are numbers. Prove the formulas

$$\sin mx \sin nx = \tfrac{1}{2}[\cos(m - n)x - \cos(m + n)x],$$

$$\sin mx \cos nx = \tfrac{1}{2}[\sin(m + n)x + \sin(m - n)x],$$

$$\cos mx \cos nx = \tfrac{1}{2}[\cos(m + n)x + \cos(m - n)x].$$

8. Show that for any positive integer k you can express $\sin^k x$ as a sum of terms $a_n \cos nx + b_n \sin nx$ where a_n, b_n are numbers. (In fact, rational numbers.) Prove the same thing for $\cos^k x$. Use induction.

§4. THE DERIVATIVES

We shall prove:

Theorem 3. *The functions* sin *x and* cos *x have derivatives and*

$$\frac{d(\sin x)}{dx} = \cos x$$

$$\frac{d(\cos x)}{dx} = -\sin x.$$

Proof. We shall first determine the derivative of sin x. We have to look at the Newton quotient of sin x. It is

$$\frac{\sin(x + h) - \sin x}{h}.$$

Using the addition formula to expand sin $(x + h)$, we see that the Newton quotient is equal to

$$\frac{\sin x \cos h + \cos x \sin h - \sin x}{h}.$$

We put together the two terms involving sin x:

$$\frac{\cos x \sin h + \sin x(\cos h - 1)}{h}$$

and separate our quotient into a sum of two terms:

$$\cos x \frac{\sin h}{h} + \sin x \frac{\cos h - 1}{h}.$$

We now face the problem of finding the limit of

$$\frac{\sin h}{h} \quad \text{and} \quad \frac{\cos h - 1}{h} \qquad \text{as } h \text{ approaches } 0.$$

This is a somewhat more difficult problem than those we encountered previously. We cannot tell right away what these limits will be. In the next section, we shall prove that

$$\lim_{h \to 0} \frac{\sin h}{h} = 1 \quad \text{and} \quad \lim_{h \to 0} \frac{\cos h - 1}{h} = 0.$$

Once we know these limits, then we see immediately that the first term approaches cos x and the second term approaches

$$(\sin x) \cdot 0 = 0.$$

Hence

$$\lim_{h \to 0} \frac{\sin(x + h) - \sin x}{h} = \cos x.$$

This proves that

$$\frac{d(\sin x)}{dx} = \cos x.$$

To find the derivative of $\cos x$, we could proceed in the same way, and we would encounter the same limits. However, there is a trick which avoids this.

We know that $\cos x = \sin\left(x + \frac{\pi}{2}\right)$. Let $u = x + \frac{\pi}{2}$ and use the chain rule. We get

$$\frac{d(\cos x)}{dx} = \frac{d(\sin u)}{du} \frac{du}{dx}.$$

However, $du/dx = 1$. Hence

$$\frac{d(\cos x)}{dx} = \cos u = \cos\left(x + \frac{\pi}{2}\right) = -\sin x,$$

thereby proving our theorem.

Remark. It is not true that the derivative of the function sin* x is cos* x. Using the chain rule, find out what its derivative is. The reason for using the radian measure of angles is to get a function $\sin x$ whose derivative is $\cos x$.

EXERCISES

1. What is the derivative of $\tan x$?

Find the derivative of the following functions:

2. $\sin (3x)$　　　　　　　　　　　　3. $\cos (5x)$

4. $\sin (4x^2 + x)$　　　　　　　　　　5. $\tan (x^3 - 5)$

6. $\tan (x^4 - x^3)$　　　　　　　　　　7. $\tan (\sin x)$

8. $\sin (\tan x)$　　　　　　　　　　　9. $\cos (\tan x)$

10. What is the slope of the curve $y = \sin x$ at the point whose x-coordinate is π? Find the slope of the following curves at the indicated point (we just give the x-coordinate of the point):

11. $y = \cos (3x)$ at $x = \pi/3$　　　　　12. $y = \sin x$ at $x = \pi/6$

13. $y = \sin x + \cos x$ at $x = 3\pi/4$　　14. $y = \tan x$ at $x = -\pi/4$

15. $y = \dfrac{1}{\sin x}$ at $x = -\pi/6$

16. Give the equation of the tangent line to the following curves at the indicated point.

　　(a) $y = \sin x$ at $x = \pi/2$　　　　　(b) $y = \cos x$ at $x = \pi/6$

(c) $y = \sin 2x$ at $x = \pi/4$

(d) $y = \tan 3x$ at $x = \pi/4$

(e) $y = 1/\sin x$ at $x = \pi/2$

(f) $y = 1/\cos x$ at $x = \pi/4$

(g) $y = 1/\tan x$ at $x = \pi/4$

(h) $y = \tan \dfrac{x}{2}$ at $x = 3\pi$

(i) $y = \sin \dfrac{x}{2}$ at $x = \pi/3$

(i) $y = \cos \dfrac{\pi x}{3}$ at $x = 1$

(k) $y = \sin \pi x$ at $x = \frac{1}{2}$

(l) $y = \tan \pi x$ at $x = \frac{1}{6}$

17. In the following right triangle, suppose that θ is decreasing at the rate of $\frac{1}{30}$ rad/sec. Find each one of the indicated derivatives:

(a) dy/dt, when $\theta = \pi/3$ and x is constant, $x = 12$.

(b) dz/dt, when $\theta = \pi/4$ if y is constant, $y = 10\sqrt{2}$.

(c) dx/dt, when $x = 1$ and $z = 2$, if x and y are both changing.

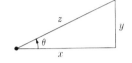

18. A Ferris wheel 50 ft in diameter makes 1 revolution every 2 min. If the center of the wheel is 30 ft above the ground, how fast is a passenger in the wheel moving vertically when he is 42.5 ft above the ground?

§5. TWO BASIC LIMITS

We shall first prove that

$$\lim_{h \to 0} \frac{\sin h}{h} = 1.$$

Both the numerator and the denominator approach 0 as h approaches 0, and we get no information by trying some cancellation procedure, the way we did it for powers.

Let us assume first that h is positive, and look at the following diagram.

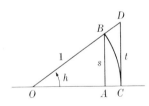

We take a circle of radius 1 and an angle of h radians. Let s be the altitude of the small triangle, and t that of the big triangle. Then

$$\sin h = \frac{s}{1} = s$$

and

$$\tan h = \frac{t}{1} = t = \frac{\sin h}{\cos h}.$$

We see that:

area of triangle OAB < area of sector OCB < area of triangle OCD.

The base OA of the small triangle is equal to cos h and its altitude is sin h.

The base OC of the big triangle is equal to 1. Its altitude is

$$t = \frac{\sin h}{\cos h}.$$

The area of each triangle is $\frac{1}{2}$ the base times the altitude.

The area of the sector is the fraction $h/2\pi$ of the area of the circle, which is π. Hence the area of the sector is $h/2$. Thus we obtain:

$$\frac{1}{2}\cos h \sin h < \frac{1}{2}h < \frac{1}{2}\frac{\sin h}{\cos h}.$$

We multiply everywhere by 2 and get

$$\cos h \sin h < h < \frac{\sin h}{\cos h}.$$

There are really two inequalities here. The first one is

$$\cos h \sin h < h.$$

Since h is positive, we can divide it by h and then divide by cos h, which is also positive. This yields

$$\frac{\sin h}{h} < \frac{1}{\cos h}.$$

The second inequality is

$$h < \frac{\sin h}{\cos h}.$$

We multiply it by cos h and divide it by h to get

$$\cos h < \frac{\sin h}{h}.$$

Putting our two inequalities together, we get

$$\cos h < \frac{\sin h}{h} < \frac{1}{\cos h}.$$

The game is almost won. Letting h approach 0, we see that $(\sin h)/h$ is squeezed between two quantities which approach 1. Hence it must approach 1 also, and our proof is complete.

We still have to consider the limit

$$\lim_{h \to 0} \frac{\cos h - 1}{h}$$

and show that it is 0. We have

$$\frac{\cos h - 1}{h} = \frac{(\cos h - 1)(\cos h + 1)}{h(\cos h + 1)}$$

$$= \frac{\cos^2 h - 1}{h(\cos h + 1)}$$

$$= \frac{-\sin^2 h}{h(\cos h + 1)}.$$

We can write this last expression in the form

$$-\frac{\sin h}{h} (\sin h) \frac{1}{\cos h + 1}.$$

Using the property concerning the product of limits, we have a product of three factors. The first is

$$-\frac{\sin h}{h}$$

and approaches -1 as h approaches 0.

The second is $\sin h$ and approaches 0 as h approaches 0.
The third is

$$\frac{1}{\cos h + 1}$$

and its limit is $\frac{1}{2}$ as h approaches 0.

Therefore the limit of the product is 0, and everything is proved!

We still have one thing to take care of. We computed our limit when $h > 0$. Suppose that $h < 0$. We can write

$$h = -k$$

with $k > 0$. Then

$$\frac{\sin (-k)}{-k} = \frac{-\sin k}{-k} = \frac{\sin k}{k}.$$

As h tends to 0, so does k. Hence we are reduced to our previous limit because $k > 0$. A similar remark applies to our other limit involving $\cos h$.

EXERCISES

Find the following limits, as h approaches 0.

1. $\dfrac{\sin 2h}{h}$ $\left[\textit{Hint:} \textbf{ Put } k = 2h. \textbf{ Then } \dfrac{\sin 2h}{h} = 2\dfrac{\sin k}{k} \cdot \right]$

2. $\dfrac{\sin 3h}{h}$ 3. $\dfrac{\sin h}{3h}$ 4. $\dfrac{\tan h}{\sin h}$

5. $\dfrac{\cos 2h}{1 + \sin h}$ 6. $\dfrac{\sin h^2}{h}$ 7. $\dfrac{\sin 2h^2}{3h}$

8. $\dfrac{\sin h^3}{h^3}$ 9. $\dfrac{\sin 2h^3}{h^3}$ 10. $\dfrac{h \sin h}{\sin 2h^2}$

11. $\dfrac{(\sin h)(\sin 2h)}{(\sin 3h)h}$

Chapter V

The Mean Value Theorem

Given a curve, $y = f(x)$, we shall use the derivative to give us information about the curve. For instance, we shall find the maximum and minimum of the graph, and regions where the curve is increasing or decreasing. We shall use the mean value theorem, which is basic in the theory of derivatives.

§1. THE MAXIMUM AND MINIMUM THEOREM

Let f be a differentiable function. A point c such that $f'(c) = 0$ is called a *critical point* of the function. The derivative being zero means that the slope of the tangent line is 0 and thus that the tangent line itself is horizontal. We have drawn three examples of this phenomenon.

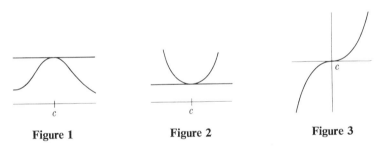

| Figure 1 | Figure 2 | Figure 3 |

The third example is that of a function like $f(x) = x^3$. We have $f'(x) = 3x^2$ and hence when $x = 0, f'(0) = 0$.

The other two examples are those of a maximum and a minimum, respectively, if we look at the graph of the function only near our point c. We shall now formalize these notions.

Let a, b be two numbers with $a < b$. We shall repeatedly deal with the interval of numbers between a and b. Sometimes we want to include the end points a and b, and sometimes we do not. We recall the standard terminology.

The collection of numbers x such that $a < x < b$ is called the *open interval* between a and b.

The collection of numbers x such that $a \leq x \leq b$ is called the *closed interval* between a and b. We denote this closed interval by the symbols $[a, b]$. (A single point will also be called a closed interval.)

If we wish to include only one end point, we shall say that the interval is *half closed*. We have of course two half-closed intervals, namely the one consisting of the numbers x with $a \leq x < b$, and the other one consisting of the numbers x with $a < x \leq b$.

Sometimes, if a is a number, we call the collection of numbers $x > a$ (or $x < a$) an open interval. The context will always make this clear.

Let f be a function, and c a number at which f is defined. We shall say that c is a *maximum* of the function if

$$f(c) \geq f(x)$$

for all numbers x at which f is defined. If we have only $f(c) \geq f(x)$ for all numbers x in some interval, then we say that c is a maximum of the function *in that interval*.

Example 1. Let $f(x) = \sin x$. Then $\pi/2$ is a maximum for f because $f(\pi/2) = 1$ and $\sin x \leq 1$ for all values of x. Note that $-3\pi/2$ is also a maximum for $\sin x$.

Example 2. Let $f(x) = 2x$, and view f as a function defined only on the interval

$$0 \leq x \leq 2.$$

Then 2 is a maximum for the function in this interval because $f(2) = 4$ and $f(x) \leq 4$ for all x in the interval.

Example 3. Let $f(x) = 1/x$. We know that f is not defined for $x = 0$. This function has no maximum. It becomes arbitrarily large when x comes close to 0 and $x > 0$.

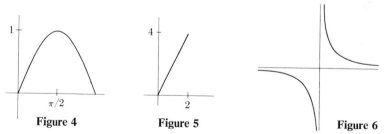

Figure 4   Figure 5   Figure 6

We have illustrated our three examples in Figs. 4, 5, and 6.

In the next theorem, we shall prove that under certain circumstances, the derivative of a function at a maximum is 0.

Theorem 1. *Let f be a function which is defined and differentiable on the open interval $a < x < b$. Let c be a number in the interval which is a maximum for the function. (In other words, $f(c) \geq f(x)$ for all x in the interval.) Then*

$$f'(c) = 0.$$

Proof. If we take small values of h (positive or negative), the number $c + h$ will lie in the interval.

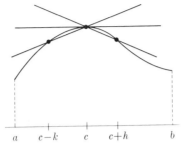

Figure 7

Let us first take h positive (see Fig. 7). We must have

$$f(c) \geqq f(c + h)$$

no matter what h is (provided h is small). Therefore $f(c + h) - f(c) \leqq 0$. Since $h > 0$, the Newton quotient

$$\frac{f(c + h) - f(c)}{h}$$

is $\leqq 0$. Hence the limit is $\leqq 0$, or in symbols:

$$\lim_{\substack{h \to 0 \\ h > 0}} \frac{f(c + h) - f(c)}{h} \leqq 0.$$

Now take h negative, say $h = -k$ with $k > 0$. Then

$$f(c - k) - f(c) \leqq 0, \qquad f(c) - f(c - k) \geqq 0$$

and the quotient is

$$\frac{f(c - k) - f(c)}{-k} = \frac{f(c) - f(c - k)}{k}.$$

Thus the Newton quotient is $\geqq 0$. Taking the limit as h (or k) approaches 0, we see that

$$\lim_{\substack{h \to 0 \\ h < 0}} \frac{f(c + h) - f(c)}{h} \geqq 0.$$

The only way in which our two limits can be equal is that they should both be 0. Therefore $f'(c) = 0$.

We can interpret our arguments geometrically by saying that the line between our two points slants to the left when we take $h > 0$ and slants to the right when we take $h < 0$. As h approaches 0, both lines must approach the tangent line to the curve. The only way this is possible is for the tangent line at the point whose x-coordinate is c to be horizontal. This means that its slope is 0, i.e. $f'(c) = 0$.

Everything we have done with a maximum could have been done with a minimum.

Let f be a function. We say that a number c is a *minimum* for f if $f(c) \leq f(x)$ for all x at which the function is defined.

Theorem 1 remains true when we replace the word "maximum" by the word "minimum". It will be a good exercise for you to prove Theorem 1 for the minimum. When we refer to Theorem 1 we shall use it in both cases.

We illustrate various minima with the graphs of certain functions.

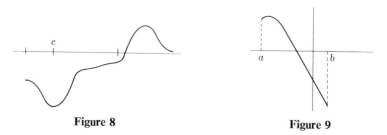

Figure 8   Figure 9

In Fig. 8 the function has a minimum. In Fig. 9 the minimum is at the end point of the interval. In Figs. 3 and 6 the function has no minimum.

In the following picture, the point c_1 looks like a maximum and the point c_2 looks like a minimum, provided we stay close to these points, and don't look at what happens to the curve farther away.

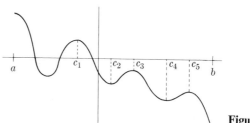

Figure 10

There is a name for such points. We shall say that a point c is a *local minimum* of the function f if there exists an interval

$$a_1 < c < b_1$$

such that $f(c) \leq f(x)$ for all numbers x with $a_1 \leq x \leq b_1$.

Similarly, we define the notion of *local maximum*. (Do it yourself.) In Fig. 10, the point c_3 is a local maximum, c_4 is a local minimum, and c_5 is a local maximum.

The actual maximum and minimum occur at the end points.

In practice, a function usually has only a finite number of critical points, and it is easy to find all points c such that $f'(c) = 0$. One can then determine by inspection which of these are maxima, which are minima, and which are neither.

Example 1. Find the critical points of the function $f(x) = x^3 - 1$.
We have $f'(x) = 3x^2$. Hence there is only one critical point, namely $x = 0$.

Example 2. Find the critical points of the function

$$y = x^3 - 2x + 1.$$

The derivative is $3x^2 - 2$. It is equal to 0 precisely when

$$x^2 = \tfrac{2}{3},$$

which means $x = \sqrt{2/3}$ or $-\sqrt{2/3}$. These are the critical points.

Example 3. Find the local maximum and minimum of the function $f(x) = x^3 - 2x + 1$.

The local maximum and minimum must be a critical point, hence we have only two possibilities, which we found in Example 2. These are $x = \sqrt{2/3}$ and $x = -\sqrt{2/3}$. We make a small table of values of our function:

x	y
0	1
-1	2
-2	-3
1	0
2	5

The number $\sqrt{2/3}$ is between 0 and 1. Since $f(1) = 0$ and $f(0) = 1$, it follows that $\sqrt{2/3}$ must be a local minimum.

Similarly, $-\sqrt{2/3}$ is between 0 and -1. But $f(0) = 1$ and $f(-1) = 2$. Hence $-\sqrt{2/3}$ is a local maximum. The sketch of the graph looks like this:

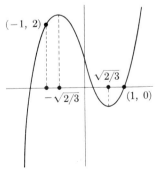

Figure 11

EXERCISES

Find the critical points of the following functions:

1. $x^2 - 2x + 5$ 　　　　　　　　　　2. $2x^2 - 3x - 1$

3. $3x^2 - x + 1$ 　　　　　　　　　　4. $-x^2 + 2x + 2$

5. $-2x^2 + 3x - 1$ 　　　　　　　　　6. $x^3 + 2$

7. $x^3 - 3x$ 　　　　　　　　　　　　8. $\sin x + \cos x$

9. $\cos x$ 　　　　　　　　　　　　　10. $\sin x$

11. A box with open top is to be made with a square base and a constant surface C. Determine the sides of the box if the volume is to be a maximum.

12. A container in the shape of a cylinder with open top is to have a fixed surface area C. Find the radius of its base and its height if it is to have maximum volume.

13. Do the above two problems when box and container are closed at the top.

(The area of a circle of radius x is πx^2 and its length is $2\pi x$. The volume of a cylinder whose base has radius x and of height y is $\pi x^2 y$.)

§2. EXISTENCE OF MAXIMA AND MINIMA

It is important to know when a function has a maximum and a minimum. We shall describe a condition under which it does.

Up to now we have defined derivatives by means of a Newton quotient taken with h positive and negative. However, in Chapter II, we also described the right derivative and the left derivative.

Let $f(x)$ be a function defined on an interval

$$a \leqq x \leqq b.$$

(*We assume throughout that $a < b$.*) We shall say that it is *differentiable* in this interval if it is differentiable in the interval

$$a < x < b,$$

and if, in addition, it has a right derivative at a, and a left derivative at b. Thus we assume that the limits

$$\lim_{\substack{h \to 0 \\ h > 0}} \frac{f(a + h) - f(a)}{h}$$

and

$$\lim_{\substack{h \to 0 \\ h < 0}} \frac{f(b + h) - f(b)}{h}$$

exist. These limits will be denoted by $f'(a)$ and $f'(b)$ just as with the ordinary derivative.

If we have a point x in the interval which is not equal to the end points, then $f'(x)$ has the usual meaning.

Since the function may not be defined outside the interval, the quotient

$$\frac{f(a + h) - f(a)}{h}$$

would not be defined when $h < 0$, and similarly the quotient

$$\frac{f(b + h) - f(b)}{h}$$

would not be defined when $h > 0$.

We need some criterion to know when a function has a maximum and a minimum in an interval.

A function f is said to be *continuous* if for every x such that f is defined, we have

$$\lim_{h \to 0} f(x + h) = f(x).$$

If f is differentiable, then it must be continuous.

In this chapter, we shall deal mostly with functions defined on an interval with end points a, b such that $a < b$, and these functions will be differentiable in the open interval, and continuous at the end points.

Theorem 2. *Let $f(x)$ be a function which is continuous on the closed interval $a \leq x \leq b$. Then f has a maximum and also has a minimum in this interval.*

This means that there is a point c_1 in the interval such that $f(c_1) \geq f(x)$ for all x in the interval, and there is a point c_2 such that $f(c_2) \leq f(x)$ for all x in the interval.

If you look back to Fig. 3 and Fig. 6 of §1, you will see graphs of functions which have no maximum or minimum. The reason for this is that the functions are not defined over closed intervals. In the case of a hyperbola, as in Fig. 6, we could define the function at 0 in an arbitrary way, for instance let $f(0) = 997$. We still would not get a maximum or a minimum.

We shall take Theorem 2 for granted, without proof. If you are interested in seeing a proof, you can look in the appendix. The proof must be carried out by using special properties of numbers.

Combining Theorems 1 and 2, we obtain:

Theorem 3. *Let a, b be two numbers, $a < b$. Let f be a function which is continuous over the closed interval*

$$a \leq x \leq b$$

and differentiable on the open interval $a < x < b$. Assume that

$$f(a) = f(b) = 0.$$

Then there exists a point c such that

$$a < c < b$$

and such that $f'(c) = 0$.

Proof. If the function is constant in the interval, then its derivative is 0 and any point in the open interval $a < x < b$ will do.

If the function is not constant, then there exists some point in the interval where the function is not 0, and this point cannot be one of the end points a or b. Suppose that some value of our function is positive. By Theorem 2, the function has a maximum. Let c be this maximum. Then $f(c)$ must be greater than 0, and c cannot be either one of the end points. Consequently

$$a < c < b.$$

By Theorem 1, we must have $f'(c) = 0$. This proves our theorem in case the function is positive somewhere in the interval.

If the function is negative for some number in the interval, then we use Theorem 2 to get a minimum, and we argue in a similar way, using Theorem 1 (applied to a minimum). (Write out the argument in full as an exercise.)

The following picture illustrates our Theorem 3.

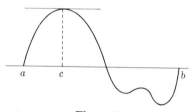

Figure 12

Example 1. Find the maximum of the function $y = 2x + 1$ on the interval $3 \leq x \leq 5$.

Let $f(x) = 2x + 1$. Then $f'(x) = 2$, and is constant $\neq 0$. Hence there is no maximum in the open interval $3 < x < 5$. Hence the maximum occurs at the end points, and one verifies by a direct computation that 5 is a maximum.

Example 2. Find a maximum for the function $f(x) = -x^2 + 3x + 5$ on the interval $[-1, 3]$.

Note that $f'(x) = -2x + 3$, and that $f'(x) = 0$ precisely when $x = 3/2$. Thus a maximum for f in the interval occurs either at the end points, or at $x = 3/2$. But $f(-1) = 1$, $f(3/2) = 29/4$ and $f(3) = 5$. Hence $3/2$ is the maximum.

Example 3. Find the maximum value of the function

$$f(x) = \sin 2x + \cos 2x$$

on the interval $0 \leq x \leq \pi/2$.

We have $f'(x) = 2 \cos 2x - 2 \sin 2x$. The derivative $f'(x)$ is equal to 0 precisely when $\sin 2x = \cos 2x$. For x in the prescribed interval, $0 \leq x \leq \pi/2$, this occurs only when $2x = \pi/4$, or $x = \pi/8$. At that point, we have

$$f(\pi/8) = \frac{2}{\sqrt{2}}.$$

At the end points of the interval, we have $f(0) = 1$ and $f(\pi/2) = -1$. Since $2/\sqrt{2} > 1$ and also > -1, it follows that the point $x = \pi/8$ is the maximum of the function.

EXERCISES

In the following exercises, sketch the graph of the function and find the maximum and minimum values in the given interval.

1. $f(x) = 2x + 1$, $[-1, 2]$ 2. $f(x) = 4 - x$, $[-2, 4]$

3. $f(x) = 1/x$, $[-2, -1]$ 4. $f(x) = x^2$, $[-2, 1]$

5. $f(x) = \sqrt{x - 2}$, $x \geq 2$ 6. $f(x) = \sqrt[3]{x + 1}$, $[-9, 7]$

7. $f(x) = x^3 - 3x + 1$, $[1, 3]$ 8. $f(x) = -x^2 + 2$, $[-1, 4]$

9. $f(x) = x^3 - x^2$, $[0, 5]$ 10. $f(x) = x^4 - 81x$, $[-2, 2]$

§2   Find the local and absolute maxima and minima of the following functions over the interval $[0, 2\pi]$.

11. $f(x) = \sin x + \cos x$ 12. $f(x) = 2 \cos x + \cos 2x$

13. $f(x) = \sin^2 x + \cos x$ 14. $f(x) = \tan x - 2x$

15. $f(x) = \sin 3x$ 16. $f(x) = \dfrac{2}{\cos x} - \tan x$

17. $f(x) = \cos^2 x$ 18. $f(x) = \sin^2 x$

§3   Find the absolute maximum of the following functions over the interval $[0, \pi/2]$.

19. $f(x) = \sin^3 x$ 20. $f(x) = 1 - \sin^3 x$

21. $f(x) = \sin^2 x + \cos x$ 22. $f(x) = \cos^2 x + \sin x$.

§3. THE MEAN VALUE THEOREM

Let $f(x)$ be a function which is differentiable in the closed interval

$$a \leq x \leq b.$$

We continue to assume throughout that $a < b$. This time we do not assume as in Theorem 3, that $f(a) = f(b) = 0$. We shall prove that there exists a point c between a and b such that the slope of the tangent line at $(c, f(c))$ is the same as the slope of the line between the end points of our graph. In other words, the tangent line is parallel to the line passing through the end points of our graph.

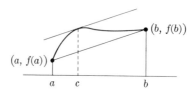

Figure 13

The slope of the line between the two end points is

$$\frac{f(b) - f(a)}{b - a}$$

because the coordinates of the end points are $(a, f(a))$ and $(b, f(b))$ respectively. Thus we have to find a point c such that

$$f'(c) = \frac{f(b) - f(a)}{b - a}.$$

Theorem 4. *Let $a < b$ as before. Let f be a function which is continuous in the closed interval $a \leq x \leq b$, and differentiable in the interval $a < x < b$. Then there exists a point c such that $a < c < b$ and*

$$f'(c) = \frac{f(b) - f(a)}{b - a}.$$

Proof. The equation of the line between the two end points is

$$y = \frac{f(b) - f(a)}{b - a}(x - a) + f(a).$$

Indeed, the slope

$$\frac{f(b) - f(a)}{b - a}$$

is the coefficient of x. When $x = a$, $y = f(a)$. Hence we have written down the equation of the line having the given slope and passing through a given point. When $x = b$, we note that $y = f(b)$.

We now consider geometrically the difference between $f(x)$ and the straight line. In other words, we consider the function

$$y = g(x) = f(x) - \frac{f(b) - f(a)}{b - a}(x - a) - f(a).$$

Then

$$g(a) = f(a) - f(a) = 0$$

and

$$g(b) = f(b) - f(b) = 0$$

also.

We can therefore apply Theorem 3 to the function $g(x)$. We know that there is a point c between a and b, and not equal to a or b, such that

$$g'(c) = 0.$$

But

$$g'(x) = f'(x) - \frac{f(b) - f(a)}{b - a}.$$

Consequently

$$0 = g'(c) = f'(c) - \frac{f(b) - f(a)}{b - a}.$$

This gives us the desired value for $f'(c)$.

The difference between $f(x)$ and the straight line becomes 0 at the end points. This is the geometric idea which allows us to apply our Theorem 3.

Example 1. Let $a = 1$ and $b = 2$. Let $f(x) = x^2$. Find a point c as in Theorem 4.

We have $f'(x) = 2x$, and

$$\frac{f(b) - f(a)}{b - a} = \frac{2^2 - 1^2}{2 - 1} = \frac{3}{1} = 3.$$

We have to solve the equation $2x = 3$. We get $x = 3/2$. Thus $c = 3/2$ is a point such that $f'(c)$ has the required value.

Example 2. Let $f(x) = x^3 + 2x$, and let $a = -1$, $b = 2$. Find a number c as in Theorem 4.

We have $f'(x) = 3x^2 + 2$, and

$$\frac{f(b) - f(a)}{b - a} = \frac{12 - (-3)}{2 - (-1)} = \frac{15}{3} = 5.$$

We must solve $3x^2 + 2 = 5$ and get

$$x = 1 \quad \text{or} \quad x = -1.$$

We take $c = 1$.

EXERCISES

Find a number c as in the mean value theorem for each one of the following functions:

1. $f(x) = x^3$, $1 \leq x \leq 3$
2. $f(x) = (x - 1)^3$, $-1 \leq x \leq 2$
3. $f(x) = x^3$, $-1 \leq x \leq 3$
4. $f(x) = x^2 + 5x$, $0 \leq x \leq 2$

§4. INCREASING AND DECREASING FUNCTIONS

Let f be a function defined on some interval (which may be open or closed). We shall say that f is *increasing* over this interval if

$$f(x_1) \leq f(x_2)$$

whenever x_1 and x_2 are two points of the interval such that $x_1 \leq x_2$.

Thus, if a number lies to the right of another, the value of the function at the larger number must be greater than or equal to the value of the function at the smaller number.

In the next figure, we have drawn the graph of an increasing function.

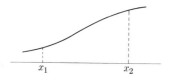

x_1 x_2 **Figure 14**

We say that a function defined on some interval is *decreasing* over this interval if

$$f(x_1) \geq f(x_2)$$

whenever x_1 and x_2 are two points of the interval such that $x_1 \leq x_2$.

Observe that a constant function (whose graph is horizontal) is both increasing and decreasing.

If we want to omit the equality sign in our definitions, we shall use the word *strictly* to qualify decreasing or increasing. Thus a function f is *strictly increasing* if

$$f(x_1) < f(x_2)$$

whenever $x_1 < x_2$, and f is *strictly decreasing* if

$$f(x_1) > f(x_2)$$

whenever $x_1 < x_2$.

The mean value theorem gives us a good test to determine when a function is increasing or decreasing.

Theorem 5. *Let f be a function which is continuous in some interval, and differentiable in the interval (excluding the end points).*

If $f'(x) = 0$ in the interval (excluding the end points), then f is constant.
If $f'(x) > 0$ in the interval (excluding the end points), then f is strictly increasing.
If $f'(x) < 0$ in the interval (excluding the end points), then f is strictly decreasing.

Proof. Let x_1 and x_2 be two points of the interval, and suppose $x_1 < x_2$. By the mean value theorem, there exists a point c such that $x_1 < c < x_2$ and

$$f'(c) = \frac{f(x_2) - f(x_1)}{x_2 - x_1}.$$

The difference $x_2 - x_1$ is positive, and we have

(1) $$f(x_2) - f(x_1) = (x_2 - x_1)f'(c).$$

If the derivative of the function is 0 throughout the interval, excluding the end points, then the right-hand side of (1) is equal to 0, and hence $f(x_1) = f(x_2)$. This means that, given any two points of the interval, the values of the function are equal, and hence the function is constant.

If the derivative $f'(x)$ is >0 for all x in the interval, excluding the end points, then $f'(c) > 0$ (because c is in the interval). Hence the product $(x_2 - x_1)f'(c)$ is positive, and

$$f(x_1) < f(x_2).$$

This proves that the function is increasing.

We leave the proof of the last assertion to you, as an exercise.

Example 1. Determine the regions of increase and decrease for the function $f(x) = x^2 + 5$.

The derivative is $f'(x) = 2x$. It is > 0 when $x > 0$ and hence f is strictly increasing when $x > 0$. The derivative is negative when $x < 0$ and hence f is strictly decreasing when $x < 0$. We leave the sketch of the graph to you.

Example 2. Determine the regions of increase and decrease for the function $f(x) = x^3 - 2x + 1$.

The derivative is $3x^2 - 2$. The condition

$$3x^2 - 2 > 0$$

is equivalent with $3x^2 > 2$ or $x^2 > 2/3$. Thus when $x > \sqrt{2/3}$ or $-x > \sqrt{2/3}$, we have $x^2 > 2/3$. The function is strictly increasing when $x > \sqrt{2/3}$ and when $x < -\sqrt{2/3}$.

The condition

$$f'(x) < 0$$

is equivalent to $3x^2 - 2 < 0$ or $x^2 < 2/3$. Thus the function is decreasing when

$$-\sqrt{2/3} < x < \sqrt{2/3}.$$

Example 3. Prove that $\sin x \leq x$ for $x \geq 0$.

We let $f(x) = x - \sin x$. Then $f(0) = 0$. Furthermore,

$$f'(x) = 1 - \cos x.$$

Since $\cos x \leq 1$ for all x, it follows that $f'(x) \geq 0$ for all x. Hence $f(x)$ is an increasing function. Hence $f(x) \geq 0$ for all $x \geq 0$ and therefore $\sin x \leq x$.

Example 3 illustrates a technique which is useful for proving certain inequalities between functions. In general, *suppose we have two functions f and g over a certain interval* $[a, b]$ *and we assume that f, g are differentiable. Suppose that* $f(a) \leq g(a)$, *and that* $f'(x) \leq g'(x)$ *throughout the interval. Then* $f(x) \leq g(x)$ *in the interval.* We see this just as in Example 3. We let $h(x) = g(x) - f(x)$. Then $h'(x) \geq 0$, so h is increasing throughout the interval, and since $h(a) = g(a) - f(a) \geq 0$, it follows that $h(x) \geq 0$ throughout the interval, whence $g(x) \geq f(x)$.

Example 4. Show that for any integer $n \geq 1$ and any number $x \geq 1$ one has the inequality $x^n - 1 \geq n(x - 1)$.

Let $f(x) = x^n - 1$ and $g(x) = n(x - 1)$. Then $f(1) = g(1) = 0$. On the other hand,

$$f'(x) = nx^{n-1}, \qquad g'(x) = n.$$

If $n = 1$, our inequality is obvious. If $n \geq 1$, then $nx^{n-1} \geq n$ because $x \geq 1$. Hence we conclude that $f(x) \geq g(x)$ for all $x \geq 1$.

The principle just stated can be visualized in the following picture: drawn for the case when $f(a) = g(a)$.

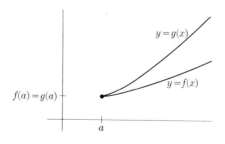

Figure 15

We shall now give a criterion which will allow us to decide when a function is positive or negative throughout an interval. For this, we need what is known as the *intermediate value theorem*.

Theorem 6. *Let x_1 and x_2 be two numbers, with $x_1 \leqq x_2$. Let f be a function which is defined on the interval*

$$x_1 \leqq x \leqq x_2$$

and assume that f is continuous. Let $y_1 = f(x_1)$ and $y_2 = f(x_2)$. Let y_3 be a number between y_1 and y_2. Then there exists a number x_3 between x_1 and x_2 such that $f(x_3) = y_3$.

The proof of Theorem 6 is given in the appendix. It is the type of proof which reduces the theorem to properties of numbers, and which we omit.

As a consequence of Theorem 6, we see that a function which is continuous in an interval, is positive at some point of the interval, and is not equal to 0 at any point of the interval, must be positive throughout the interval. Indeed, if it were negative at some point of the interval, the intermediate value theorem would ensure that there is a point in the interval at which it is equal to 0. For our purposes, we therefore have the following criterion.

Theorem 7. *Let f be a function having a derivative f' at every point of an interval, and assume that f' is continuous. If f' is positive at some point of the interval, and $f'(x) \neq 0$ for any x in the interval except possibly at the end points, then f is strictly increasing in the interval.*

In practice, we can use Theorem 7 by checking that f' is not equal to 0 at any point. This is easier than checking that $f'(x) > 0$ at every point of an interval.

Needless to say, an analogous statement holds when f' is assumed to be negative throughout the interval. State it yourself as an exercise.

Example 5. Determine the intervals on which the function

$$f(x) = x^3 + 5x^2 - 1$$

is increasing and decreasing.

We have $f'(x) = 3x^2 + 10x = x(3x + 10)$. The derivative $f'(x)$ is therefore equal to 0 precisely when $x = 0$ or $x = -10/3$. Thus the sign of the derivative is constant on the intervals

$$x < -10/3, \qquad -10/3 < x < 0, \qquad 0 < x.$$

Since $f'(-5) = 25 > 0$, it follows that the function is strictly increasing for $x < -10/3$. Since $f'(-1) = -7$, it follows that f is strictly decreasing for $-10/3 < x < 0$. Since $f'(1) = 13$, it follows that f is strictly increasing for $x > 0$. This determines what we wanted.

Example 6. Show that among all rectangles of given area, the one with least perimeter is a square.

Let a be the given area, and let x be the length of one side of the possible rectangle with area a. We take $0 < x$. If y is the length of the other side, then $xy = a$, so that $y = a/x$ is the length of the other side. Hence

$$f(x) = 2\left(x + \frac{a}{x}\right)$$

is the perimeter. We have $f'(x) = 2(1 - a/x^2)$, so that $f'(x) = 0$ precisely when $x^2 = a$, i.e. $x = \sqrt{a}$ (because we consider only $x > 0$). When $0 < x < \sqrt{a}$ one sees that $f'(x) < 0$ so that f is decreasing, and when $x > \sqrt{a}$, one sees that $f'(x) > 0$ so that f is increasing. Hence $x = \sqrt{a}$ is a minimum for f, and in that case $y = \sqrt{a}$ also, thus proving that the rectangle is a square.

Example 7. A function f has a derivative equal to

$$f'(x) = (x - 1)(x - 2)(x + 3).$$

Determine the intervals where the function is increasing.

We consider the intervals $x < -3$, $-3 < x < 1$, $1 < x < 2$ and $x > 2$ successively. In the interval $x < -3$, all three factors $(x - 1)$, $x - 2$, $x + 3$ are negative, and hence $f'(x) < 0$ so that the function is decreasing. In the interval $-3 < x < 1$, both factors $x - 1$ and $x - 2$ are negative, but $x + 3$ is positive. Hence the derivative $f'(x)$ is positive, and the function is increasing. Similarly, the function is decreasing in $1 < x < 2$, and increasing for $x > 2$.

Before closing this chapter, we emphasize the first assertion of Theorem 5. We had already seen that the derivative of a constant is 0. We now have proved the converse. It gives us the following very important result:

Theorem 8. *Let $f(x)$ and $g(x)$ be two functions which are differentiable in some interval and assume that*

$$f'(x) = g'(x)$$

for all x in the interval. Then there is a constant C such that

$$f(x) = g(x) + C$$

for all x in the interval.

Proof. Let $\varphi(x) = f(x) - g(x)$ be the difference of our two functions. Then

$$\varphi'(x) = f'(x) - g'(x) = 0.$$

Hence $\varphi(x)$ is constant, i.e. $\varphi(x) = C$ for some number C.

EXERCISES

Determine the intervals on which the following functions are increasing and decreasing.

1. $f(x) = x^3 + 1$ ✓

2. $f(x) = (x - 1)(x - 2)(x - 3)$

3. $f(x) = x^2 - x + 5$ ✓

4. $f(x) = \sin x + \cos x$

5. $f(x) = \sin 2x \quad (0 \leq x \leq 2\pi)$

6. $f(x) = x^4 - 3x^2 + 1$

7. $f(x) = x^3 + x - 2$

8. $f(x) = -x^3 + 2x + 1$

9. $f(x) = 2x^3 + 5$ ✓

10. $f(x) = 5x^2 + 1$ ✓

11. Consider only values of $x \geq 0$, and let

$$f_1(x) = x - \sin x \qquad f_2(x) = -1 + \frac{x^2}{2} + \cos x$$

$$f_3(x) = -x + \frac{x^3}{3 \cdot 2} + \sin x \qquad f_4(x) = 1 - \frac{x^2}{2} + \frac{x^4}{4 \cdot 3 \cdot 2} - \cos x$$

$$f_5(x) = x - \frac{x^3}{3 \cdot 2} + \frac{x^5}{5 \cdot 4 \cdot 3 \cdot 2} - \sin x$$

(a) Determine whether $f_1(x)$ is increasing or decreasing. Using the value of $f_1(x)$ at 0, show that $\sin x \leq x$.

(b) Determine which of the other functions are increasing or decreasing. Using the value of each function at 0, prove the following inequalities:

$$x - \frac{x^3}{3 \cdot 2} \leq \sin x \leq x - \frac{x^3}{3 \cdot 2} + \frac{x^5}{5 \cdot 4 \cdot 3 \cdot 2}$$

$$1 - \frac{x^2}{2} \leq \cos x \leq 1 - \frac{x^2}{2} + \frac{x^4}{4 \cdot 3 \cdot 2}$$

(c) Show how the above procedure can be continued to get further inequalities for $\sin x$ and $\cos x$. Give the general formula.

12. Assume that there is a function $f(x)$ such that $f(x) \neq 0$ for any x, and $f'(x) = f(x)$. Let $g(x)$ be any function such that $g'(x) = g(x)$. Show that there is a constant C such that $g(x) = Cf(x)$. [*Hint:* Differentiate the quotient g/f.]

For each of the following functions, find the maximum, minimum (a) for all x and (b) in the given interval. Also (c) find where each function is increasing and decreasing.

13. $x^2 - 2x - 8, \quad [0, 4]$

14. $x^2 - 2x + 1, \quad [-1, 4]$

15. $4 - 4x - x^2, \quad [-1, 4]$

16. $x - x^2, \quad [-1, 2]$

17. $3x - x^3, \quad [-2, \sqrt{3}]$

18. $(x - 4)^5, \quad [3, 6]$

19. $x^4 - 2x^2, \quad [-2, 1]$

20. $(x - 1)^{1/3} + \frac{1}{2}(x + 1)^{2/3}, \quad [-2, 7]$

21. $x^{2/5} + 1, \quad [-1, 1]$

22. $\sqrt{x^2 + 1}, \quad [0, \sqrt{8}]$

23. Let f, g be two differential functions on an open interval $a < x < b$. Assume that $f'(x) > g'(x)$ for all x in this interval, and that there exists a number c in this interval such that $f(c) = g(c)$. Show that if x is a point in the interval, then $f(x) > g(x)$ if $x > c$ and $f(x) < g(x)$ if $x < c$.

24. Let f be a function which is infinitely differentiable. Let $c_1 < c_2 < \cdots < c_r$ be numbers such that $f(c_i) = 0$ for all i. Show that f' has at least $r - 1$ zeros [i.e. numbers b such that $f'(b) = 0$].

25. Apply the preceding exercise to a polynomial

$$f(x) = a_n x^n + \cdots + a_0$$

where $a_0, \ldots, a_n$ are numbers, and $a_n \neq 0$. Conclude that such a polynomial has at most n roots. [*Hint:* What is the n-th derivative of f?]

26. Show that among all triangles with given area, the equilateral triangle has the least perimeter.

27. Show that among all triangles with given perimeter, the equilateral triangle has the maximum area.

28. Prove that $\tan x \geq x$ if $0 \leq x \leq \pi/2$.

Supplementary Exercises

1. Find the length of the sides of a rectangle of largest area which can be inscribed in a semicircle, the lower base being on the diameter.

2. A rectangular box has a square base and no top. The combined area of the sides and bottom is 48 ft^2. Find the dimensions of the box of maximum volume meeting these requirements.

3. Prove that, among all rectangles of given area, the square has the least perimeter.

4. A truck is to be driven 300 mi at a constant speed of x mph. Speed laws require $30 \leq x \leq 60$. Assume that gasoline costs 30 cents/gallon and is consumed at the rate of $2 + x^2/600$ gal/hr. If the driver's wages are D dollars per hour, find the most economical speed and the cost of the trip if (a) $D = 0$, (b) $D = 1$, (c) $D = 2$, (d) $D = 3$, (e) $D = 4$.

5. A rectangle is to have an area of 64 in^2. Find its dimensions so that the distance from one corner to the mid-point of a non-adjacent side shall be a minimum.

6. Express the number 4 as the sum of two positive numbers in such a way that the sum of the square of the first and the cube of the second is as small as possible.

7. A wire 24 in. long is cut in two, and one part is bent into the shape of a circle, and the other into the shape of a square. How should it be cut if the sum of the areas of the circle and the square is to be (a) minimum, (b) maximum?

8. Find the point on the graph of the equation $y^2 = 4x$ which is nearest to the point $(2, 1)$.

9. Find the points on the hyperbola $x^2 - y^2 = 1$ nearest to the point $(0, 1)$.

10. Show that $(2, 2)$ is the point on the graph of the equation $y = x^3 - 3x$ that is nearest the point $(11, 1)$.

11. Find the coordinates of the points on the curve $x^2 - y^2 = 16$ which are nearest to the point $(0, 6)$.

12. Find the coordinates of the points on the curve $y^2 = x + 1$ which are nearest to the origin.

13. Find the coordinates of the point on the curve $y^2 = \frac{5}{2}(x + 1)$ which is nearest to the origin.

14. Find the coordinates of the points on the curve $y = 2x^2$ which are closest to the point $(9, 0)$.

15. A circular ring of radius b is uniformly charged with electricity, the total charge being Q. The force exerted by this charge on a particle at a distance x from the center of the ring, in a direction perpendicular to the plane of the ring, is given by $F(x) = Qx(x^2 + b^2)^{-3/2}$. Find the maximum of F for all $x \geq 0$.

16. Let F be the rate of flow of water over a certain spillway. Assume that F is proportional to $y(h - y)^{1/2}$, where y is the depth of the flow, and h is the head, and is constant. What value of y makes F a maximum?

17. Find the point on the x-axis the sum of whose distances from $(2, 0)$ and $(0, 3)$ is a minimum.

18. A piece of wire of length L is cut into two parts, one of which is bent into the shape of an equilateral triangle and the other into the shape of a circle. How should the wire be cut so that the sum of the enclosed areas is (a) a minimum, (b) a maximum?

19. A fence $13\frac{1}{2}$ ft high is 4 ft from the side wall of a house. What is the length of the shortest ladder, one end of which will rest on the level ground outside the fence and the other on the side wall of the house?

20. A tank is to have a given volume V and is to be made in the form of a right circular cylinder with hemispheres attached to each end. The material for the ends costs twice as much per square foot as that for the sides. Find the most economical proportions.

21. Find the length of the longest rod which can be carried horizontally around a corner from a corridor 8 ft wide into one 4 ft wide.

22. Let P, Q be two points in the plane on the same side of the x-axis. Let R be a point on the x-axis (Figure 16). Show that the sum of the distances PR and QR is smallest when the angles θ_1 and θ_2 are equal.

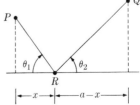

Figure 16

[*Hint:* Let $f(x)$ be the sum of the distances. Show that the condition $f'(x) = 0$ means that $\cos \theta_1 = \cos \theta_2$. Using values of x near 0 and a, and Theorem 7, conclude that $f(x)$ is decreasing for $0 \leq x \leq d$ and increasing for $d \leq x \leq a$ if d is the critical point of f.]

23. Suppose the velocity of light is v_1 in air and v_2 in water. A ray of light traveling from a point P_1 above the surface of water to a point P_2 below the surface will travel by the path which requires the least time. Show that the ray will cross the surface at the point Q in the vertical plane through P_1 and P_2 so placed that

$$\frac{\sin \theta_1}{v_1} = \frac{\sin \theta_2}{v_2},$$

where θ_1 and θ_2 are the angles shown in the following figure:

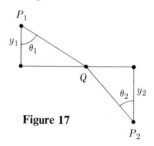

Figure 17

(You may assume that the light will travel in the vertical plane through P_1 and P_2. You may also assume that when the velocity is constant, equal to v, throughout a region, and s is the distance traveled, then the time t is equal to $t = s/v$.)

24. Let p be the probability that a certain event will occur, at any trial. In n trials, suppose that s successes have been observed. The likelihood function L is defined as $L(p) = p^s(1 - p)^{n-s}$. Find the value of p which maximizes the likelihood function. (Take $0 \leq p \leq 1$.)

25. Find an equation for the line through the point $(3, 2)$ making with the coordinate axes a triangle of minimum area in the first quadrant.

26. Let $a_1, \ldots, a_n$ be numbers. Find the number x for which

$$(a_1 - x)^2 + \cdots + (a_n - x)^2$$

is a minimum.

27. When light from a point source strikes a plane surface, the intensity of illumination is proportional to the cosine of the angle of incidence and inversely proportional to the square of the distance from the source. How high should a light be located above the center of a circle of radius 25 cm to give the best illumination along the circumference? (The angle of incidence is measured from the perpendicular to the plane.)

28. A horizontal reservoir has a cross section which is an inverted isosceles triangle, where the length of a leg is 60 ft. Find the angle between the equal legs to give maximum capacity.

29. A reservoir has a horizontal plane bottom and a cross section as shown on the figure. Find the angle of inclination of the sides from the horizontal to give maximum capacity.

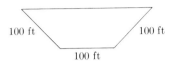

100 ft   100 ft

100 ft   **Figure 18**

30. Determine the constant a such that the function

$$f(x) = x^2 + \frac{a}{x}$$

has (a) a local minimum at $x = 2$, (b) a local minimum at $x = -3$. (c) Show that the function cannot have a local maximum for any value of a.

31. The intensity of illumination at any point is proportional to the strength of the light source and varies inversely as the square of the distance from the source. If two sources of strengths a and b respectively are a distance c apart, at what point on the line joining them will the intensity be a minimum?

32. A window is in the shape of a rectangle surmounted by a semicircle. Find the dimensions when the perimeter is 12 ft and the area is as large as possible.

33. Find the radius and angle of the circular sector of maximum area having a perimeter of 16 ft.

34. Two points P and Q are diametrically opposite each other on the shore of a circular pond whose radius is 1 mi. A man wishes to go from P to Q by swimming from P to a point R on the shore and then walking along the shore from R to Q. He can swim 2 mph and walk 4 mph. Find the minimum possible time from P to Q and also the maximum possible time under the stated conditions.

35. A ladder is to reach over a fence 12 ft high to a wall 2 ft behind the fence. What is the length of the shortest ladder that can be used?

36. A cannon, resting on level ground, is aimed upward at an angle of inclination θ. Let r be the range of the cannon, that is, the distance from the cannon to the point of impact of the ball. Then r is given by

$$r = \frac{2v^2}{g} \sin \theta \cos \theta,$$

where v, g are constants. For what angle is the range a maximum?

Chapter VI

Sketching Curves

We have developed enough techniques to be able to sketch curves and graphs of functions much more efficiently than before. We shall investigate systematically the behavior of a curve, and the mean value theorem will play a fundamental role.

We shall especially look for the following aspects of the curve:
1. Intersections with the coordinate axes.
2. Critical points.
3. Regions of increase.
4. Regions of decrease.
5. Maxima and minima (including the local ones).
6. Behavior as x becomes very large positive and very large negative.
7. Values of x near which y becomes very large positive or very large negative.

These seven pieces of information will be quite sufficient to give us a fairly accurate idea of what the graph looks like. We shall devote a section to considering one other aspect, namely:
8. Regions where the curve is convex upwards or downwards. This tells us how the curve is bending.

We shall also introduce a new way of describing points of the plane and functions, namely polar coordinates. These are especially useful in connection with the trigonometric functions.

§1. BEHAVIOR AS x BECOMES VERY LARGE

Suppose we have a function f defined for all sufficiently large numbers. Then we get substantial information concerning our function by investigating how it behaves as x becomes large.

For instance, $\sin x$ oscillates between -1 and $+1$.

However, polynomials don't oscillate. When $f(x) = x^2$, as x becomes large positive, so does x^2. Similarly with the function x^3, or x^4 (etc.).

Example 1. Consider a polynomial

$$f(x) = x^3 + 2x - 1.$$

108

We can write it in the form

$$x^3\left(1 + \frac{2}{x^2} - \frac{1}{x^3}\right).$$

When x becomes very large, the expression

$$1 + \frac{2}{x^2} - \frac{1}{x^3}$$

approaches 1. In particular, given a small number $\delta > 0$, we have, for all x sufficiently large, the inequality

asymptotic

$$1 - \delta < 1 + \frac{2}{x^2} - \frac{1}{x^3} < 1 + \delta.$$

Therefore $f(x)$ satisfies the inequality

$$x^3(1 - \delta) < f(x) < x^3(1 + \delta).$$

This tells us that $f(x)$ behaves very much like x^3 when x is very large.

A similar argument can be applied to any polynomial.

Example 2. Consider a quotient of polynomials like

$$Q(x) = \frac{x^3 + 2x - 1}{2x^3 - x + 1}.$$

Dividing numerator and denominator by x^3, we get

$$Q(x) = \frac{1 + \dfrac{2}{x^2} - \dfrac{1}{x^3}}{2 - \dfrac{1}{x^2} + \dfrac{1}{x^3}}.$$

As x becomes very large, the numerator approaches 1 and the denominator approaches 2. Thus our fraction approaches $\frac{1}{2}$.

Example 3. Consider the quotient

$$Q(x) = \frac{x^2 - 1}{x^3 - 2x + 1}.$$

Does it approach a limit as x becomes very large?

If we divide numerator and denominator by x^3, then we see that our quotient can be written

$$\frac{\dfrac{1}{x} - \dfrac{1}{x^3}}{1 - \dfrac{2}{x^2} + \dfrac{1}{x^3}}.$$

As x becomes very large, the numerator approaches 0 and the denominator approaches 1. Consequently the quotient approaches 0.

Example 4. Consider the quotient

$$Q(x) = \frac{x^3 - 1}{x^2 + 5}$$

and determine what happens when x becomes very large.

We divide numerator and denominator by x^2. This gives

$$Q(x) = \frac{x - \dfrac{1}{x^2}}{1 + \dfrac{5}{x^2}}.$$

As x becomes very large, the numerator is approximately equal to x and the denominator approaches 1. Thus the quotient is approximately equal to x.

These four examples are typical of what happens when we deal with quotients of polynomials.

Instead of saying "when x becomes very large", we shall also say "as x approaches infinity", or even better, "as x approaches plus infinity". Thus in Example 2 we would write

$$\lim_{x \to \infty} Q(x) = \tfrac{1}{2}.$$

In Example 3 we would write

$$\lim_{x \to \infty} Q(x) = 0.$$

In Example 4, we would write

$$\lim_{x \to \infty} Q(x) = \infty.$$

We emphasize that this way of writing is an *abbreviation*, a shorthand, for the sentences we wrote in our various examples. There is NO NUMBER WHICH IS CALLED INFINITY. The symbol ∞ will not be used except in the context we have just described.

Of course, we could also investigate what happens when x becomes very large *negative*, or, as we shall also say, when x approaches minus infinity, which we write $-\infty$.

In Example 2, we see that as x becomes very large negative, our quotient $Q(x)$ still approaches $\tfrac{1}{2}$, because a fraction like $1/x^3$ becomes very small. (For instance $1/-10,000 = -1/10,000$ is very small negative.) Thus we would write

$$\lim_{x \to -\infty} Q(x) = \tfrac{1}{2}.$$

EXERCISES

Find the limits of the following quotients $Q(x)$ as x becomes very large positive or negative. In other words, find

$$\lim_{x \to \infty} Q(x) \quad \text{and} \quad \lim_{x \to -\infty} Q(x).$$

1. $\dfrac{2x^3 - x}{x^4 - 1}$

2. $\dfrac{\sin x}{x}$

3. $\dfrac{\cos x}{x}$

4. $\dfrac{x^2 + 1}{\pi x^2 - 1}$

5. $\dfrac{\sin 4x}{x^3}$

6. $\dfrac{5x^4 - x^3 + 3x + 2}{x^3 - 1}$

7. $\dfrac{-x^2 + 1}{x + 5}$

8. $\dfrac{2x^4 - 1}{-4x^4 + x^2}$

9. $\dfrac{2x^4 - 1}{-4x^3 + x^2}$

10. $\dfrac{2x^4 - 1}{-4x^5 + x^2}$

Describe the behavior of the following polynomials as x becomes very large positive and very large negative.

11. $x^3 - x + 1$

12. $-x^3 - x + 1$

13. $x^4 + 3x^3 + 2$

14. $-x^4 + 3x^3 + 2$

15. $2x^5 + x^2 - 100$

16. $-3x^5 + x + 1000$

17. $10x^6 - x^4$

18. $-3x^6 + x^3 + 1$

19. A function $f(x)$ which can be expressed as follows:

$$f(x) = a_n x^n + a_{n-1} x^{n-1} + \cdots + a_0,$$

where n is a positive integer and the $a_n, a_{n-1}, \ldots, a_0$ are numbers, is called a polynomial. If $a_n \neq 0$, then n is called the *degree* of the polynomial. Describe the behavior of $f(x)$ as x becomes very large positive or negative, n is odd or even, and $a_n > 0$ or $a_n < 0$. (You will have eight cases to consider.)

20. Using the intermediate value theorem, show that any polynomial of odd degree has a root.

§2. CURVE SKETCHING

We shall put together all the information we have gathered up to now to get an accurate picture of the graph of a function. We deal systematically with the seven properties stated in the introduction, and our discussion will take the form of working out examples.

Example 1. Sketch the graph of the curve

$$y = f(x) = \frac{x - 1}{x + 1}$$

and determine the seven properties stated in the introduction.

1. When $x = 0$, we have $f(x) = -1$. When $x = 1, f(x) = 0$.
2. The derivative is

$$f'(x) = \frac{2}{(x + 1)^2}.$$

(You can compute it using the quotient rule.) It is never 0, and therefore the function has no critical points.

3. The denominator is a square and hence is always positive. Thus $f'(x) > 0$ for all x. The function is increasing for all x. Of course, the function is not defined for $x = -1$ and neither is the derivative. Thus it would be more accurate to say that the function is increasing in the region

$$x < -1$$

and is increasing in the region $x > -1$.

4. There is no region of decrease.

5. Since the derivative is never 0, there is no relative maximum or minimum.

6. As x becomes very large positive, our function approaches 1 (using the method of the preceding section). As x becomes very large negative, our function also approaches 1.

Finally, there is one more useful piece of information which we can look into, when $f(x)$ itself becomes very large positive or negative:

7. As x approaches -1, the denominator approaches 0 and the numerator approaches -2. If x approaches -1 from the right, then the denominator is positive, and the numerator is negative. Hence the fraction

$$\frac{x - 1}{x + 1}$$

is negative, and is very large negative.

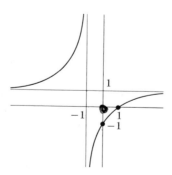

If x approaches -1 from the left, then $x - 1$ is negative, but $x + 1$ is negative also. Hence $f(x)$ is positive and very large, since the denominator is small when x is close to -1. Putting all this information together, we see that the graph looks like that in the preceding figure.

We have drawn the two lines $x = -1$ and $y = 1$, as these play an important role when x approaches -1 and when x becomes very large, positive or negative.

Example 2. Sketch the graph of the curve

$$y = -x^3 + 3x - 5.$$

1. When $x = 0$, we have $y = -5$.
2. The derivative is

$$f'(x) = -3x^2 + 3.$$

It is 0 when $3x^2 = 3$, which is equivalent to saying that

$$x^2 = 1, \quad \text{or} \quad \boxed{x = \pm 1.} \qquad x = 1$$
$$x = -1$$

These are the critical points.

3. The derivative is positive when $-3x^2 + 3 > 0$, which amounts to saying that

$$3x^2 < 3 \quad \text{or} \quad x^2 < 1.$$

This is equivalent to the condition

$$-1 < x < 1,$$

which is therefore a region of increase.

4. When $-3x^2 + 3 < 0$, the function decreases. This is the region given by the inequality

$$3x^2 > 3$$

or $x^2 > 1$. Thus when

$$x > 1 \quad \text{or} \quad x < -1,$$

the function decreases.

5. Since the function decreases when $x < -1$ and increases when $x > -1$ (and is close to -1), we conclude that the point -1 is a local minimum. Also, $f(-1) = -7$.

Similarly, the point 1 is a relative maximum and $f(1) = -3$.

6. As x becomes very large positive, x^3 is very large positive and $-x^3$ is very large negative. Hence our function becomes very large negative, as we see if we put it in the form

$$f(x) = -x^3 \left(1 - \frac{3}{x^2} + \frac{5}{x^3} \right).$$

Similarly, as x becomes very large negative, our function becomes very large positive.

Putting all this information together, we see that the graph looks like this:

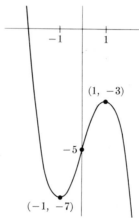

(1, −3)

−5

(−1, −7)

EXERCISES

Sketch the following curves, indicating all the information stated in the introduction:

1. $y = \dfrac{x^2 + 2}{x - 3}$

2. $y = \dfrac{x - 3}{x^2 + 1}$

3. $y = \dfrac{x + 1}{x^2 + 1}$

4. $y = \sin^2 x$

5. $y = \cos^2 x$

6. $y = \dfrac{x^2 - 1}{x}$

7. $y = \tan^2 x$

8. $y = \dfrac{x^3 + 1}{x + 1}$

9. $y = x^4 - 2x^3 + 1$

10. $y = \dfrac{2x^2 - 1}{x^2 - 2}$

11. $y = \dfrac{2x - 3}{3x + 1}$

12. $y = x^4 + 4x$

13. $y = x^5 + x$

14. $y = x^6 + 6x$

15. $y = x^7 + x$

16. $y = x^8 + x$

17. Which of the following polynomials have a minimum (for all x)?

   (a) $x^6 - x + 2$ (b) $x^5 - x + 2$
   (c) $-x^6 - x + 2$ (d) $-x^5 - x + 2$
   (e) $x^6 + x + 2$ (f) $x^5 + x + 2$

Sketch the graphs of these polynomials.

18. Which of the polynomials in Exercise 17 have a maximum (for all x)?

19. Sketch the following curves:

   (a) $x^3 + x - 1$ (b) $x^3 - x - 1$ (c) $-x^3 + 2x + 5$
   (d) $-2x^3 + x + 2$ (e) $x^3 - x^2 + 1$ (f) $x^3 + x$

20. Let a, b, c, d be four distinct numbers. What would the following curves look like? You may assume $a < b < c < d$.

   (i) $(x - a)(x - b)$
   (ii) $(x - a)(x - b)(x - c)$
   (iii) $(x - a)(x - b)(x - c)(x - d)$

Sketch the graphs of the following functions and find the regions of increase and decrease, relative maxima and minima, etc.

21. $4x - \frac{1}{3}x^3$

22. $(x - 1)^{2/3} + 3$

23. $x^2 + 4x + 2$

24. $\dfrac{4x}{x^2 - 9}$

25. $x + \dfrac{3}{x}$

26. $\dfrac{x^2 - 4}{x^3}$

27. $\frac{1}{3}x^3 + x^2 - 2x$

28. $x^3 - 3x^2 + 6x - 3$

29. $\dfrac{x^2 - 4}{(x - 2)^2}$

30. $\dfrac{3x - 2}{2x + 3}$

31. $\dfrac{x}{3x - 5}$

32. $\dfrac{2x}{x + 4}$

33. $\dfrac{x^2}{\sqrt{x + 1}}$

34. $\dfrac{x + 1}{x^2 + 5}$

35. $\dfrac{x + 1}{x^2 - 5}$

36. $\dfrac{x^2 + 1}{x^2 - 1}$

37. $\dfrac{x^2 - 1}{x^2 - 4}$

38. $\dfrac{(x + 1)^2}{x^2 - 1}$

39. $x^{2/3}\sqrt{9 - x^2}$ for $-3 \leq x \leq 3$.

40. $(x - 4)^{4/3} + 2(x + 4)^{2/3}$

41. $(x - 1)^{1/3} + \frac{1}{2}(x + 1)^{2/3}$ for $-2 \leq x \leq 7$

42. $(x - 1)^{1/3} - \frac{1}{2}(x + 1)^{2/3}$ for $2 \leq x \leq 3$

43. $\sin x + \cos x$

44. $x - \sin x$

45. $\sin 2x + \sqrt{3} \cos 2x$

46. $x + 2 \cos \dfrac{x}{2}$

47. $\sin x + \sin x \cos x$

48. $\sin 2x - \sin 2x \cos 2x$

49. $\sin x - \sin^3 x$

50. $\cos x - \cos^3 x$

51. If $a_1, \ldots, a_n$ are numbers ≥ 0, show that

$$(a_1 \cdots a_n)^{1/n} \leq \frac{a_1 + \cdots + a_n}{n}.$$

[*Hint:* By induction. The statement is obvious if $n = 1$. Assume it for some integer $n - 1 \geq 1$. Taking the n-th power of both sides, it suffices to prove that

$$a_1 \cdots a_n \leq \left(\frac{a_1 + \cdots + a_n}{n}\right)^n.$$

Let

$$f(x) = \left(\frac{a_1 + \cdots + a_{n-1} + x}{n}\right)^n - a_1 \cdots a_{n-1} x.$$

Compute $f'(x)$. Note that $f(0) \geq 0$. Show that $f'(x) = 0$ for exactly one value of x, say $x = c$. If $c \leq 0$, then the sign of f' is constant for $x > 0$, so that f is either decreasing or increasing for $x \geq 0$. But as x becomes large, $f(x)$ becomes large. Hence f is increasing for $x \geq 0$ and we are done in this case. If on the other hand $c > 0$, compute explicitly the value $f(c)$, and using the induction hypothesis, show that $f(c) \geq 0$. Since c is the only critical point, and since $f(x)$ becomes large when x becomes large, it follows that c must be a minimum, and hence finally that $f(x) \geq 0$ whenever $x \geq 0$.] Another proof for this inequality can be given using the convexity of the log, in a later chapter.

§3. CONVEXITY

Let a, b be numbers, $a < b$. Let f be a continuous function defined on the interval $[a, b]$. Assume that f' and f'' exist on the interval $a < x < b$. We view the second derivative f'' as the rate of change of the slope of the curve $y = f(x)$ over the interval. If the second derivative is positive in the interval $a < x < b$, then the slope of the curve is increasing, and we interpret this as meaning that the curve is bending upward. If the second derivative is negative, we interpret this as meaning that the curve is bending downward. The following two pictures illustrate this.

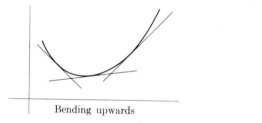

Bending upwards   Bending downwards

One can actually characterize the preceding geometric behavior more analytically. What does it mean to say that a curve is bending upwards? An equivalent condition should be that, given two points P and Q on the curve, the line segment joining P and Q should lie *above* the curve between P and Q, in which case we say that the curve is *convex* upwards. This is illustrated on the picture at the right. We can put this in terms of inequalities. Suppose our curve is given by a function, $y = f(x)$, and the points P and

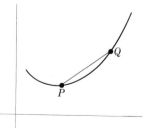

Q are given in terms of their coordinates, $(a, f(a))$ and $(b, f(b))$, for numbers a and b with $a < b$. The equation of the line passing through our two points is

$$y - f(a) = \frac{f(b) - f(a)}{b - a}(x - a),$$

or in other words,

$$y = f(a) + \frac{f(b) - f(a)}{b - a}(x - a).$$

The equation of the given curve is

$$y = f(x).$$

Thus the condition that the line segment between P and Q should lie above the curve between these points can be expressed by the inequality

(*) $$f(a) + \frac{f(b) - f(a)}{b - a}(x - a) \geq f(x) \qquad \text{for } a < x < b.$$

Thus we define the curve $y = f(x)$ to be *convex upwards* on an interval if for every $a < b$ in that interval, inequality (*) is satisfied. If inequality (*) holds when the sign $\geq$ is replaced by the sign $>$, then we say that the curve is *strictly* convex upwards.

Theorem 1. *Let a, b be numbers, $a < b$. Let f be a continuous function defined over the interval $[a, b]$. Assume that f' and f'' exist on the interval $a < x < b$, and that $f''(x) > 0$ for all x in this interval. Then the curve $y = f(x)$ is strictly convex upwards.*

Proof. Given any numbers c, d with $a \leq c < d \leq b$, all our hypotheses are satisfied for the interval $[c, d]$. Hence it will suffice to prove that the line segment between $(a, f(a))$ and $(b, f(b))$ lies above the curve in the interval $[a, b]$. Let φ be the function giving the difference between the line segment and the curve, i.e.

$$\varphi(x) = f(a) + \frac{f(b) - f(a)}{b - a}(x - a) - f(x).$$

Then

$$\varphi'(x) = \frac{f(b) - f(a)}{b - a} - f'(x),$$

and using the mean value theorem, we conclude that there exists some number c such that $a < c < b$ and

$$\varphi'(x) = f'(c) - f'(x)$$

for all x such that $a < x < b$. Now we may apply the mean value theorem to the function f' itself, with respect to the two numbers x and c. Suppose first that $a < x \leqq c$. Then

$$f'(c) - f'(x) = f''(d)(c - x)$$

for some number d between x and c. Since $f''(d) > 0$, it follows that $\varphi'(x) > 0$ for all x with $a < x < c$. Hence φ is a strictly increasing function in the interval $[a, c]$. Since $\varphi(a) = 0$ (as one verifies at once), it follows that $\varphi(x) > 0$ if $a < x \leqq c$. This proves the desired condition (*) when $a < x \leqq c$.

On the other hand, suppose that $c < x < b$. Then again by the mean value theorem, applied to f', we find

$$f'(x) - f'(c) = f''(e)(x - c)$$

for some number e between c and x. This shows that

$$\varphi'(x) = f'(c) - f'(x) < 0$$

in the present case, and hence that φ is strictly decreasing in the interval $c < x \leqq b$. Since $\varphi(b) = 0$ by a direct computation, we conclude again that $\varphi(x) > 0$, which is the desired condition (*) when $c < x < b$. This proves Theorem 1.

Example 1. Show that the curve $y = x^2$ is convex upwards over all intervals.

This is easily done, since the second derivative is the constant 2, which is certainly >0. We can thus apply Theorem 1.

Example 2. Let $f(x) = \sin x$. Show that the curve $y = \sin x$ is convex upwards in the interval $\pi \leqq x \leqq 2\pi$.

Again, we compute $f''(x) = -\sin x$, and we note that $f''(x) > 0$ in the interval $\pi < x < 2\pi$. Thus we can apply the theorem once more.

Of course, Theorem 1 has an analogue for curves which are convex downwards, i.e. such that the line segment between two points of the curve lies below the curve.

Theorem 2. *Let a, b be numbers, $a < b$. Let f be a continuous function defined over the interval $[a, b]$. Assume that f' and f'' exist on the interval $a < x < b$, and that $f''(x) < 0$ for all x in this interval. Then the curve $y = f(x)$ is strictly convex downwards.*

Proof. The proof is entirely similar to that of Theorem 1, and will be left as an exercise.

Example 3. Determine the intervals where the curve

$$y = -x^3 + 3x - 5$$

is convex upwards and convex downwards.

Let $f(x) = -x^3 + 3x - 5$. Then $f''(x) = -6x$. Thus $f''(x) > 0$ for $x < 0$ and $f''(x) < 0$ for $x > 0$. Hence the curve is convex upwards for $x \leq 0$ and is convex downwards for $x \geq 0$ according to Theorems 1 and 2. The graph of this curve has been discussed in Example 2 of §2, but the present considerations justify theoretically the convexity behaviour which we had already exhibited on this graph.

A point where a curve changes its behaviour from convex upwards to downwards (or vice versa) is called an *inflection point*. If the curve is the graph of a function f whose second derivative exists and is continuous, then we must have $f''(x) = 0$ at that point. The following picture illustrates this:

Inflection point

In Example 3 above, the point $(0, -5)$ is an inflection point. Again the reader can see the illustration given in Example 2 of §2.

The determination of regions of convexity, and inflection points gives us worthwhile pieces of information concerning curves. For instance, knowing that a curve in a region of decrease is actually convex downwards tells us that the decrease occurs essentially as in this example:

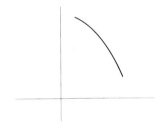

and not as in these examples:

One can give another condition characterizing convex curves. This comes from the fact that an arbitrary point in an interval $[a, b]$ can be written in the form

$$ta + (1 - t)b$$

for some t such that $0 \leq t \leq 1$. To see this, suppose that $a \leq x \leq b$. Then we let

$$t = \frac{b - x}{b - a}.$$

A direct computation shows that $x = ta + (1 - t)b$. Conversely, for any t with $0 \leq t \leq 1$, we have

$$a \leq ta + (1 - t)b \leq b.$$

Indeed, the left and right inequalities follow from these

$$ta + (1 - t)b - a = (1 - t)(b - a) \geq 0$$

and

$$ta + (1 - t)b - b = t(a - b) \leq 0.$$

If we let $u = 1 - t$, then as t goes from 0 to 1, we see that u goes from 1 to 0. Thus the points of the interval $[a, b]$ can also be written in the form

$$(1 - u)a + ub = a + u(b - a).$$

Theorem 3. *Let f be a function defined on the interval $[a, b]$. Then the following two conditions are equivalent.*

CON 1. *The line segment between the points $(a, f(a))$ and $(b, f(b))$ lies above the curve $y = f(x)$ in the interval $[a, b]$.*

CON 2. *For all numbers t with $0 \leq t \leq 1$ we have*

$$f(ta + (1 - t)b) \leq tf(a) + (1 - t)f(b).$$

Proof. Assume CON 1. For any x between a and b, write

$$x = ta + (1 - t)b$$

with $0 \leq t \leq 1$. Then referring to inequality (*), we find

$$f(ta + (1 - t)b) \leq f(a) + \frac{f(b) - f(a)}{b - a}(ta + b - tb - a)$$

$$= f(a) + \frac{f(b) - f(a)}{b - a}(b - a)(1 - t)$$

$$= tf(a) + (1 - t)f(b),$$

thereby proving CON 2. The converse will be left as an exercise.

A function satisfying the hypotheses of Theorem 2 for every pair of points $a \leq b$ in some interval of definition is said to be *convex (upwards)* in that interval.

Instead of writing t and $1 - t$ for the coefficients of a and b, we observe that $t + (1 - t) = 1$, and let $s = 1 - t$. Then CON 2 can be rewritten in the form

$$f(ta + sb) \leq tf(a) + sf(b)$$

for all numbers t, $s \geq 0$ such that $t + s = 1$. Similarly, we define a function g to be *convex downwards* on an interval if

$$g(ta + sb) \geq tg(a) + sg(b)$$

for all numbers t, $s \geq$ such that $t + s = 1$, and all $a < b$ in that interval.

EXERCISES

1. Write out in full the proof of Theorem 2.

2. Determine the intervals of convexity for the curves given in the exercises of §2, thereby justifying the convexity aspects of the sketches which you made previously of these curves.

3. Let the hypotheses be as in Theorem 1. Let x_0 be a number such that $a < x_0 < b$. Show that the tangent line to the curve $y = f(x)$ at $x = x_0$ lies below the graph of f except at $x = x_0$ where it touches the graph.

4. State and prove the analogous statement to Exercise 3, corresponding to Theorem 2.

5. (a) Find the equation for the tangent to the hyperbola $xy = 1$ at the point $(\frac{1}{2}, 2)$.
   (b) Prove that the tangent line is below the hyperbola for all $x > 0$ (except $x = \frac{1}{2}$ where it touches).

6. Let the hypotheses be as in Theorem 1. Show that

$$f\left(\frac{a + b}{2}\right) < \frac{f(a) + f(b)}{2}.$$

$$\left[Hint: \text{ Put } x = \frac{a + b}{2} \right].$$

7. Prove that CON 2 implies CON 1 in Theorem 3, i.e. prove the converse of the statement whose proof was given.

8. Determine all inflection points of $\sin x$ and $\cos x$.

9. Determine the inflection points of the curves given in the exercises of §2.

10. Let f, g be functions defined for all numbers, and convex (upwards). Assume that f is an increasing function. Show that $f \circ g$ is convex (upwards).

11. Determine the intervals of convexity for the following curves, and sketch these curves.

(a) $y = x + \dfrac{1}{x}$ (b) $y = \dfrac{x}{x^2 + 1}$ (c) $y = \dfrac{x}{x^2 - 1}$

12. Let f be a function defined for all $x > 0$ and convex downwards. Prove by induction that for all numbers $t_1, \ldots, t_n \geq 0$ such that $t_1 + \cdots + t_n = 1$, and all numbers $x_1, \ldots, x_n > 0$ we have

$$t_1 f(x_1) + \cdots + t_n f(x_n) \leq f(t_1 x_1 + \cdots + t_n x_n).$$

[*Hint*: If $t_n \neq 0$, let $s_i = t_i / (1 - t_n)$ for $i = 1, \ldots, n - 1$. Then by induction, $s_1 f(x_1) + \cdots + s_{n-1} f(x_{n-1}) \leq f(s_1 x_1 + \cdots + s_{n-1} x_{n-1})$. Now add

$$\frac{t_n}{1 - t_n} f(x_n)$$

to both sides, multiply by $(1 - t_n)$, and use the convexity of f to conclude the proof.]

13. Let f be a function which is defined for all $x > 0$ and convex upwards. Prove that for all numbers $x_1, \ldots, x_n > 0$ we have

$$f\left(\frac{x_1 + \cdots + x_n}{n}\right) \leq \frac{1}{n} f(x_1) + \cdots + \frac{1}{n} f(x_n).$$

What is the corresponding inequality if f is assumed to be convex downwards?

§4. POLAR COORDINATES

Instead of describing a point in the plane by its coordinates with respect to two perpendicular axes, we can also describe it as follows. We draw a line between the point and a given origin. The angle which this line makes with the horizontal axis and the distance between the point and the origin determine our point. Thus the point is described by a pair of numbers (r, θ), which are called its *polar coordinates*.

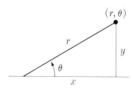

If we have our usual axes and x, y are the ordinary coordinates of our point, then we see that

$$\frac{x}{r} = \cos \theta \quad \text{and} \quad \frac{y}{r} = \sin \theta,$$

whence $x = r \cos \theta$ and $y = r \sin \theta$.

This allows us to change from polar coordinates to ordinary coordinates.

It is to be understood that r is always supposed to be ≥ 0. In terms of the ordinary coordinates, we have

$$r = \sqrt{x^2 + y^2}.$$

Example 1. Find polar coordinates of the point whose ordinary coordinates are $(1, \sqrt{3})$.

We have $x = 1$ and $y = \sqrt{3}$, so that $r = \sqrt{1 + 3} = 2$. Also $\cos \theta = \frac{1}{2}$, $\sin \theta = \sqrt{3}/2$. Hence $\theta = \pi/3$, and the polar coordinates are $(2, \pi/3)$.

We observe that we may have several polar coordinates corresponding to the same point. The point whose polar coordinates are $(r, \theta + 2\pi)$ is the same as the point (r, θ). Thus in our example above, $(2, \pi/6 + 2\pi)$ would also be polar coordinates for our point. In practice, we usually use the value for the angle which lies between 0 and 2π.

Let f be a function whose values are ≥ 0. If we set $r = f(\theta)$, then the set of points $(\theta, f(\theta))$ is the graph of the function in polar coordinates. We can also view $r = f(\theta)$ as the equation of a curve.

Example 2. Sketch the graph of the function $r = \sin \theta$ for $0 \leq \theta \leq \pi$. If $\pi < \theta < 2\pi$, the $\sin \theta < 0$ and hence for such θ we don't get a point on the curve.

First we make a table of values, as indicated. As θ ranges from 0 to $\pi/2$, $\sin \theta$ increases until it reaches 1. As θ goes from $\pi/2$ to π, the sine decreases back to 0. Hence the graph looks like this:

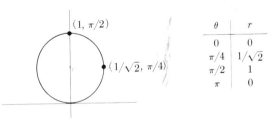

θ	r
0	0
$\pi/4$	$1/\sqrt{2}$
$\pi/2$	1
π	0

Example 3. Change the equation $r = \sin \theta$ of Example 2 to rectangular coordinates.

We substitute the expressions

$$r = \sqrt{x^2 + y^2}   \text{and}   \sin \theta = y/r = y/\sqrt{x^2 + y^2}$$

in the polar equation, to obtain

$$\sqrt{x^2 + y^2} = \frac{y}{\sqrt{x^2 + y^2}} \cdot$$

Of course, this substitution is valid only when $r \neq 0$, i.e. $r > 0$. We can then simplify the equation we have just obtained, multiplying both sides by $\sqrt{x^2 + y^2}$. We then obtain

$$x^2 + y^2 = y,$$

which after completing the square yields

$$x^2 + (y - \tfrac{1}{2})^2 = \tfrac{1}{4}.$$

Thus we recognize the equation of Example 2 as that of a circle, of center $(0, \tfrac{1}{2})$ and radius $\tfrac{1}{2}$. The point corresponding to the polar coordinate $r = 0$ is the point with rectangular coordinates $x = 0$ and $y = 0$.

Example 4. The equation of the circle of radius 3 and center at the origin in polar coordinates is simply $r = 3$.

Example 5. Consider the equation $\theta = 1$ in polar coordinates. A point whose polar coordinates satisfy this equation can be described as $(r, 1)$ for any value of $r \geq 0$. Thus geometrically, this set of points can be described as a half line, or a ray:

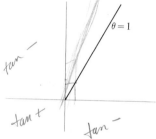

The slope of this ray is equal to tan 1. Thus the equation in rectangular coordinates is

$$y = (\tan 1)x \qquad \text{and} \qquad x \geq 0.$$

EXERCISES

1. Plot the following points in polar coordinates:

   (a) $(2, \pi/4)$ (b) $(3, \pi/6)$ (c) $(1, -\pi/4)$ (d) $(2, -3\pi/6)$

2. Same directions as in Exercise 1.

   (a) $(1, 1)$ (b) $(4, -3)$

   (These are polar coordinates. Just show approximately the angle represented by the given coordinates.)

3. Find polar coordinates for the following points given in the usual x- and y-coordinates:

   (a) $(1, 1)$ (b) $(-1, -1)$ (c) $(3, 3\sqrt{3})$ (d) $(-1, 0)$

Sketch the graphs of the following curves given in polar coordinates:

4. $r = 5$ 5. $r = \sin 2\theta$ 6. $r = \theta$

7. $r = \sin \theta + \cos \theta$ 8. $r = \dfrac{2}{2 - \cos \theta}$ 9. $r = \sin 3\theta$

10. $r^2 = 2a^2 \cos 2\theta$ $(a > 0)$ 11. $r = 1 + \cos \theta$

12. $r = a \cos \theta$ $(a > 0)$ 13. $r = a \sin \theta$ $(a > 0)$

Sketch the following curves in polar coordinates.

14. $r = 1 + 2 \sin \theta$ 15. $r = 5 + 2 \sin \theta$

16. $r = 6 \cos \theta$ 17. $r = 3/\cos \theta$

18. $r = 2 \tan \theta$ 19. $r = 1 + \sqrt{2} \cos \theta$

20. $r = \sin 2\theta$ 21. $r = \cos 2\theta$

22. $r = 4 \sin^2 \theta$ 23. $r = 2 + \sin 2\theta$

24. $r^2 = \cos \theta$ 25. $r^2 = \sin \theta$

26. $r = 1/\theta$ 27. $r = \sin 4\theta$

28. $r = 1 - \sin \theta$ 29. $r = \dfrac{4}{1 + 2 \cos \theta}$

30. $r = \dfrac{4}{2 - \cos \theta}$ 31. $r = \dfrac{1}{\sin \theta}$

Change the following equations to rectangular coordinates:

32. $\theta = 2$ 33. $r = 4$ 34. $r = 2 \sin \theta$

35. $r = 3 \cos \theta$ 36. $r = 1 - \cos \theta$ 37. $r = 1 - 2 \sin \theta$

38. $r = \dfrac{1}{\cos \theta}$ 39. $r = \dfrac{1}{\sin \theta}$ 40. $r = \dfrac{1}{1 - \cos \theta}$

41. $r = \dfrac{2}{2 - \cos \theta}$ 42. $\theta = \pi$ 43. $\theta = 3$

44. $\theta = 2.5$ 45. $\theta = \pi/2$ 46. $\theta = 0.3$

47. $\theta = 0.5$

§5. PARAMETRIC CURVES

There is one other way in which we can describe a curve. Suppose that we look at a point which moves in the plane. Its coordinates can be given as a function of time t. Thus, when we give two functions of t, say

$$x = f(t), \qquad y = g(t),$$

we may view these as describing a point moving along a curve.

For example, if we let $x = \cos t$ and $y = \sin t$, then our point moves along a circle, counterclockwise, with uniform speed.

When (x, y) is described by two functions of t as above, we say that we have a *parametrization of the curve* in terms of the *parameter t*.

Example 1. Sketch the curve $x = t^2$, $y = t^3$.

We can make a table of values as usual. We also investigate when x and y are increasing or decreasing functions of t. For instance, taking the derivative, we get

$$\frac{dx}{dt} = 2t, \quad \text{and} \quad \frac{dy}{dt} = 3t^2.$$

Thus x increases when $t > 0$ and decreases when $t < 0$. The y-coordinate is increasing since $t^2 > 0$ (unless $t = 0$). Furthermore, the x-coordinate is always positive (unless $t = 0$). Thus the graph looks like this:

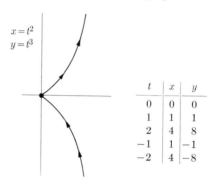

t	x	y
0	0	0
1	1	1
2	4	8
-1	1	-1
-2	4	-8

Example 2. We look at the circle

$$x = \cos \theta, \quad y = \sin \theta.$$

We shall find another parametrization. Consider the circle of radius 1 and the point (x, y) on it:

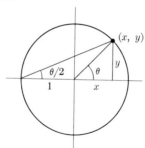

Let

$$t = \frac{y}{x + 1} \quad (x \neq -1).$$

The equation of the circle is

$$x^2 + y^2 = 1.$$

Then we can interpret t geometrically to be $\tan \dfrac{\theta}{2}$.

From our expression for t we obtain

$$y = (x + 1)t \quad \text{and} \quad y^2 = (x + 1)^2 t^2.$$

On the other hand,

$$y^2 = 1 - x^2 = (x + 1)(1 - x).$$

In the two expressions for y^2, we cancel $(x + 1)(x \neq -1)$ and obtain

$$1 - x = (x + 1)t^2.$$

From this we solve for x, and get

$$x = \frac{1 - t^2}{1 + t^2}.$$

From the formula $y = t(x + 1)$, we get

$$y = \frac{2t}{1 + t^2}.$$

Thus, for $x \neq -1$, we can get t from x and y, but *conversely* we can recover x, y from values of t, which can be given arbitrarily. This allows us to find points on the circle explicitly simply by giving t arbitrary values, which may be selected to be rational numbers. Points (x, y) such that x and y are rational numbers are called *rational points*. The above parametrization shows us how to get all of them (except when $x = -1$).

Example 3. We shall prove that the points on the parametric curve

(*) $x = 2t - 1, \quad y = t + 4$

are precisely the points on a straight line. Eliminating t from these equations, i.e. multiplying the second by 2 and subtracting from the first, we obtain

(**) $x - 2y = -9.$

Thus all points satisfying (*) satisfy (**), which is the equation of a line. Conversely, given a point (x, y) satisfying equation (**), let $t = y - 4$. Then $y = t + 4$, and

$$x = -9 + 2y = 2(t + 4) - 9 = 2t + 8 - 9 = 2t - 1.$$

Hence (x, y) satisfy (*), as was to be shown.

In general, suppose that we have two points (x, y) and (x_1, y_1) in the plane. We define the sum

$$(x, y) + (x_1, y_1) = (x + x_1, y + y_1),$$

and if c is a number, the product

$$c(x, y) = (cx, cy).$$

Thus sum and product are defined componentwise. In Example 3, let $P = (2, 1)$ and $Q = (-1, 4)$. Let $X = (x, y)$. Then the parametric curve of Example 3 can be written in a shorter notation in the form

$$X = Q + tP.$$

When we study vectors in the next course, we shall see that this can be interpreted as the line through Q, in the direction of P.

EXERCISES

Sketch the following curves given in parametric form:

1. $x = t + 1, \quad y = 3t + 4$
2. $x = 1 + t^2, \quad y = 3 - t$
3. $x = 1 - t^2, \quad y = t \quad (-1 \leq t \leq 1)$
4. $x = t - \sin t, \quad y = 1 - \cos t$
5. $x = 2(t - \sin t), \quad y = 2(1 - \cos t)$

One can also give a parametrization of curves in polar coordinates. Sketch the following curves in polar coordinates:

6. $r = t^3, \quad \theta = \pi t^2$ 7. $r = t, \quad \theta = t^2$

8. Find at least five rational points on the circle of radius 1. (It is very difficult in general to find rational points on curves. It is rather remarkable that we did it on the circle.)

9. Using the method above, find an analogous parametrization of the circle

$$x^2 + y^2 = 9.$$

10. Prove that on any curve

$$x^n + y^n = 1$$

(n = positive integer $\geq$ 3), there is only a finite number of rational points. (If you solve this, you will be instantly world-famous among mathematicians. It is in fact believed that the only rational points are those for which x or $y = 0$. This is Fermat's problem, and has been verified for many values of n. It is also unknown whether there exist infinitely many rational points on a curve of type

$$y^2 = f(x),$$

where f is a polynomial of degree $\geq$ 5, having distinct roots, for instance

$$y^2 = (x - 1)(x - 2)(x - 3)(x - 4)(x - 5).$$

This is a special case of a more general conjecture made by Mordell some forty years ago, and unproved to this day.)

11. Sketch the following curves given in parametric form.

(a) $x = t$, $y = t^3$ (b) $x = t$, $y = t^4$

(c) $x = t^2$, $y = t^4$ (d) $x = t$, $y = \sqrt{t}$

12. Show that all points on the parametric curve $x = 2t + 1$, $y = 3t - 1$ lie on a straight line, and determine the ordinary equation of this line. Conversely, show that every point on this line satisfies the parametric equation for some value of t.

13. Show that the points on the parametric curve

$$x = 5t - 1, \qquad y = -2t + 4$$

are precisely the points on a straight line, and determine the equation of this line.

14. Show that the points on the parametric curve

$$x = 2t, \qquad y = 3t^2$$

are precisely the points on a parabola, and determine the ordinary equation of this parabola.

15. Show that the points on the parametric curve

$$x = 2t^2, \qquad y = 3t - 1$$

are precisely the points on a parabola, and determine the ordinary equation of this parabola.

16. Determine the ordinary equation for the following parametrized curves and sketch the graphs.

(a) $x = t$, $y = 1/2t$ (b) $x = 3t$, $y = 1/t$

(c) $x = t^2$, $y = 1/t^2$

(In this case, you may need an inequality in addition to an equation.)

17. Show that the parametric curve given by $x = t^2$, $y = t^4$ is part of a parabola. What is the ordinary equation of this parabola, and which part is parametrized as above?

18. Sketch the parametric curve $x = t^2$, $y = 1/t^4$.

Chapter VII

Inverse Functions

Suppose that we have a function, for instance

$$y = 3x - 5.$$

Then we can solve for x in terms of y, namely

$$x = \tfrac{1}{3}(y + 5).$$

Thus x can be expressed as a function of y.

Although we are able to solve by means of an explicit formula, there are interesting cases where x can be expressed as a function of y, but without such an explicit formula. In this chapter, we shall investigate such cases.

§1. DEFINITION OF INVERSE FUNCTIONS

Let $y = f(x)$ be a function, defined for all x in some interval. If, for each value y_1 of y, there exists exactly *one* value x_1 of x in the interval such that $f(x_1) = y_1$, then we can define an *inverse function*

$$x = g(y)$$

by the rule: Given a number y, we associate with it the unique number x in the interval such that $f(x) = y$.

Our inverse function is defined only at those numbers which are values of f. We have the fundamental relation $f(g(y)) = y$ and $g(f(x)) = x$.

For example, consider the function $y = x^2$, which we view as being defined only for $x \geq 0$. Every positive number (or 0) can be written uniquely as the square of a positive number (or 0). Hence we can define the inverse function, which will also be defined for $y \geq 0$, but not for $y < 0$. It is nothing but the square root function.

The next theorem gives us a good criterion when the inverse function is defined.

Theorem 1. Let $f(x)$ be a function which is strictly increasing. Then the inverse function exists.

Proof. This is practically obvious: Given a number y_1 and a number x_1 such that $f(x_1) = y_1$, there cannot be another number x_2 such that

130

$f(x_2) = y_1$ unless $x_2 = x_1$, because if $x_2 \neq x_1$, then either $x_2 > x_1$, in which case $f(x_2) > f(x_1)$, or $x_2 < x_1$, in which case $f(x_2) < f(x_1)$.

Since the positivity of the derivative gives us a good test when a function is strictly increasing, we are able to define inverse functions whenever the function is differentiable and its derivative is positive.

As usual, what we have said above applies as well to functions which are strictly decreasing, and whose derivatives are negative.

Using the intermediate value theorem, we now conclude:

Theorem 2. *Let f be a continuous function on the closed interval*

$$a \leqq x \leqq b$$

and assume that f is strictly increasing. Let $f(a) = \alpha$ and $f(b) = \beta$. Then the inverse function is defined on the closed interval $[\alpha, \beta]$.

Proof. Given any number γ between α and β, there exists a number c between a and b such that $f(c) = \gamma$, by the intermediate value theorem. Our assertion now follows from Theorem 1.

If we let g be this inverse function, then $g(\alpha) = a$ and $g(\beta) = b$. Furthermore, the inverse function is characterized by the relation

$$f(x) = y \qquad \text{if and only if} \qquad x = g(y).$$

Example 1. Let $f(x) = x^3 - 2x + 1$, viewed as a function on the interval $x > \sqrt{2/3}$. Can we define the inverse function? For what numbers? If g is the inverse function, what is $g(0)$? What is $g(5)$?

Since $f'(x) = 3x^2 - 2$, the derivative is positive when $x > \sqrt{2/3}$. Hence our function is strictly increasing and the inverse function is defined. We know (from the techniques of the previous chapter) that $x = \sqrt{2/3}$ is a minimum of f, and $f(\sqrt{2/3}) = (2/3)^{3/2} - 2(2/3)^{1/2} + 1$. The inverse function is defined therefore for $y > f(\sqrt{2/3})$.

Since $f(1) = 0$, we get $g(0) = 1$. Since $f(2) = 5$, we get $g(5) = 2$.

Please note that we do not give an explicit formula for our inverse function.

Example 2. Let $f(x) = x^n$ (n being a positive integer). We view f as defined only for numbers $x > 0$. Since $f'(x)$ is nx^{n-1}, the function is strictly increasing. Hence the inverse function exists. This inverse function g is in fact what we mean by the n-th root. In particular, we have proved that every positive number has an n-th root.

In all the exercises of the previous chapter you determined intervals over which certain functions increase and decrease. You can now define inverse functions for such intervals. In most cases, you cannot write down an explicit formula for such inverse functions.

EXERCISES

For each of the following functions, determine whether there is an inverse
function g, and determine those numbers at which g is defined.

1. $f(x) = 3x + 2$, all x.

2. $f(x) = x^2 + 2x - 3$, $0 \leq x$

3. $f(x) = x^3 + 4x - 5$, all x

4. $f(x) = \dfrac{x}{x + 1}$, $-1 < x$

5. $f(x) = \dfrac{x}{x + 2}$, $-2 < x$

6. $f(x) = \dfrac{x + 1}{x - 1}$, $1 < x$

7. $f(x) = \dfrac{1}{x^2}$, $0 < x \leq 1$

8. $f(x) = \dfrac{x^2}{x^2 + 1}$, $0 \leq x \leq 5$

9. $f(x) = \dfrac{x + 2}{x - 2}$, $0 \leq x < 2$

10. $f(x) = x + \dfrac{1}{x}$, $1 \leq x \leq 10$

11. $f(x) = x + \dfrac{1}{x}$, $0 < x \leq 1$

12. $f(x) = x - \dfrac{1}{x}$, $0 < x \leq 1$

13. $f(x) = \dfrac{2x}{1 + x^2}$, $-1 \leq x \leq 1$

14. $f(x) = \dfrac{2x}{1 + x^2}$, $1 \leq x$

§2. DERIVATIVE OF INVERSE FUNCTIONS

We shall state a theorem which allows us to determine the derivative of
an inverse function when we know the derivative of the given function.

Theorem 3. *Let a, b be two numbers, $a < b$. Let f be a function which
is differentiable on the interval $a < x < b$ and such that its derivative
$f'(x)$ is > 0 for all x in this open interval. Then the inverse function
$x = g(y)$ exists, and we have*

$$g'(y) = \frac{1}{f'(x)} = \frac{1}{f'(g(y))}.$$

Proof. We are supposed to investigate the Newton quotient

$$\frac{g(y + k) - g(y)}{k}.$$

The following picture illustrates the situation:

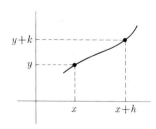

By the intermediate value theorem, every number of the form $y + k$ with small values of k can be written as a value of f. We let $x = g(y)$ and we let $h = g(y + k) - g(y)$. Then

$$x = g(y) \qquad \text{and} \qquad g(y + k) = x + h.$$

Furthermore, $y + k = f(x + h)$ and hence

$$k = f(x + h) - f(x).$$

The Newton quotient for g can therefore be written

$$\frac{h}{f(x + h) - f(x)},$$

and we see that it is the reciprocal of the Newton quotient for f, namely

$$\frac{1}{\dfrac{f(x + h) - f(x)}{h}}.$$

As h approaches 0, we know that k approaches 0. Conversely, as k approaches 0, we know that there exists exactly one value of h such that $f(x + h) = y + k$, because the inverse function is defined. Consequently, the corresponding value of h must also approach 0.

If we now take the limit of the reciprocal of the Newton quotient of f, as h (or k) approaches 0, we get

$$\frac{1}{f'(x)}.$$

By definition, this is the derivative $g'(y)$ and our theorem is proved.

Example 1. Let $f(x) = x^3 - 2x + 1$, viewed as a function on the interval $x > \sqrt{2/3}$. Let g be the inverse function. What is $g'(0)$? What is $g'(5)$?

Since $f'(x) = 3x^2 - 2$ we know that

$$g'(y) = \frac{1}{f'(x)}$$

whenever $y = f(x)$ or $x = g(y)$. But

$$f(1) = 0 \qquad \text{and} \qquad g(0) = 1.$$

Therefore

$$g'(0) = \frac{1}{f'(1)} = 1.$$

Similarly, $f(2) = 5$ and $g(5) = 2$. Hence

$$g'(5) = \frac{1}{f'(2)} = \frac{1}{10},$$

because $f'(2) = 10$.

Please note that the derivative $g'(y)$ is given in terms of $f'(x)$. We don't have a formula in terms of y.

The theorem giving us the derivative of the inverse function could also be expressed by saying that

$$\frac{dx}{dy} = \frac{1}{dy/dx}.$$

Here also, the derivative behaves *as if* we were taking a quotient. Thus the notation is very suggestive and we can use it from now on without thinking, because we proved a theorem justifying it.

Remark. In Theorem 3, we have proved that in fact, the derivative of the inverse function g exists, and is given by $g'(y) = 1/f'(x)$. If one *assumes* that this derivative exists, then one can give a much shorter argument to find its value, using the chain rule. Indeed, we have

$$f(g(y)) = y.$$

Differentiating with respect to y, we find by the chain rule,

$$f'(g(y))g'(y) = 1.$$

Hence

$$g'(y) = \frac{1}{f'(g(y))},$$

as was to be shown.

EXERCISES

In the exercises of Chapter V, §4, restrict f to an interval so that the inverse function is defined in an interval containing the indicated point, and find the derivative of the inverse function at that point. (Let g denote this inverse function in every case.)

1. $g'(2)$ 2. $g'(6)$ 3. $g'(7)$ 4. $g'(-1)$ 5. $g'(\sqrt{3}/2)$
6. $g'(-1)$ 7. $g'(0)$ 8. $g'(2)$ 9. $g'(21)$ 10. $g'(11)$

11. Let f be a continuous function on the interval $[a, b]$. Assume that f is twice differentiable on the open interval $a < x < b$, and that $f'(x) > 0$ and $f''(x) > 0$ on this interval. Let g be the inverse function of f.
    (a) Find an expression for the second derivative of g.
    (b) Show that $g''(y) < 0$ on its interval of definition. Thus g is convex in the opposite direction to f.

§3. THE ARCSINE

It is impossible to define an inverse function for the function $y = \sin x$ because to each value of y there correspond infinitely many values of x (differing by 2π). However, if we restrict our attention to special intervals, we can define the inverse function.

We restrict the sine function to the interval

$$-\frac{\pi}{2} \le x \le \frac{\pi}{2}.$$

The derivative of sin x is cos x and in that interval, we have

$$0 < \cos x$$

except when $x = \pi/2$ or $x = -\pi/2$ in which case the cosine is 0.
    Therefore, in the interval

$$-\frac{\pi}{2} \le x \le \frac{\pi}{2}$$

the function is strictly increasing by Theorem 2 of Chapter V, §4. The inverse function exists, and is called the *arcsine*.
    Let $f(x) = \sin x$, and $x = \arcsin y$, the inverse function. Since $f(0) = 0$ we have arcsin $0 = 0$.   Furthermore, since sin $(-\pi/2) = -1$ and sin $(\pi/2) = 1$, we know that the inverse function is defined over the interval going from -1 to $+1$, i.e. for

$$-1 \le y \le 1.$$

In words, we can say loosely that arcsin x *is the angle whose sine is x.* (We throw in the word *loosely* because, strictly speaking, arcsin x is a number, and not an angle, and also because we mean the angle between $-\pi/2$ and $\pi/2$.)
    The derivative of sin x is positive for

$$-\pi/2 < x < \pi/2.$$

Since the derivative of the inverse function $x = g(y)$ is $1/f'(x)$, the derivative of arcsin y is also positive, in the interval

$$-1 < y < 1.$$

Therefore the inverse function is strictly increasing in that interval. Its graph looks like the figure shown below.

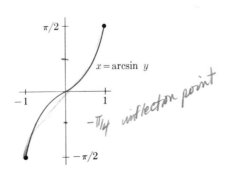

At this point, we cannot call the horizontal axis simultaneously the *x*- and *y*-axis. Thus for the moment, the horizontal axis as drawn above is the *y*-axis and the vertical axis is the *x*-axis.

According to the general rule for the derivative of inverse functions, we know that when $y = \sin x$ and $x = \arcsin y$ the derivative is

$$\frac{dx}{dy} = \frac{1}{\cos x}.$$

When *x* is very close to $\pi/2$, we know that $\cos x$ is close to 0. Therefore the derivative is very large. Hence the curve is almost vertical. Similarly, when *x* is close to $-\pi/2$ and *y* is close to -1, the curve is almost vertical, as drawn.

Finally, it turns out that we can express our derivative explicitly as a function of *y*. Indeed, we have the relation

$$\sin^2 x + \cos^2 x = 1,$$

whence

$$\cos^2 x = 1 - \sin^2 x.$$

In the interval between $-\pi/2$ and $\pi/2$, the cosine is ≥ 0. Hence we can take the square root, and we get

$$\cos x = \sqrt{1 - \sin^2 x}$$

in that interval. Since $y = \sin x$, we can write our derivative in the form

$$\frac{dx}{dy} = \frac{1}{\sqrt{1 - y^2}}$$

which is expressed entirely in terms of *y*.

Having now obtained all the information we want concerning the arcsine, we shift back our letters to the usual ones. We state the main properties as a theorem.

Theorem 4. *View the sine function as defined on the interval*

$$[-\pi/2, \pi/2].$$

Then the inverse function is defined on the interval $[-1, 1]$. *Call it*

$$g(x) = \arcsin x.$$

Then g is differentiable in the open interval $-1 < x < 1$, *and*

$$g'(x) = \frac{1}{\sqrt{1 - x^2}}.$$

EXERCISES

1. Define the inverse function arccosine, viewing the cosine only on the interval $[0, \pi]$.

2. What is the derivative of arccosine?

3. Let $g(x) = \arcsin x$. What is $g'(\frac{1}{2})$? What is $g'(1/\sqrt{2})$? What is $g(\frac{1}{2})$? What is $g(1/\sqrt{2})$?

4. Let $g(x) = \arccos x$. What is $g'(\frac{1}{2})$? What is $g'(1/\sqrt{2})$? What is $g(\frac{1}{2})$? What is $g(1/\sqrt{2})$?

5. Let $\sec x = 1/\cos x$. Define the inverse function of the secant over a suitable interval and obtain a formula for the derivative of this inverse function.

Find the following numbers.

6. $\arcsin (\sin 3\pi/2)$ 7. $\arcsin (\sin 2\pi)$ 8. $\arccos (\cos 3\pi/2)$

9. $\arccos (\cos -\pi/2)$ 10. $\arcsin (\sin -3\pi/4)$

Find the derivatives of the following functions:

11. $\arcsin (x^2 - 1)$ 12. $\arccos (2x + 5)$ 13. $\dfrac{1}{\arcsin x}$ 14. $\dfrac{2}{\arccos 2x}$

15. Determine the intervals over which the function arcsin is convex upward, and convex downward. $f''(x) > 0 \quad \text{convex up}$

§4. THE ARCTANGENT

Let $f(x) = \tan x$ and view this function as defined over the interval

$$-\frac{\pi}{2} < x < \frac{\pi}{2}.$$

As x goes from $-\pi/2$ to $\pi/2$, the tangent goes from very large negative values to very large positive values. As x approaches $\pi/2$, the tangent has in fact arbitrarily large positive values, and similarly when x approaches $-\pi/2$, the tangent has arbitrarily large negative values.

We recall that the graph of the tangent looks like that in the figure below.

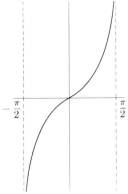

The derivative of tan x is

$$\frac{d(\tan x)}{dx} = 1 + \tan^2 x.$$

Hence the derivative is always positive, and our function is strictly increasing. Therefore the inverse function is defined for all numbers. We call it the *arctangent*. Its derivative is also positive (because it is the reciprocal of the derivative of the tangent) and hence the arctan is strictly increasing also.

The graph looks like this:

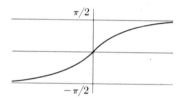

Let $x = g(y) = \arctan y$. Then

$$g'(y) = \frac{1}{1 + \tan^2 x}$$

so that

$$g'(y) = \frac{1}{1 + y^2}.$$

Here again we are able to get an explicit formula for the derivative of the inverse function.

As with the arcsine, when dealing simultaneously with the function and its inverse function, we have to keep our letters x, y separate. However, we now summarize the properties of the arctan in terms of our usual notation.

Theorem 5. *The inverse function of the tangent is defined for all numbers. Call it the arctangent. Then it has a derivative, and that derivative is given by the relation*

$$\frac{d(\arctan x)}{dx} = \frac{1}{1 + x^2}.$$

As x becomes very large positive, arctan x approaches $\pi/2$.
As x becomes very large negative, arctan x approaches $-\pi/2$.
The arctangent is strictly increasing for all x.

In words, we can say that arctan x is the angle whose tangent is x, between $-\pi/2$ and $\pi/2$.

Example. A balloon leaves the ground 100 ft from an observer at the rate of 50 ft/min. How fast is the angle of elevation of the observer's line of sight increasing when the balloon is at an altitude of 100 ft? The picture is as follows.

$\rightarrow \dfrac{d\theta}{dt} = ?$

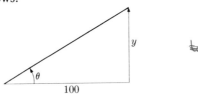

We have to determine $d\theta/dt$. We know that $dy/dt = 50$. We have

$$\frac{y}{100} = \tan \theta, \quad = \quad \frac{\mathbf{y}}{\mathbf{x}}$$

whence

$$\theta = \arctan\left(\frac{y}{100}\right).$$

Hence

$$\frac{d\theta}{dy} = \frac{1}{1 + \left(\frac{y}{100}\right)^2} \cdot \frac{1}{100} \quad \text{and} \quad \frac{d\theta}{dt} = \frac{d\theta}{dy}\frac{dy}{dt}.$$

$$= \frac{d\theta}{dt} \cdot 50$$

It follows that

$$\frac{d\theta}{dt} \quad \text{when} \quad y = 100 \quad \text{is equal to} \quad \frac{1}{1 + 1^2} \cdot \frac{1}{100} \cdot 50$$

and hence the answer is $\frac{1}{4}$ rad/min (where rad is radians).

EXERCISES

1. Let g be the arctan function. What is $g(1)$? What is $g(1/\sqrt{3})$? What is $g(-1)$? What is $g(\sqrt{3})$?

2. Let g be the arctan function. What is $g'(1)$? What is $g'(1/\sqrt{3})$? What is $g'(-1)$? What is $g'(\sqrt{3})$?

3. Suppose you were to define an inverse function for the tangent in the interval $\pi/2 < x < 3\pi/2$. What would be the derivative of this inverse function?

4. What is
   (a) arctan $(\tan 3\pi/4)$?   (b) arctan $(\tan 2\pi)$?
   (c) arctan $(\tan 5\pi/6)$?   (d) arctan $(\tan -5\pi/6)$?

Find the derivatives of the following functions.

5. arctan $3x$

6. arctan $\sqrt{x}$

7. arcsin $x +$ arccos x

8. x arcsin x

9. $\arctan (\sin 2x)$

10. $x^2 \arctan 2x$

11. $\dfrac{\sin x}{\arcsin x}$

12. $\arcsin (\cos x - x^2)$

13. $\arctan \dfrac{1}{x}$

14. $\arctan \dfrac{1}{2x}$

15. $(1 + \arcsin 3x)^3$

16. $(\arcsin 2x + \arctan x^2)^{3/2}$

Find the equation of the tangent line at the indicated point for the following curves.

17. $y = \arcsin x, \quad x = 1/\sqrt{2}$

18. $y = \arccos x, \quad x = 1/\sqrt{2}$

19. $y = \arctan 2x, \quad x = \sqrt{3}/2$

20. $y = \arctan x, \quad x = -1$

21. $y = \arcsin x, \quad x = -\tfrac{1}{2}$

22. A balloon leaves the ground 500 ft from an observer at the rate of 200 ft/min. How fast is the angle of elevation of the observer's line of sight increasing when the balloon is at an altitude of 1000 ft?

23. An airplane at an altitude of 4400 ft is flying horizontally directly away from an observer. When the angle of elevation is $\pi/4$, the angle is decreasing at the rate of 0.05 rad/sec. How fast is the airplane flying at that instant?

24. A man is walking along a sidewalk at the rate of 5 ft/sec. A searchlight on the ground 30 ft from the walk is kept trained on him. At what rate is the searchlight revolving when the man is 20 ft from the point on the sidewalk nearest the light?

25. A tower stands at the end of a street. A man drives towards the tower at the rate of 50 ft/sec. The tower is 500 ft tall. How fast is the angle subtended by the tower at the man's eye increasing when the man is 1000 ft from the tower?

26. A police car approaches an intersection at 80 ft/sec. When it is 200 ft from the intersection, a car crosses the intersection traveling at a right angle from the police car at the rate of 60 ft/sec. If the policeman directs his beam of light on this second car, how fast is the light beam turning 2 sec later, assuming that both cars continue at their original rate?

27. A weight is drawn along a level floor by means of a rope which passes over a hook 6 ft above the floor. If the rope is pulled over the hook at the rate of 1 ft/sec find an expression for the rate of change of the angle θ between the rope and the floor as a function of the angle θ.

28. A man standing at a fixed point on a wharf pulls in a small boat. The wharf is 20 ft above the level of the water. If he is pulling the rope at 2 ft/sec, how fast is the angle that the rope makes with the water increasing when the distance from the man to the boat is 50 ft?

29. A helicopter leaves the ground 1000 ft from an observer and rises vertically at 20 ft/sec. At what rate is the observer's angle of elevation of the helicopter changing when the helicopter is 800 ft above the ground?

30. Determine those intervals where arctan is convex upward and convex downward.

Chapter VIII

Exponents and Logarithms

We remember that we had trouble at the very beginning with the function 2^x (or 3^x, or 10^x). It was intuitively very plausible that there should be such functions, satisfying the fundamental equation

$$2^{x+y} = 2^x 2^y$$

for all numbers x, y, and $2^0 = 1$, but we had difficulties in saying what we meant by $2^{\sqrt{2}}$ (or 2^π).

It is the purpose of this chapter to give a systematic treatment of this function, and others like it.

We shall see that its inverse function is defined for positive numbers. It is called the log (or rather the log to the base 2). Thus $y = 2^x$ if and only if $x = \log_2 y$. For instance,

$$3 = \log_2 8 \quad \text{and} \quad 8 = 2^3$$

are two ways of saying the same thing.

Let us assume for the moment that we can make sense of the function 2^x, and let us see how we could find its derivative.

We form the Newton quotient. It is

$$\frac{2^{x+h} - 2^x}{h}.$$

Using the fundamental equation we see that this quotient is equal to

$$\frac{2^x 2^h - 2^x}{h} = 2^x \frac{2^h - 1}{h}.$$

As h approaches 0, 2^x remains fixed, but it is very difficult to see what happens to

$$\frac{2^h - 1}{h}.$$

It is not at all clear that this quotient approaches a limit. Roughly speaking, we meet a difficulty which is analogous to the one we met when we tried to find the derivative of $\sin x$. However, in the present situation, a direct approach would lead to much greater difficulties than those which we met when we discussed

$$\lim_{h \to 0} \frac{\sin h}{h}.$$

It is in fact true that

$$\lim_{h \to 0} \frac{2^h - 1}{h}$$

exists. We see that it does not depend on x. It depends only on 2.

If we tried to take the derivative of 10^x, we would end up with the problem of determining the limit

$$\lim_{h \to 0} \frac{10^h - 1}{h},$$

which is also independent of x.

There seems to be no reason for selecting 2, or 10, or any other number a in investigating the function a^x. However, we shall see that there exists a number called e such that

$$\lim_{h \to 0} \frac{e^h - 1}{h} = 1$$

is equal to 1. This is perfectly marvelous, because if we then form the Newton quotient for e^x, we get

$$\frac{e^{x+h} - e^x}{h} = e^x \cdot \frac{e^h - 1}{h}.$$

Therefore its limit as h approaches 0 is e^x and hence

$$\frac{d(e^x)}{dx} = e^x.$$

We shall find out eventually how to compute e. Its value is 2.718.... In Chapter XIV you will have the technique to compute e to any degree of accuracy you wish.

The sales talk which precedes must now be set aside in your mind. We start from scratch, and in order to develop the theory in the easiest way, it is best to start with the log, and not with the exponential function. We shall then have no difficulties in determining all the limits which arise.

§1. THE LOGARITHM

We define a function $\log x$ to be the area under the curve $1/x$ between 1 and x if $x \geq 1$, and the negative of the area of the curve $1/x$ between 1 and x if $0 < x < 1$. In particular, $\log 1 = 0$.

The shaded portion of our picture at the top of page 143 represents the area under the curve between 1 and x and we have taken an instance where $x > 1$.

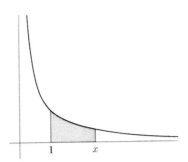

If $x < 1$ and $x > 0$, we would have the picture shown below. If $0 < x < 1$, we have said that log x is equal to the negative of the area. Thus log $x < 0$ if $0 < x < 1$ and log $x > 0$ if $x > 1$.

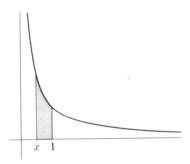

(In defining the log, we have appealed to our geometric intuition of area, just as we did when we defined the sine and cosine. In the next chapter, we shall see how one can avoid this appeal to geometry, and give a purely analytic definition.)

The fundamental fact concerning the logarithm is the following.

Theorem 1. *The function* log x *is differentiable, and*

$$\frac{d(\log x)}{dx} = \frac{1}{x}.$$

Proof. We form the Newton quotient

$$\frac{\log (x + h) - \log x}{h}$$

and have to prove that it approaches $1/x$ as a limit when h approaches 0.

Let us take $h > 0$ for the moment. Then log $(x + h) - $ log x is the area under the curve between x and $x + h$. Since the curve $1/x$ is decreasing, this area satisfies the following inequalities:

$$h\,\frac{1}{x + h} < \log (x + h) - \log x < h\,\frac{1}{x}.$$

Indeed, $1/x$ is the height of the big rectangle as drawn on the next figure, and $1/(x + h)$ is the height of the small rectangle. Since h is the base of the rectangle, and since the area under the curve $1/x$ between x and $x + h$ is in between the two rectangles, we see that it satisfies our inequalities.

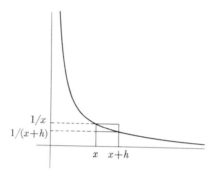

We divide both sides of our inequalities by the positive number h. Then the inequalities are preserved, and we get

$$\frac{1}{x + h} < \frac{\log (x + h) - \log x}{h} < \frac{1}{x}.$$

As h approaches 0, our Newton quotient is squeezed between $1/(x + h)$ and $1/x$ and consequently approaches $1/x$. This proves our theorem in case $h > 0$.

When $h < 0$ we use an entirely similar argument, which we leave as an exercise. (You have to pay attention to the sign of the log. Also when you divide an inequality by h and $h < 0$ then the inequality gets reversed. However, you will again see that the Newton quotient is squeezed between $1/x$ and $1/(x + h)$.)

From now on, we do not need our geometric intuition any more. The notion of area was used only to give us the existence of a function whose derivative is $1/x$, and whose value at 1 is 0. All the arguments which follow depend only on the fact that we have such a function.

Let, therefore, $\log x$ be a function defined for $x > 0$, such that $\log 1 = 0$, and such that

$$\frac{d(\log x)}{dx} = \frac{1}{x}.$$

If $g(x)$ is another such function, then it differs from $\log x$ by a constant C, i.e.

$$g(x) = \log x + C$$

for all $x > 0$. (Use Theorem 8 of Chapter V, §4.) Setting $x = 1$ gives $g(1) = C$. Since we assume that $g(1) = 0$ we see that $g(x) = \log x$. Thus there is only one function having the properties mentioned above.

Theorem 2. *If a, b are two numbers > 0, then*

$$\log (ab) = \log a + \log b.$$

Proof. Consider the function $f(x) = \log (ax)$, defined for all $x > 0$. We can take its derivative by the chain rule, and we obtain

$$\frac{df}{dx} = \frac{1}{ax} \cdot a = \frac{1}{x}.$$

$\left(\text{Put } u = ax \text{ and remember that } \frac{df}{dx} = \frac{df}{du} \frac{du}{dx} \cdot\right)$ Therefore, our functions $f(x)$ and $\log x$ have the same derivative. Consequently, they differ by a constant:

$$\log (ax) = \log x + C.$$

This is true for *all* $x > 0$. In particular, it is true for $x = 1$. This yields

$$\log a = C$$

and determines the constant C as being equal to $\log a$.

But the above relation being true for *all* $x > 0$, it is also true if we set $x = b$. In that case, we obtain

$$\log (ab) = \log b + \log a,$$

thereby proving our theorem.

Please appreciate the elegance and efficiency of the arguments!

Theorem 3. *The function* $\log x$ *is strictly increasing for* $x > 0$. *It takes on arbitrarily large positive and negative values.*

Proof. Since the derivative is $1/x$, which is positive for all $x > 0$, our function is strictly increasing. Since $\log 1 = 0$, we conclude for instance that $\log 2 > 0$.

Using Theorem 2 we now see that

$$\log 4 = \log (2 \cdot 2) = 2 \log 2,$$
$$\log 8 = \log (4 \cdot 2) = \log 4 + \log 2 = 3 \log 2,$$
$$\log 16 = \log (8 \cdot 2) = \log 8 + \log 2 = 4 \log 2,$$

and so on. In general, by induction, assume that $\log 2^{n-1} = (n - 1) \log 2$. Then

$$\log 2^n = \log 2 \cdot 2^{n-1} = \log 2 + \log 2^{n-1}$$
$$= \log 2 + (n - 1) \log 2 = n \log 2$$

for any positive integer n. As n becomes very large, $n \log 2$ also becomes very large.

Concerning the negative values, observe that

$$0 = \log 1 = \log (2 \cdot \tfrac{1}{2}) = \log 2 + \log (\tfrac{1}{2}).$$

Therefore

$$\log \left(\tfrac{1}{2}\right) = -\log 2,$$

and similarly,

$$\log \left(\frac{1}{2^n}\right) = -n \log 2.$$

For large positive integers n, the number $-n \log 2$ is very large negative. These same arguments can be applied to prove the following theorem.

Theorem 4. *If n is an integer, positive or negative, and a is a number > 0, then*

$$\log (a^n) = n \log a.$$

Proof. We proceed stepwise, assuming first that n is positive. Then

$$\log (a^2) = \log a + \log a = 2 \log a.$$

By induction, assuming $\log (a^{n-1}) = (n - 1) \log a$, we have

$$\log (a^n) = \log (a \cdot a^{n-1}) = \log a + \log (a^{n-1})$$
$$= \log a + (n - 1) \log a = n \log a.$$

Suppose that n is negative, say $n = -m$ with m positive. Then

$$0 = \log 1 = \log (a^m \cdot a^{-m}) = \log (a^m) + \log (a^{-m}).$$

Therefore

$$\log (a^n) = \log (a^{-m}) = -m \log (a) = n \log a,$$

thereby proving our theorem.

By the intermediate value theorem, the function log takes on *all* values. Its graph looks like that in the next figure. It is convex downwards because the second derivative of $\log x$ is $-1/x^2 < 0$ for all $x > 0$.

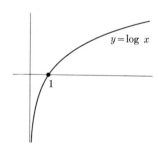

Remark. We shall sometimes consider composite functions of the type $\log (f(x))$. Since the log is not defined for numbers < 0, this expression is defined only for numbers x such that $f(x) > 0$. This is to be understood whenever we write such an expression.

Thus when we write $\log (x - 2)$, this is defined only when $x - 2 > 0$, in other words $x > 2$. When we write $\log (\sin x)$, this is meaningful only when $\sin x > 0$. It is not defined when $\sin x \leq 0$.

EXERCISES

1. What is the tangent line to the curve $y = \log x$ at the point whose x-coordinate is (a) 2, (b) 5, (c) $\frac{1}{2}$?

2. What is the equation of the tangent line of the curve $y = \log (x^2 + 1)$ at the point whose x-coordinate is (a) -1, (b) 2, (c) -3?

3. Find the derivatives of the following functions:

   (a) $\log (\sin x)$ (b) $\sin (\log (2x + 3))$ (c) $\log (x^2 + 5)$ (d) $\dfrac{\log 2x}{\sin x}$

4. What is the equation of the tangent line of the curve $y = \log (x + 1)$ at the point whose x-coordinate is 3?

5. What is the equation of the tangent line of the curve $y = \log (2x - 5)$ at the point whose x-coordinate is 4?

6. (a) Prove that $\log x < x$ for all $x > 1$. [*Hint:* Let $f(x) = x - \log x$, find $f(1)$ and show that f is strictly increasing.]
   (b) Prove that $\log (1 + x) < x$ for all $x > 0$.

7. Let h be a positive number. Compare the area under the curve $1/x$ between 1 and $1 + h$ with the area of suitable rectangles to show that

$$\frac{h}{1 + h} < \log (1 + h) < h.$$

8. Prove that

$$\lim_{h \to 0} \frac{1}{h} \log (1 + h) = 1.$$

9. Prove that for every positive integer n, we have

$$\frac{1}{n + 1} < \log \left(1 + \frac{1}{n} \right) < \frac{1}{n}.$$

10. (a) Let

$$a_n = 1 + \tfrac{1}{2} + \cdots + \frac{1}{n} - \log n$$

   for each integer $n \geq 2$. Show that $a_{n+1} < a_n$.

   (b) Let $b_n = a_n - \dfrac{1}{n}$. Show that $b_{n+1} > b_n$.

   (c) The sequence of positive numbers a_n decreases, and the sequence of positive numbers b_n increases. Since $b_n - a_n$ becomes arbitrarily small as n becomes large, it follows that there is a unique number C such that

$$b_n < C < a_n$$

for all positive integers n. This number is called *Euler's constant*. Prove that this constant is not a rational number. (Undying fame awaits you if you can do this exercise.)

Differentiate the following functions.

11. $\log (2x + 5)$ 12. $\log (x^2 + 3)$ 13. $\log (\arcsin x)$ 14. $\log (\arccos 2x)$

15. $\dfrac{1}{\log x}$ 16. $\dfrac{x}{\log x}$ 17. $x(\log x)^{1/3}$ 18. $\log \sqrt{1 - x^2}$

Sketch the following curves.

19. $y = \log (-x), \quad x < 0$ 20. $y = \log 2x, \quad x \neq 0$
21. $y = \log (x + 1), \quad x > -1$ 22. $y = \log (1 - x), \quad x < 1$
23. $y = x - \log x, \quad x > 0$

24. Let $a > 0$ and let $b = a^{1/n}$. Show that

$$\log b = \frac{1}{n} \log a.$$

25. Let $a_1, \ldots, a_n$ be numbers > 0. Show that

$$(a_1 \cdots a_n)^{1/n} \leqq \frac{a_1 + \cdots + a_n}{n}.$$

[*Hint:* Take the log, and use the convexity, referring back to Exercises 12 and 13 of Chapter VI, §3.]

§2. THE EXPONENTIAL FUNCTION

We can apply the theory of the inverse function. Since the function log is strictly increasing, the inverse function is defined and we call it exp. Since log takes on *all* values, the inverse function is defined for *all* numbers, positive or negative.

Since $0 = \log 1$, we have by definition

$$1 = \exp (0).$$

Theorem 5. *If z, w are two numbers, then*

$$\exp (z + w) = \exp (z) \cdot \exp (w).$$

Proof. Let $a = \exp z$ and $b = \exp w$. Then $z = \log a$ and $w = \log b$ by definition of the inverse function. By Theorem 2, we know that

$$z + w = \log (ab).$$

By the definition of the inverse function, this means that

$$\exp (z + w) = ab.$$

However, $ab = \exp (z) \cdot \exp (w)$. Our theorem is proved.

We *define* the number e to be exp (1). This is the same as saying that $\log e = 1$ or exp (1) $= e$.

(With the geometric interpretation of the log as area under the curve $1/x$, this means that e is the number such that the area between 1 and e is equal to 1.)

Using Theorem 5, we conclude that

$$\exp (2) = \exp (1 + 1) = \exp (1) \exp (1) = e^2.$$

Similarly,

$$\exp (3) = \exp (2 + 1) = \exp (2) \exp (1) = e^2 \cdot e = e^3.$$

Proceeding by induction, we conclude that

$$\exp (n) = e^n$$

for every positive integer n.

If n is a negative integer, write $n = -m$ where m is positive. Then

$$1 = \exp (0) = \exp (m - m) = \exp (m) \exp (-m).$$

Dividing by exp (m), which is e^m, we get

$$\exp (-m) = \frac{1}{e^m}.$$

We see therefore that our exp function gives us the power function for positive and negative integers m.

Theorem 6. *The function* exp *is differentiable, and*

$$\frac{d(\exp x)}{dx} = \exp x.$$

Proof. By the theory of the derivatives of the inverse function, we know that it is differentiable. If $y = \exp x$ and $x = \log y$, then the theory of the derivatives of inverse functions gives us

$$\frac{dy}{dx} = \frac{1}{dx/dy}.$$

But $dx/dy = 1/y$. Hence

$$\frac{dy}{dx} = \frac{1}{1/y} = y = \exp x,$$

thereby proving our theorem.

From now on, we agree to write e^x instead of exp (x). In view of Theorem 5, we have the rule

$$e^{z+w} = e^z e^w$$

for all numbers z, w, and $e^0 = 1$.

The preceding theorem then looks like

$$\frac{d(e^x)}{dx} = e^x.$$

By definition, the derivative of e^x is the limit of the Newton quotient

$$\frac{e^{x+h} - e^x}{h} = e^x \frac{e^h - 1}{h}$$

as h approaches 0. Hence, at the very end of our theory, we now obtain in a very natural way the fact that

$$\lim_{h \to 0} \frac{e^h - 1}{h} = 1.$$

As we said in the introduction, this fact would have been very troublesome to obtain directly.

The function e^x is strictly increasing, and since $e > 1$, e^n becomes very large as n becomes very large. Hence so does e^x for any x.

Actually, e^x increases quite fast. We shall make this more precise in §4.

Finally, the second derivative of e^x is e^x and is > 0 for all x. Hence e^x is convex upwards.

We are now in a position to see that the graph of e^x looks like this:

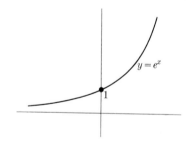

$y = e^x$

EXERCISES

1. What is the equation of the tangent line to the curve $y = e^{2x}$ at the point whose x-coordinate is (a) 1, (b) -2, (c) 0?

2. What is the equation of the tangent line to the curve $y = e^{x/2}$ at the point whose x-coordinate is (a) -4, (b) 1, (c) 0?

3. What is the equation of the tangent line to the curve $y = xe^x$ at the point whose x-coordinate is 2?

4. Find the derivatives of the following functions:

(a) $e^{\sin 3x}$

(b) $\log (e^x + \sin x)$

(c) $\sin (e^{x+2})$

(d) $\sin (e^{4x-5})$

5. Find the derivatives of the following functions.

(a) $\arctan \log x$ (b) $\log \cos (3x + 5)$
(c) $e^{\sin 2x}$ (d) $e^{\arccos x}$
(e) $\log e^x$ (f) x/e^x
(g) e^{e^x} (h) $e^{-\arcsin x}$
(i) $\tan (e^x)$ (j) $x^{\sqrt{x}}$
(k) $x^{\sqrt[3]{x}}$ (l) $\arcsin (e^x + x)$
(m) $e^{\tan x}$ (n) $\tan e^x$

6. (a) Show by induction that the n-th derivative of xe^x is $(x + n)e^x$ for all integers $n \geq 1$.
   (b) Show by induction that the n-th derivative of xe^{-x} is $(-1)^n(x - n)e^{-x}$.
   (c) Show that the $(n + 1)$-th derivative of $x^n \log x$ is $n!/x$.

7. (a) Sketch the curve $y = e^{-1/x}$ (defined for $x \neq 0$).
   (b) Sketch the curve $y = e^{-1/x^2}$ (defined for $x \neq 0$).

8. (a) Let $f(x)$ be a differentiable function over some interval satisfying the relation $f'(x) = Kf(x)$ for some constant K. Show that there is a constant C such that $f(x) = Ce^{Kx}$.
   (b) Let f be a differentiable function such that $f'(x) = -2xf(x)$. Show that there is a constant C such that $f(x) = Ce^{-x^2}$.
   (c) In general suppose there is a function h such that $f'(x) = h'(x)f(x)$. Show that $f(x) = Ce^{h(x)}$.

Find the tangent line to the curve at the indicated point.

9. $y = \log x, \quad x = e$ 10. $y = x \log x, \quad x = e$

11. $y = x \log x, \quad x = 2$ 12. $y = \log (x^3), \quad x = e$

13. $y = \dfrac{1}{\log x}, \quad x = e$ 14. $y = \dfrac{1}{\log x}, \quad x = 2$

15. $y = e^{2x}, \quad x = 1$ 16. $y = xe^x, \quad x = 2$

17. $y = xe^x, \quad x = 5$ 18. $y = xe^{-x}, \quad x = 0$

19. $y = e^{-x}, \quad x = 0$ 20. $y = x^2e^{-x}, \quad x = 1$

21. Show that $1 + x < e^x < \dfrac{1}{1 - x}$ for $0 < x < 1$, and for $-1 < x < 0$.

22. Prove that there is a unique number x such that $e^x + x = 0$.

23. Prove that there is a unique number x such that $\log x + x = 0$.

24. Sketch the graph of the function $\log \dfrac{1 + x}{1 - x}$ for $-1 < x < 1$.

25. Sketch the graph of the function $\log \dfrac{1 + x^2}{1 - x^2}, \quad -1 < x < 1$.

26. Does the function of Exercise 24 have an inverse function? If yes, for what values is this inverse function defined?

27. Determine an interval for which the inverse function of Exercise 25 will exist, and determine for what values this inverse is defined.

28. Sketch the graph of the function

$$f(x) = e^{x/2} + e^{-x/2}.$$

29. Sketch the graph of the function

$$f(x) = e^{x/2} - e^{-x/2}.$$

30. Let f be a differentiable function in the open interval $-1 < x < 1$. Assume that

$$f'(x) = \frac{1}{1 - x^2}$$

in this interval. Determine whether f is increasing or decreasing in this interval. Assume that $f(0) = 0$. Sketch the graph of f.

31. Let f be a differentiable function in the open interval $-1 < x < 1$. Assume that

$$f(0) = 0 \quad \text{and} \quad f'(x) = \frac{1}{(1 - x^2)^2}.$$

Determine whether f is increasing or decreasing in this interval. What happens to $f(x)$ as x approaches 1, and as x approaches -1? [*Hint:* Compare the derivative of f with that of the function in the preceding exercise.]

32. *Hyperbolic functions*

(a) Define functions

$$\cosh t = \frac{e^t + e^{-t}}{2} \quad \text{and} \quad \sinh t = \frac{e^t - e^{-t}}{2}.$$

Show that their derivatives are given by

$$\cosh' = \sinh \quad \text{and} \quad \sinh' = \cosh.$$

(b) Show that for all t we have

$$\cosh^2 t - \sinh^2 t = 1.$$

(c) Sketch the graph of the curve $x^2 - y^2 = 1$.
(d) If you let $x = \cosh t$ and $y = \sinh t$, which portion of the curve in (c) is parametrized by these functions?
(e) For a suitable interval of values of t, determine inverse functions for $\cosh t$ and $\sinh t$, and determine their derivatives.

§3. THE GENERAL EXPONENTIAL FUNCTION

Let a be a positive number, and x any number. We *define*

$$a^x = \exp(x \log a) = e^{x \log a}.$$

Thus

$$a^{\sqrt{2}} = e^{\sqrt{2} \log a}.$$

Using the properties of the log and exp, it is easy to prove that

$$a^{x+y} = a^x a^y$$

for all numbers x and y and that $a^0 = 1$. Furthermore, $(a^x)^y = a^{xy}$.

We leave the proof as an exercise. However, we observe that when x is a positive integer n, then a^x is indeed the product of a with itself n times. For instance, take $x = 2$. Then

$$e^{2\log a}$$

is equal to

$$e^{\log a + \log a} = (e^{\log a})^2 = a \cdot a,$$

and similarly,

$$e^{3\log a}$$

is equal to

$$e^{(\log a)+(\log a)+(\log a)}$$

which is equal to $(e^{\log a})^3$. The general case is proved by induction. Thus our definition of a^x as $e^{x\log a}$ is consistent with our original notation of a^n when x is a positive integer n. This is the justification for the definition in the general case.

The moral of the story is that, by going all the way around the difficulties, and giving up on a frontal attack on the function a^x, we have recovered it at the end, together with all of the desired properties. For instance, we have its derivative:

Theorem 7. *The derivative of a^x is $a^x (\log a)$.*

Proof. We use the chain rule. Let $u = (\log a)x$. Then $du/dx = \log a$ and $a^x = e^u$. Hence

$$\frac{d(a^x)}{dx} = a^x(\log a)$$

as desired.

In particular,

$$\frac{d(2^x)}{dx} = 2^x \log 2.$$

This result clarifies the mysterious limit

$$\lim_{h \to 0} \frac{2^h - 1}{h}$$

which we encountered in the introduction. We are now able to see that this limit is log 2, and it arises in a very natural way. We also see that when we take $a = e$ we obtain the only exponential function which is equal to its own derivative. For any other choice of the constant a, we would get an extraneous constant appearing in the derivative.

As an application of our theory of the exponential function, we also can take care of the general power function (which we had left dangling in Chapter III).

Theorem 8. *Let c be any number, and let*

$$f(x) = x^c$$

be defined for $x > 0$. Then $f'(x)$ exists and is equal to

$$f'(x) = cx^{c-1}.$$

Proof. By definition,

$$f(x) = e^{c \log x} = e^u$$

if we put $u = c \log x$. Then

$$\frac{du}{dx} = \frac{c}{x}.$$

Using the chain rule, we see that

$$f'(x) = e^u \cdot \frac{du}{dx} = e^{c \log x} \cdot \frac{c}{x} = x^c \cdot \frac{c}{x} = cx^{c-1}.$$

This proves our theorem.

When x, y are two numbers such that $y = 2^x$, it is customary to say that x is the log of y to the base 2. Similarly, if a is a number > 0, and $y = a^x = e^{x \log a}$, we say that x is the log of y to the base a. When $y = e^x$, we simply say that $x = \log y$.

The log to the base a is sometimes written $\log_a$. It occurs very infrequently, and you might as well forget about it.

We conclude this section by discussing two limits, which are now very easy to handle.

First, we have

$$\lim_{h \to 0} \frac{1}{h} \log (1 + h) = 1.$$

Indeed, the limit on the left is nothing else but the limit of the Newton quotient

$$\lim_{h \to 0} \frac{\log (1 + h) - \log 1}{h} = \log' (1).$$

Since $\log' (x) = 1/x$, it follows that $\log' (1) = 1$, as desired.

Now observe that

$$\log (1 + h)^{1/h} = \frac{1}{h} \log (1 + h),$$

because in general if a, b are numbers, $a > 0$, we have (Exercise 5)

$$\log a^b = b \log a.$$

Taking the exponential function, and using the fact that the exponential is continuous at 1, we find

$$\lim_{h \to 0} \exp \log (1 + h)^{1/h} = \lim_{h \to 0} \exp \frac{1}{h} \log (1 + h)$$

$$= \exp \lim_{h \to 0} \frac{1}{h} \log (1 + h)$$

$$= \exp (1) = e.$$

But $\exp \log (x) = x$ for all $x > 0$ by definition, so that for $x = (1 + h)^{1/h}$ we find

$$\lim_{h \to 0} (1 + h)^{1/h} = e.$$

If we let $h = 1/n$ where n is an integer, then our limit implies

$$\lim_{n \to \infty} \left(1 + \frac{1}{n}\right)^n = e.$$

EXERCISES

1. What is the derivative of 10^x? 7^x?

2. What is the derivative of 3^x? π^x?

3. What is the derivative of the function x^x (defined for $x > 0$)? [*Hint:* $x^x = e^{x \log x}$.]

4. What is the derivative of the function $x^{(x^x)}$?

5. If a, b are numbers, $a > 0$, show that $\log a^b = b \log a$.

6. Sketch the curves $y = 3^x$ and $y = 3^{-x}$.

7. Sketch the curves $y = 2^x$ and $y = 2^{-x}$.

8. Find the equation of the tangent line to the curve $y = x^x$ at the point $x = 1$.

9. Find the equation of the tangent line to each curve of Exercise 1 at $x = 0$.

10. Find the equation of the tangent line to each curve of Exercise 2 at $x = 2$.

11. If a is a number > 1 and $x > 0$, show that

$$x^a - 1 \geq a(x - 1).$$

12. Let p, q be numbers ≥ 1 such that $\dfrac{1}{p} + \dfrac{1}{q} = 1$. If $x \geq 1$, show that

$$x^{1/p} \leq \frac{x}{p} + \frac{1}{q}.$$

13. Let α, β be positive numbers such that $\alpha/\beta \geq 1$, and let p, q be as in Exercise 12. Show that

$$\alpha^{1/p}\beta^{1/q} \leq \frac{\alpha}{p} + \frac{\beta}{q}.$$

14. Let a be a number > 0. Find the minimum and maximum of the function $f(x) = x^2/a^x$.

15. Let a, b be two numbers > 0, and $0 < t < 1$. Show that

$$a^t b^{1-t} \leq ta + (1 - t)b.$$

[*Hint:* Take the log and use convexity.]

§4. ORDER OF MAGNITUDE

The area under the curve $1/x$ between 1 and 2 is at least equal to $\frac{1}{2}$. (Visualize a rectangle like that in the picture below.)

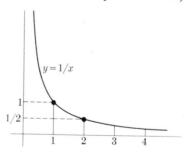

Since $\log e = 1$ and $\log 4 = 2 \log 2 \geq 1$, it follows that $e < 4$. On the other hand, the area under our curve between 1 and 2 is less than 1 because $1/x$ is at most equal to 1 in that interval. Thus we have

$$2 < e < 4.$$

We shall learn how to compute e to any degree of accuracy in a later chapter.

In order to prove Theorem 10, we need an auxiliary statement.

Theorem 9. *Let a be a number > 0. Then*

$$\frac{(1 + a)^n}{n}$$

becomes very large as n becomes very large.

Proof. We can write

$$(1 + a)^n = 1 + na + \frac{n(n-1)}{2} a^2 + b,$$

where b is some number ≥ 0. This is easily seen by expanding the product of $(1 + a)$ with itself n times. Consequently, dividing by n, we obtain

$$\frac{(1 + a)^n}{n} = \frac{1}{n} + a + \frac{n-1}{2} a^2 + \frac{b}{n},$$

and b/n is ≥ 0. As n becomes large, we see that the term $\dfrac{n-1}{2} a^2$ becomes large. All the other terms are ≥ 0. Hence we have proved our theorem.

We apply this to the case of e^n/n. We know that e can be written in the form $1 + a$ with $a > 0$. Hence we see that e^n/n becomes arbitrarily large as n increases indefinitely.

Theorem 10. *The function $f(x) = e^x/x$ is strictly increasing for $x > 1$. As x becomes very large positive, so does $f(x)$.*

Proof. To verify the first assertion, take the derivative

$$f'(x) = \frac{xe^x - e^x}{x^2} = \frac{e^x}{x^2}(x - 1).$$

We know that e^x and x^2 are > 0 for all $x > 0$. Hence our derivative $f'(x)$ is positive when $x > 1$, and so our function is strictly increasing.

When x is an integer n, we know that the values $f(n)$ become arbitrarily large when n becomes large. It follows that it does also for all x when x becomes arbitrarily large. This proves our theorem.

Observe that we can conclude that

$$\frac{x}{e^x} \quad \text{and} \quad \frac{n}{e^n}$$

approach 0 as x and n become large. In fact, for any number $a > 0$ we also observe that

$$\frac{n}{(1 + a)^n}$$

approaches 0 as n becomes large.

Corollary 1. *As x becomes arbitrarily large, the function $x - \log x$ also becomes arbitrarily large.*

Proof. The log of e^x/x is $x - \log x$. Our assertion follows from the properties of the log proved previously, namely when y becomes very large, so does $\log y$.

Corollary 2. *As x becomes very large, the quotient*

$$\frac{x}{\log x}$$

also becomes very large.

Proof. Let $y = \log x$. Then $x = e^y$ and our quotient is of the form

$$\frac{e^y}{y}.$$

We know that $\log x$ becomes large when x becomes large. Thus our assertion follows from the theorem.

Corollary 3. *As x becomes very large, $x^{1/x}$ approaches 1 as a limit.*

Proof. We have $x^{1/x} = e^{(\log x)/x}$. As x becomes very large, $(\log x)/x$ approaches 0 and hence its exponent approaches 1.

This corollary is used frequently when we look at integers n instead of arbitrary numbers x. Thus

$$n^{1/n}$$

approaches 1 as n becomes very large.

The next theorem is a refinement of some previous ones.

Theorem 11. *Let m be a positive integer. Then the function*

$$\frac{e^x}{x^m}$$

is strictly increasing for $x > m$ and becomes very large when x becomes very large.

Proof. Let $f(x) = e^x/x^m$. Since

$$x = e^{\log x},$$

we have

$$x^m = e^{m \log x}.$$

Therefore

$$f(x) = e^{x - m \log x}.$$

We have

$$f'(x) = e^{x - m \log x} \left(1 - \frac{m}{x} \right).$$

This is > 0 when $x > m$ and our first assertion is proved.

As to the second, to prove that e^x/x^m becomes very large when x does, it suffices to do it for its log. Taking the log we see that

$$\log f(x) = x - m(\log x),$$

which can also be written

$$(\log x) \left(\frac{x}{\log x} - m \right).$$

As x becomes large, so does $\log x$, and so does $x/\log x$ by Corollary 2 above. Since m is fixed, our expression becomes very large, as desired.

Example. We shall sketch the curve $y = xe^x$. Let $f(x) = xe^x$. Then $f'(x) = xe^x + e^x = e^x(x + 1)$. Thus the only critical point of f is at $x = -1$. When $x < -1$, e^x is > 0 and $x + 1 < 0$. Hence when $x < -1$, $f'(x) < 0$ and f is decreasing. When $x > -1$, we see that $f'(x) > 0$ and f is increasing.

As x becomes very large positive, xe^x also becomes very large. When x is very large negative, say $x = -y$ and y very large positive, then

$$xe^x = -ye^{-y} = -y/e^y$$

approaches 0.

We have $f(-1) = -1/e$ and $f(0) = 0$. Thus the graph looks like this:

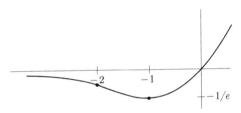

The convexity behavior is as we have drawn it. We test this by taking the second derivative, namely $f''(x) = e^x(x + 2)$. Thus the second derivative is positive when $x > -2$ and negative when $x < -2$. Hence the function is convex downwards when $x < -2$ and convex upwards when $x > -2$.

EXERCISES

1. Sketch the graph of the curve $y = xe^{2x}$. In this and other exercises, you may treat the convexity properties as optional.

Sketch the graphs of the following functions. (In Exercises 6 through 10, $x \neq 0$.)

2. xe^{-x} 3. xe^{-x^2} 4. $x^2e^{-x^2}$

5. x^2e^{-x} 6. e^x/x 7. e^x/x^2

8. e^x/x^3 9. $e^{1/x}$ 10. $xe^{1/x}$

11. Show that the equation $e^x = ax$ has at least one solution for any number a except when $0 \leq a < e$.

12. Let $f(x)$ be the function e^{-1/x^2} when $x \neq 0$ and $f(0) = 0$. Show that f has a derivative at 0 and that $f'(0) = 0$.

13. Does f' have a derivative? If yes, what is it?

14. Does f have any further derivatives at 0?

15. Sketch the curve $f(x) = x^x$.

16. Show that the curve

$$y = \frac{\log_a x}{x}$$

has its maximum value at $x = e$ for all numbers $a > 0$.

17. Does $x \log x$ approach a limit as $x \to 0$? What about $x^2 \log x$? [*Hint:* Let $x = 1/t$ and let t become very large.]

18. Sketch the following curves.

(a) $y = x \log x$ (b) $y = x^2 \log x$
(c) $y = x(\log x)^2$ (d) $y = x/\log x$

19. Show that the function $f(x) = x^x$ is strictly increasing for $x > 0$. Let g be its inverse function.

(a) Show that if $y = f(x)$ then

$$\frac{\log \log x}{\log \log y} \to 0 \quad \text{as} \quad x \to \infty.$$

(b) Show that

$$g(y) = \frac{\log y}{\log \log y} \psi(y)$$

where $\psi(y)$ approaches 1 as $y \to \infty$. [*Hint:* Take the log twice in the expression $y = e^{x \log x}$.]

20. Let $f(x) = 2^x x^x$. Show that f is strictly increasing for $x > 0$. Let g be its inverse function. Show that

$$g(y) = \frac{\log y}{\log \log y} \varphi(y)$$

where $\varphi(y)$ approaches 1 as $y \to \infty$.

21. Sketch the curves (a) $y = x - e^x$ and (b) $y = x + e^x$.

22. Find the following limits as $n \to \infty$.

(a) $(\log n)^{1/n}$ (b) $[(\log n)/n]^{1/n}$
(c) $(n/e^n)^{1/n}$ (d) $(n \log n)^{1/n}$

§5. SOME APPLICATIONS

It is worth while to mention briefly some applications of the exponential function to physics and chemistry.

It is known (from experimental data) that when a piece of radium is left to disintegrate, the rate of disintegration is proportional to the amount of radium left.

Suppose that at time $t = 0$ we have 10 grams of radium and let $f(t)$ be the amount of radium left at time t. Then

$$\frac{df}{dt} = kf(t)$$

for some constant k. We take k negative since the physical interpretation is that the amount of substance decreases.

If we take the derivative of the quotient

$$\frac{f(t)}{e^{kt}}$$

and use the rule for the derivative of a quotient, we find

$$\frac{e^{kt}f'(t) - f(t)ke^{kt}}{e^{2kt}},$$

and this is equal to 0 [using our hypothesis concerning $f'(t)$]. Hence there is a constant C such that

$$f(t) = Ce^{kt}.$$

Let $t = 0$. Then $f(0) = C$. Thus $C = 10$, if we assumed that we started with 10 grams. In general, C is interpreted as the amount of initial substance when $t = 0$.

Similarly, consider a chemical reaction. It is frequently the case that the rate of the reaction is proportional to the quantity of reacting substance present. If $f(t)$ denotes the amount of substance left after time t, then

$$\frac{df}{dt} = Kf(t)$$

for some constant K (determined experimentally in each case). We are therefore in a similar situation as before, and

$$f(t) = Ce^{Kt}$$

where C is the amount of substance at $t = 0$.

Example. Suppose $f(t) = 10e^{Kt}$ where K is constant. Assume that $f(3) = 5$. Find K.

We have

$$5 = 10e^{K3}.$$

Taking the log yields

$$\log 5 = \log 10 + 3K$$

whence

$$K = \frac{\log 5 - \log 10}{3}.$$

$$\frac{1}{2} = e^{K3}$$

$$\log(e^{3K}) = \log\left(\frac{1}{2}\right) = K3$$

$$3K = \log\left(\frac{1}{2}\right) = -\log_e(2)$$

$$K = -3\log_e(2)$$

$$= -\log 8$$

EXERCISES

1. Let $f(t) = 10e^{Kt}$ for some constant K. Suppose that you know that $f(1/2) = 2$. Find K.

2. Let $f(t) = Ce^{2t}$. Suppose that you know $f(2) = 5$. Determine the constant C.

3. One gram of radium is left to disintegrate. After one million years, there is 0.1 gram left. What is the formula giving the rate of disintegration?

4. A certain chemical substance reacts in such a way that the rate of reaction is equal to the quantity of substance present. After one hour, there are 20 grams of substance left. How much substance was there at the beginning?

5. A radioactive substance disintegrates proportionally to the amount of substance present at a given time, say

$$f(t) = Ce^{Kt}.$$

At what time will there be exactly half the original amount left?

6. Suppose $K = -4$ in the preceding exercise. At what time will there be one-third of the substance left?

7. If bacteria increase in number at a rate proportional to the number present, how long will it take before 1,000,000 bacteria increase to 10,000,000 if it takes 12 minutes to increase to 2,000,000?

8. A substance decomposes at a rate proportional to the amount present. At the end of 3 minutes, 10 percent of the original substance has decomposed. When will half the original amount have decomposed?

9. Let f be a function of a variable t and increasing at the rate $df/dt = kf$ where k is a constant. Let $a_n = f(nt_1)$ where t_1 is a fixed value of t, $t_1 > 0$. Show that $a_0, a_1, a_2, \ldots$ is a geometric progression.

10. In 1900 the population of a city was 50,000. In 1950 it was 100,000. If the rate of increase of the population is proportional to the population, what will be the population in 1984? In what year will it be 200,000?

11. Assume that the rate of change with respect to height of atmospheric pressure at any height is proportional to the pressure there. If the barometer reads 30 at sea level and 24 at 6000 ft above sea level, find the barometric reading 10,000 ft above sea level.

12. Sugar in water decomposes at a rate proportional to the amount still unchanged. If 30 lb of sugar reduces to 10 lb in 4 hr, when will 95% of the sugar be decomposed?

13. A particle moves with speed $s(t)$ satisfying $ds/dt = -ks$, where k is some constant. If the initial speed is 16 units/min and if the speed is halved in 2 min, find the value of t when the speed is 10 units/min.

14. Assume that the difference x between the temperature of a body and that of surrounding air decreases at a rate proportional to this difference. If $x = 100°$ when $t = 0$, and $x = 40°$ when $t = 40$ minutes, find t (a) when $x = 70°$, (b) when $x = 16°$, (c) the value of x when $t = 20$.

15. A moron loses money in gambling at a rate equal to the amount he owns at any given time. At what time t will he have lost half of his initial capital?

Chapter IX

Integration

In this chapter, we solve, more or less simultaneously, the following problems:

(1) Given a function $f(x)$, find a function $F(x)$ such that

$$F'(x) = f(x).$$

This is the inverse of differentiation, and is called integration.

(2) Given a function $f(x)$ which is ≥ 0, give a definition of the area under the curve $y = f(x)$ which does not appeal to geometric intuition.

Actually, in this chapter, we give the ideas behind the solutions of our two problems. The techniques which allow us to compute effectively when specific data are given will be postponed to the next chapter.

In carrying out (2) we shall follow an idea of Archimedes. It is to approximate the function f by horizontal functions, and the area under f by the sum of little rectangles.

The slightly theoretical sections 5 and 6 should be omitted for any class especially allergic to pure theory. The geometric argument involving area should suffice to justify the definite integral, and a mild sales talk on the integral as a limit of sums of small rectangles would be sufficient for the physical applications. Our axiomatization of the fundamental theorem allows the greatest flexibility concerning the extent to which these sections should be carried out in detail.

§1. THE INDEFINITE INTEGRAL

Let $f(x)$ be a function defined over some interval. If $F(x)$ is a function defined over the same interval and such that

$$F'(x) = f(x),$$

then we say that F is an *indefinite integral* of f. If $G(x)$ is another indefinite integral of f, then $G'(x) = f(x)$ also. Hence the derivative of the difference $F - G$ is 0:

$$(F - G)'(x) = F'(x) - G'(x) = f(x) - f(x) = 0.$$

Consequently, by Theorem 3 of Chapter V, §4, there is a constant C such that

$$F(x) = G(x) + C$$

for all x in the interval.

Example 1. An indefinite integral for $\cos x$ would be $\sin x$. But $\sin x + 5$ is also an indefinite integral for $\cos x$.

Example 2. $\log x$ is an indefinite integral for $1/x$. So is $\log x + 10$ or $\log x - \pi$.

In the next chapter, we shall develop techniques for finding indefinite integrals. Here, we merely observe that every time we prove a formula for a derivative, it has an analogue for the integral.

It is customary to denote an indefinite integral of a function f by

$$\int f \quad \text{or} \quad \int f(x)\, dx.$$

In this second notation, the dx is meaningless by itself. It is only the full expression $\int f(x)\, dx$ which is meaningful. When we study the method of substitution in the next chapter, we shall get further confirmation for the practicality of our notation.

We shall now make a table of some indefinite integrals, using the information which we have obtained about derivatives.

Let n be an integer, $n \neq -1$. Then we have

$$\int x^n\, dx = \frac{x^{n+1}}{n+1}.$$

If $n = -1$, then

$$\int \frac{1}{x}\, dx = \log x.$$

(This is true only in the interval $x > 0$.)

In the interval $x > 0$ we also have

$$\int x^c\, dx = \frac{x^{c+1}}{c+1}$$

for any number $c \neq -1$.

The following indefinite integrals are valid for all x.

$$\int \cos x\, dx = \sin x \qquad \int \sin x\, dx = -\cos x$$

$$\int e^x\, dx = e^x \qquad \int \frac{1}{1+x^2}\, dx = \arctan x$$

Finally, for $-1 < x < 1$, we have

$$\int \frac{1}{\sqrt{1 - x^2}} \, dx = \arcsin x.$$

In practice, one frequently omits mentioning over what interval the various functions we deal with are defined. However, in any specific problem, one has to keep it in mind. For instance, if we write

$$\int x^{-1/3} \, dx = \tfrac{3}{2} \cdot x^{2/3},$$

this is valid for $x > 0$ and is also valid for $x < 0$. But 0 cannot be in any interval of definition of our functions. Thus we could have

$$\int x^{-1/3} \, dx = \tfrac{3}{2} \cdot x^{2/3} + 5$$

when $x < 0$ and

$$\int x^{-1/3} \, dx = \tfrac{3}{2} \cdot x^{2/3} - 2$$

when $x > 0$.

We agree throughout that indefinite integrals are defined only over intervals. Thus in considering the function $1/x$, we have to consider *separately* the cases $x > 0$ and $x < 0$. For $x > 0$, we have already remarked that $\log x$ is an indefinite integral. It turns out that for the interval $x < 0$ we can also find an indefinite integral, and in fact we have for $x < 0$,

$$\int \frac{1}{x} \, dx = \log(-x).$$

Observe that when $x < 0$, $-x$ is positive, and thus $\log(-x)$ is meaningful. The fact that the derivative of $\log(-x)$ is equal to $1/x$ is true by the chain rule.

For $x < 0$, any other indefinite integral is given by

$$\log(-x) + C,$$

where C is a constant.

It is sometimes stated that in all cases,

$$\int \frac{1}{x} \, dx = \log|x| + C.$$

With our conventions, we do not attribute any meaning to this, because our functions are not defined over intervals (the missing point 0 prevents this). In any case, the formula would be *false*. Indeed, for $x < 0$ we have

$$\int \frac{1}{x} \, dx = \log|x| + C_1,$$

and for $x > 0$ we have

$$\int \frac{1}{x}\,dx = \log|x| + C_2.$$

However, the two constants need not be equal, and hence we cannot write

$$\int \frac{1}{x}\,dx = \log|x| + C$$

in all cases.

We prefer to stick to our convention that integrals are defined only over intervals. When we deal with the log, it is to be understood that we deal only with the case $x > 0$.

EXERCISES

Find indefinite integrals for the following functions:

1. $\sin 2x$ 2. $\cos 3x$ 3. $\dfrac{1}{x+1}$ 4. $\dfrac{1}{x+2}$

(In these last two problems, specify the intervals over which you find an indefinite integral.)

§2. CONTINUOUS FUNCTIONS

Let $f(x)$ be a function. We shall say that f is *continuous* if

$$\lim_{h \to 0} f(x + h) = f(x)$$

for all x at which the function is defined.

It is understood that in taking the limit, only values of h for which $f(x + h)$ is defined are considered. For instance, if f is defined on an interval

$$a \leqq x \leqq b$$

(assuming $a < b$), then we would say that f is continuous at a if

$$\lim_{\substack{h \to 0 \\ h > 0}} f(a + h) = f(a).$$

We cannot take $h < 0$, since the function would not be defined for $a + h$ if $h < 0$.

Geometrically speaking, a function is continuous if there is no break in its graph. All differentiable functions are continuous. We have already remarked this fact, because if a quotient

$$\frac{f(x + h) - f(x)}{h}$$

has a limit, then the numerator $f(x + h) - f(x)$ must approach 0, because

$$\lim_{h \to 0} f(x + h) - f(x) = \lim_{h \to 0} h \frac{f(x + h) - f(x)}{h}$$

$$= \lim_{h \to 0} h \lim_{h \to 0} \frac{f(x + h) - f(x)}{h} = 0.$$

The following are graphs of functions which are not continuous.

In Fig. 1, we have the graph of a function like

$$f(x) = -1 \quad \text{if} \quad x \leqq 0$$
$$f(x) = 1 \quad \text{if} \quad x > 0.$$

We see that

$$f(a + h) = f(h) = 1$$

for all $h > 0$. Hence

$$\lim_{\substack{h \to 0 \\ h > 0}} f(a + h) = 1,$$

which is unequal to $f(0)$.

A similar phenomenon occurs in Fig. 2 where there is a break. (Cf. Example 5 of Chapter III, §2.)

Figure 1

Figure 2

§3. AREA

Let $a < b$ be two numbers, and let $f(x)$ be a continuous function defined on the interval $a \leqq x \leqq b$.

We wish to find a function $F(x)$ which is differentiable in this interval, and such that

$$F'(x) = f(x).$$

In this section, we appeal to our geometric intuition concerning area. We assume that $f(x) \geqq 0$ for all x in the interval, and we define geometrically the function $F(x)$ by saying that it is the numerical measure of the area under the curve between a and x.

The following picture illustrates this.

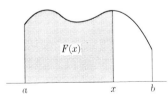

We thus have $F(a) = 0$. The area between a and a is 0.

Theorem 1. *The function $F(x)$ is differentiable, and its derivative is $f(x)$.*

Proof. Since we defined F geometrically, we shall have to argue geometrically.

We have to consider the Newton quotient

$$\frac{F(x + h) - F(x)}{h}.$$

Suppose first that x is unequal to the end point b, and also suppose that we consider only values of $h > 0$.

Then $F(x + h) - F(x)$ is the area between x and $x + h$. A magnified picture may look like this.

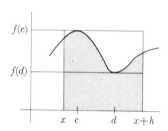

The shaded area represents $F(x + h) - F(x)$.

We let c be a point in the closed interval $[x, x + h]$ which is a maximum for our function f *in that small interval.* We let d be a point in the same closed interval which is a minimum for f in that interval. Thus

$$f(d) \leqq f(t) \leqq f(c)$$

for all t satisfying

$$x \leqq t \leqq x + h.$$

(We are forced to use another letter, t, since x is already being used.)

The area under the curve between x and $x + h$ is bigger than the area of the small rectangle in the figure above, i.e. the rectangle having base h and height $f(d)$.

The area under the curve between x and $x + h$ is smaller than the area of the big rectangle, i.e. the rectangle having base h and height $f(c)$.

This gives us

$$h \cdot f(d) \leqq F(x + h) - F(x) \leqq h \cdot f(c).$$

Dividing by the positive number h yields

$$f(d) \leqq \frac{F(x + h) - F(x)}{h} \leqq f(c).$$

Since c, d are between x and $x + h$, as h approaches 0 both $f(c)$ and $f(d)$

approach $f(x)$. Hence the Newton quotient for F is squeezed between two numbers which approach $f(x)$. It must therefore approach $f(x)$ itself, and we have proved Theorem 1, when $h > 0$.

The proof is essentially the same as the proof which we used to get the derivative of $\log x$. The only difference in the present case is that we pick a maximum and a minimum without being able to give an explicit value for it, the way we could for the function $1/x$. Otherwise, there is no difference in the arguments.

If $x = b$, we look at negative values for h. The argument in that case is entirely similar to the one we have written down in detail, and we find again that the Newton quotient of F is squeezed between $f(c)$ and $f(d)$. We leave it as an exercise.

Suppose that we are able to guess at a function $G(x)$ whose derivative is $f(x)$. Then we know that there is a constant C such that

$$F(x) = G(x) + C.$$

Let $x = a$. We get

$$0 = F(a) = G(a) + C.$$

This shows that $C = -G(a)$. Hence letting $x = b$ yields

$$F(b) = G(b) - G(a).$$

Thus the area under the curve between a and b is $G(b) - G(a)$. This is very useful to know in practice, because we can usually guess the function G.

If we deal with a continuous function f which may be negative in the interval $[a, b]$, then we could still use our notion of area to find the function $F(x)$. However, in those portions where the function is negative, we have to take F to be *minus* the area under the curve. We illustrate this by the following picture. In this case, $F(x)$ would be the area between a_1 and a_2, minus the area between a_2 and x (for the point x indicated in the picture). The argument that $F'(x) = f(x)$ goes through in the same way.

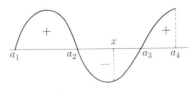

Thus by using our geometric intuition, we have found a function $F(x)$ whose derivative is $f(x)$.

Example 1. Find the area under the curve $y = x^2$ between $x = 1$ and $x = 2$.

Let $f(x) = x^2$. If $G(x) = x^3/3$ then $G'(x) = f(x)$. Hence the area under the curve between 1 and 2 is

$$G(2) - G(1) = \frac{2^3}{3} - \frac{1^3}{3} = \frac{7}{3}.$$

Example 2. Find the area under one arch of the function sin x.

We have to find the area under the curve between 0 and π. Let

$$G(x) = -\cos x.$$

Then $G'(x) = \sin x$. Hence the area is

$$\begin{aligned} G(\pi) - G(0) &= -\cos \pi - (-\cos 0) \\ &= -(-1) + 1 \\ &= 2. \end{aligned}$$

Note how remarkable this is. The arch of the sine curve going from 0 to π seems to be a very irrational curve, and yet the area turns out to be the integer 2!

EXERCISES

Find the area under the given curves between the given bounds.

1. $y = x^3$ between $x = 1$ and $x = 5$.
2. $y = x$ between $x = 0$ and $x = 2$.   3. $y = \cos x$, one arch.
4. $y = 1/x$ between $x = 1$ and $x = 2$.
5. $y = 1/x$ between $x = 1$ and $x = 3$.
6. $y = x^4$ between $x = -1$ and $x = 1$.
7. $y = e^x$ between $x = 0$ and $x = 1$.

§4. FUNDAMENTAL THEOREM

The argument which we gave in the preceding section, to show that the derivative of the area is equal to the function f, can be made completely general. In fact, if we do this, then we shall be able to apply this argument to many more cases, both for theoretical purposes (in §6, for instance), and in applications, when dealing with lengths of curves or work in Chapter XII. Thus we shall now describe the general framework in which we can carry out the arguments of Theorem 1.

Theorem 2. *Let a, d be two numbers, with $a < d$. Let f be a continuous function on the interval $[a, d]$. Suppose that for each pair of numbers $b \leq c$ in the interval we are able to associate a number denoted by $I_b^c(f)$ satisfying the following properties:*

Property 1. If M, m are two numbers such that

$$m \leqq f(x) \leqq M$$

for all x in the interval [b, c] then

$$m(c - b) \leqq I_b^c(f) \leqq M(c - b).$$

Property 2. We have

$$I_a^b(f) + I_b^c(f) = I_a^c(f).$$

Then the function $x \mapsto I_a^x(f)$ is differentiable in the interval [a, d] and its derivative at x is f(x). An association as above is uniquely determined.

Proof. We have to form the Newton quotient

$$\frac{I_a^{x+h}(f) - I_a^x(f)}{h}$$

and see if it approaches a limit as $h \to 0$. (If $x = a$ then it is to be understood that $h > 0$, and if $x = b$ then $h < 0$. As usual, we prove that the function $I_a^x(f)$ is right differentiable at a and left differentiable at b.)

Assume for the moment that $h > 0$. By Property 2, applied to the three numbers a, x, $x + h$, we conclude that our Newton quotient is equal to

$$\frac{I_a^x(f) + I_x^{x+h}(f) - I_a^x(f)}{h} = \frac{I_x^{x+h}(f)}{h}.$$

This reduces our investigation of the Newton quotient to the interval between x and $x + h$.

Let s be a point between x and $x + h$ such that f reaches a maximum in this small interval $[x, x + h]$ and let t be a point in this interval such that f reaches a minimum.

We let

$$m = f(t) \qquad \text{and} \qquad M = f(s)$$

and apply Property 1 to the interval $[x, x + h]$. We obtain

$$f(t)(x + h - x) \leqq I_x^{x+h}(f) \leqq f(s)(x + h - x),$$

which we can rewrite as

$$f(t) \cdot h \leqq I_x^{x+h}(f) \leqq f(s) \cdot h.$$

Dividing by the positive number h preserves the inequalities, and yields

$$f(t) \leqq \frac{I_x^{x+h}(f)}{h} \leqq f(s).$$

Since s, t lie between x and $x + h$, we must have (by continuity)

$$\lim_{h \to 0} f(s) = f(x) \qquad \text{and} \qquad \lim_{h \to 0} f(t) = f(x).$$

Thus our Newton quotient is squeezed between two numbers which approach $f(x)$. It must therefore approach $f(x)$, and our theorem is proved when $h > 0$.

The argument when $h < 0$ is entirely similar. We omit it, except for the following remark concerning Property 2.

✗ Suppose that we have two numbers b, c with $c < b$. We define

$$I_b^c(f) = -I_c^b(f),$$

whenever f is a continuous function on the interval $[c, b]$. Then it is easy to verify that Property 2 holds no matter what the numbers b, c are. For instance, suppose $c < b$. We show you how to prove the statement of Property 2 in that case.

By definition

$$I_b^c(f) = -I_c^b(f).$$

We know that

$$I_a^c(f) + I_c^b(f) = I_a^b(f)$$

if we use the ordinary case of Property 2 when the numbers are increasing. Substituting the value for $I_b^c(f)$, we find

$$I_a^c(f) - I_b^c(f) = I_a^b(f),$$

whence

$$I_a^c(f) = I_a^b(f) + I_b^c(f).$$

In the next sections, we shall prove that there exists a way of assigning a number $I_a^b(f)$ satisfying the properties stated in Theorem 2. We shall now prove that any such assignment is *uniquely determined*. Indeed, if $J_a^b(f)$ also satisfies the properties of Theorem 2, then the functions of x given by

$$I_a^x(f) \qquad \text{and} \qquad J_a^x(f)$$

have the same derivative, and consequently there is a constant C such that

$$I_a^x(f) = J_a^x(f) + C$$

for all x in the interval $[a, b]$. But if we let $x = a$, we can use Property 1 to see that $I_a^a(f) = J_a^a(f) = 0$. Hence $C = 0$, whence

$$I_a^x(f) = J_a^x(f)$$

for all x in the interval. In view of this, we define the *definite integral of f* between a and b to be $I_a^b(f)$, provided that it exists. It is usually denoted by $\int_a^b f$.

§5. UPPER AND LOWER SUMS

To show the existence of the integral, we still use the idea of approximating our curves by constant functions.

Let a, b be two numbers, with $a \leq b$. Let f be a continuous function in the interval $a \leq x \leq b$.

By a *partition of the interval* $[a, b]$ we mean a sequence of numbers

$$a = x_0 \leq x_1 \leq x_2 \leq \cdots \leq x_n = b$$

between a and b, such that $x_i \leq x_{i+1}$ $(i = 0, 1, \ldots, n - 1)$. For instance, we could take just two numbers,

$$x_0 = a \qquad \text{and} \qquad x_1 = b.$$

This will be called the *trivial partition*.

A partition divides our interval in a lot of smaller intervals $[x_i, x_{i+1}]$.

$$\underset{a=x_0 \quad x_1 \qquad x_2 \quad x_3 \quad \cdots \quad x_{n-1} \ x_n=b}{\vdash\!\!-\!\!+\!\!-\!\!+\!+\!\!-\!\!-\!\!-\!\!+\!\!-\!\!\dashv}$$

Given any number between a and b, in addition to $x_0, \ldots, x_n$, we can add it to the partition to get a new partition having one more small interval. If we add enough intermediate numbers to the partition, then the intervals can be made arbitrarily small.

Let f be a function defined on the interval

$$a \leq x \leq b$$

and continuous. If c_i is a point between x_i and x_{i+1}, then we form the sum

$$f(c_0)(x_1 - x_0) + f(c_1)(x_2 - x_1) + \cdots + f(c_{n-1})(x_n - x_{n-1}).$$

Such a sum will be called a *Riemann sum*. Each value $f(c_i)$ can be viewed as the height of a rectangle, and each $(x_{i+1} - x_i)$ can be viewed as the length of the base.

Let s_i be a point between x_i and x_{i+1} such that f has a maximum in this small interval $[x_i, x_{i+1}]$ at s_i. In other words,

$$f(x) \leq f(s_i)$$

for all x between x_i and x_{i+1}. The rectangles then look like those in the next figure. In the picture, s_0 happens to be equal to $x_1, s_2 = x_2, s_3 = x_4$.

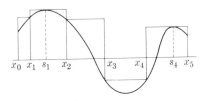

The main idea which we are going to carry out is that, as we make the intervals of our partitions smaller and smaller, the sum of the areas of the rectangles will approach a limit, and this limit can be used to define the area under the curve.

Observe however that when $f(x)$ becomes negative, the value $f(s_i)$ may be negative. Thus the corresponding rectangle gives a negative contribution

$$f(s_i)(x_{i+1} - x_i)$$

to the sum.

If P is the partition given by the numbers

$$x_0 \leqq x_1 \leqq x_2 \leqq \cdots \leqq x_n,$$

then the sum

$$f(s_0)(x_1 - x_0) + f(s_1)(x_2 - x_1) + \cdots + f(s_{n-1})(x_n - x_{n-1})$$

will be called the *upper sum* associated with the function f, and the partition P of the interval $[a, b]$. We shall denote it by the symbols

$$U_a^b(P, f).$$

Also, it is tiresome to write the sum by repeating each term, and so we shall use the abbreviation

$$\sum_{i=0}^{n-1} f(s_i)(x_{i+1} - x_i)$$

to mean the sum from 0 to $n - 1$ of the terms $f(s_i)(x_{i+1} - x_i)$. Thus, by definition,

$$U_a^b(P, f) = \sum_{i=0}^{n-1} f(s_i)(x_{i+1} - x_i).$$

Instead of taking a maximum s_i in the interval $[x_i, x_{i+1}]$ we could have taken a minimum. Let t_i be a point in this interval, such that

$$f(t_i) \leqq f(x)$$

for all x in the small interval $[x_i, x_{i+1}]$. We call the sum

$$f(t_0)(x_1 - x_0) + f(t_1)(x_2 - x_1) + \cdots + f(t_{n-1})(x_n - x_{n-1})$$

the *lower sum* associated with the function f, and the partition P of the interval $[a, b]$. The lower sum will be denoted by

$$L_a^b(P, f).$$

With our convention concerning sums, we can therefore write

$$L_a^b(P, f) = \sum_{i=0}^{n-1} f(t_i)(x_{i+1} - x_i).$$

On the next picture, we have drawn a typical term of the sum.

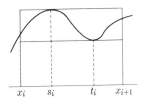

For all numbers x in the interval $[x_i, x_{i+1}]$ we have

$$f(t_i) \leq f(x) \leq f(s_i).$$

Since $x_{i+1} - x_i$ is ≥ 0, it follows that each term of the lower sum is less than or equal to each term of the upper sum. Therefore

$$L_a^b(P, f) \leq U_a^b(P, f).$$

Furthermore, any Riemann sum taken with points c_i (which are not necessarily maxima or minima) is between the lower and upper sum.

What happens to our sums when we add a new point to a partition? We shall see that the lower sum increases and the upper sum decreases.

Theorem 3. *Let f be a continuous function on the interval $[a, b]$. Let $P = (x_0, \ldots, x_n)$ be a partition of $[a, b]$. Let $\bar{x}$ be any number in the interval, and let Q be the partition obtained from P by adding $\bar{x}$ to $(x_0, \ldots, x_n)$. Then*

$$L_a^b(P, f) \leq L_a^b(Q, f) \leq U_a^b(Q, f) \leq U_a^b(P, f).$$

Proof. Let us look at the lower sums, for example. Suppose that our number $\bar{x}$ is between x_j and x_{j+1}:

$$x_j \leq \bar{x} \leq x_{j+1}.$$

When we form the lower sum for P, it will be the same as the lower sum for Q except that the term

$$f(t_j)(x_{j+1} - x_j)$$

will now be replaced by two terms. If u is a minimum for f in the interval between x_j and $\bar{x}$, and v is a minimum for f in the interval between $\bar{x}$ and x_{j+1}, then these two terms are

$$f(u)(\bar{x} - x_j) + f(v)(x_{j+1} - \bar{x}).$$

We can write $f(t_j)(x_{j+1} - x_j)$ in the form

$$f(t_j)(x_{j+1} - x_j) = f(t_j)(\bar{x} - x_j) + f(t_j)(x_{j+1} - \bar{x}).$$

Since $f(t_j)$ is less than or equal to $f(u)$ or $f(v)$ (because t_j was a minimum in the whole interval between x_j and x_{j+1}), it follows that

$$f(t_j)(x_{j+1} - x_j) \leqq f(u)(\bar{x} - x_j) + f(v)(x_{j+1} - \bar{x}).$$

Thus when we replace the term in the sum for P by the two terms in the sum for Q, the value of the contribution of these two terms increases. Since all other terms are the same, our assertion is proved.

The assertion concerning the fact that the upper sum decreases is left as an exercise. The proof is very similar.

As a consequence of our theorem, we obtain:

Corollary. *Every lower sum is less than or equal to every upper sum.*

Proof. Let P and Q be two partitions. If we add to P all the points of Q and add to Q all the points of P, we obtain a partition R such that every point of P is a point of R and every point of Q is a point of R. Thus R is obtained by adding points to P and to Q. Consequently, we have the inequalities

$$L_a^b(P, f) \leqq L_a^b(R, f) \leqq U_a^b(R, f) \leqq U_a^b(Q, f).$$

This proves our assertion.

It is now a very natural question to ask whether there is a *unique* point between the lower sums and the upper sums. In the next sections, we shall prove:

Theorem 4. *There exists a unique number which is greater or equal to every lower sum and less than or equal to every upper sum.*

This number will be called the *definite integral* of f between a and b, and is denoted by

$$\int_a^b f.$$

Example. Let $f(x) = x^2$ and let the interval be $[0, 1]$. Write out the upper and lower sums for the partition consisting of $(0, \frac{1}{2}, 1)$.

The minimum of the function in the interval $[0, \frac{1}{2}]$ is at 0, and $f(0) = 0$. The minimum of the function in the interval $[\frac{1}{2}, 1]$ is at $\frac{1}{2}$ and $f(\frac{1}{2}) = \frac{1}{4}$. Hence the lower sum is

$$f(0)(\tfrac{1}{2} - 0) + f(\tfrac{1}{2})(1 - \tfrac{1}{2}) = \tfrac{1}{4} \cdot \tfrac{1}{2} = \tfrac{1}{8}.$$

The maximum of the function in the interval $[0, \frac{1}{2}]$ is at $\frac{1}{2}$ and the maximum of the function in the interval $[\frac{1}{2}, 1]$ is at 1. Thus the upper sum is

$$f(\tfrac{1}{2})(\tfrac{1}{2} - 0) + f(1)(1 - \tfrac{1}{2}) = \tfrac{1}{8} + \tfrac{1}{2} = \tfrac{5}{8}.$$

EXERCISES

Write out the lower and upper sums for the following functions and intervals. Use a partition such that the length of each small interval is $\frac{1}{2}$.

1. $f(x) = x^2$ in the interval $[1, 2]$.   2. $f(x) = 1/x$ in the interval $[1, 3]$.

3. $f(x) = x$ in the interval $[0, 2]$.   4. $f(x) = 3$ in the interval $[0, 5]$.

5. Let $f(x) = 1/x$ and let the interval be $[1, 2]$. Let n be a positive integer. Write out the upper and lower sum, using the partition such that the length of each small interval is $1/n$.

6. Prove that

$$\frac{1}{n+1} + \frac{1}{n+2} + \cdots + \frac{1}{n+n} \leq \log 2 \leq \frac{1}{n} + \frac{1}{n+1} + \cdots + \frac{1}{2n-1}.$$

7. Let $f(x) = \log x$. Let n be a positive integer. Write out the upper and lower sums, using the partition of the interval between 1 and n consisting of the integers from 1 to n, i.e. the partition $(1, 2, \ldots, n)$.

§6. THE BASIC PROPERTIES

This section will contain the proof of Theorem 4. We first need to discuss a special property of numbers.

Let S be a collection of numbers, with at least one number in the collection. (We also say that S is not empty.) An *upper bound* for S is a number B such that

$$x \leq B$$

for all x in the collection S. A *least upper bound* for S is an upper bound which is smallest among all upper bounds.

For instance, let S be the collection of numbers whose square is ≤ 4. Then 5 is an upper bound for S and so is 3. However, 2 is the least upper bound.

Another example: Let S be the collection of numbers whose square is < 2. Then $\sqrt{2}$ is the least upper bound. (In this example, the least upper bound does not belong to our collection S.)

The property of numbers which we accept without proof is that *every collection of numbers which is not empty and has an upper bound also has a least upper bound.*

Similarly, we shall say that a number A is a *lower bound* for S if

$$A \leq x$$

for all x in the collection S. A *greatest lower bound* for S is a lower bound which is largest among all lower bounds.

We shall also accept without proof that every non-empty collection of numbers which has a lower bound has a greatest lower bound.

For example, the collection of numbers $1, \frac{1}{2}, \frac{1}{3}, \frac{1}{4}, \ldots$ has a greatest lower bound, which is the number 0. Observe again that this greatest lower bound is not in the collection.

We return to our upper and lower sums.

Let f be as in §5. We consider the collection of numbers consisting of all lower sums

$$L_a^b(P, f)$$

for all partitions P. This collection certainly has an upper bound (any upper sum will be an upper bound). We denote by

$$L_a^b(f)$$

its least upper bound, and call it the *lower integral* of f, over the interval $[a, b]$.

Every upper sum is an upper bound for the collection of lower sums. Therefore

$$L_a^b(f) \leqq U_a^b(P, f)$$

for every partition P. Thus $L_a^b(f)$ is a lower bound for the collection of upper sums. We denote by

$$U_a^b(f)$$

the greatest lower bound of the collection of upper sums, and call it the upper integral of f over the interval $[a, b]$. Then

$$L_a^b(f) \leqq U_a^b(f).$$

If x is any point in the interval, then we have the numbers

$$L_a^x(f) \quad \text{and} \quad U_a^x(f).$$

Thus $L_a^x(f)$ is the value at x of a function defined on the interval. Similarly, $U_a^x(f)$ is the value at x of another function defined on the interval.

Our purpose is to prove that these functions are equal for all x. The way we shall do this is to prove that $L_a^b(f)$ and $U_a^b(f)$ each satisfy the properties stated in Theorem 2. This will both give the existence of the integral, and in view of the remarks at the end of §4, it will also show that $L_a^b(f) = U_a^b(f)$.

Proof of Property 1. Suppose that we have two numbers m, M such that

$$m \leqq f(x) \leqq M$$

for all x between b and c. Let P be the partition of the interval b, c consisting only of the end points. Then

$$m(c - b) \leq L_b^c(P, f) \leq L_b^c(f).$$

On the other hand,

$$L_b^c(f) \leq U_b^c(f) \leq M(c - b).$$

This proves our property.

Proof of Property 2. Let a, b, c be three numbers with $a \leq b \leq c$. Let f be a continuous function on the interval $[a, c]$. We shall prove:

$$L_a^b(f) + L_b^c(f) = L_a^c(f).$$

A similar statement holds for the upper integrals, namely

$$U_a^b(f) + U_b^c(f) = U_a^c(f).$$

We shall first prove that

$$L_a^b(f) + L_b^c(f) \leq L_a^c(f).$$

Since $L_a^b(f)$ is the *least* upper bound of the lower sums built up with partitions, we can find such a lower sum which comes arbitrarily close to it. Thus, given any small number $\epsilon > 0$, we can find a partition P of the interval $[a, b]$ such that

$$L_a^b(f) - \epsilon \leq L_a^b(P, f).$$

Similarly, we can find a partition Q of the interval $[b, c]$ such that

$$L_b^c(f) - \epsilon \leq L_b^c(Q, f).$$

Adding, we get

$$L_a^b(f) + L_b^c(f) - 2\epsilon \leq L_a^b(P, f) + L_b^c(Q, f).$$

We can view P and Q together as giving a partition of the whole interval $[a, c]$.

We denote this partition simply by (P, Q). The two sums occurring on the right-hand side of our inequality are then equal to the lower sum built up from the partition (P, Q) over the whole interval $[a, c]$. Thus we can write

$$L_a^b(f) + L_b^c(f) - 2\epsilon \leq L_a^c((P, Q), f).$$

But any lower sum made up from a partition is smaller than the lower integral, which is an upper bound (even a least upper bound) of such lower sums. Thus our expression on the right satisfies the inequality

$$L_a^c((P, Q), f) \leqq L_a^c(f).$$

We obtain finally

$$L_a^b(f) + L_b^c(f) - 2\epsilon \leqq L_a^c(f).$$

This is true for every $\epsilon > 0$. Let ϵ approach 0. Then the left-hand side approaches

$$L_a^b(f) + L_b^c(f)$$

and our inequality follows.

We shall now prove the reverse inequality.

Let R be any partition of $[a, c]$. If we add b to R, then we get a partition of $[a, c]$ which splits up into a partition of $[a, b]$ and a partition of $[b, c]$. Call these P and Q. Then

$$L_a^c(R, f) \leqq L_a^c((P, Q), f) = L_a^b(P, f) + L_b^c(Q, f).$$

Since the lower integral is an upper bound for these lower sums, we know that the expression on the right is less than or equal to

$$L_a^b(f) + L_b^c(f),$$

which is therefore an upper bound for $L_a^c(R, f)$. The least upper bound $L_a^c(f)$ is therefore less than or equal to our sum on the right, and the property is proved.

The proof that the upper integral U satisfies the two properties is entirely similar, and will be left as an exercise.

§7. INTEGRABLE FUNCTIONS

In general, let f be a bounded function on $[a, b]$. This means that there exists a number C such that $|f(x)| \leqq C$ for all x in $[a, b]$. Then f may not have a minimum on a closed interval, but we can still form lower sums by replacing the minimum by a greatest lower bound. Thus if P is a partition of $[a, b]$ say

$$a = x_0 \leqq x_1 \leqq \cdots \leqq x_n = b,$$

we let

$m_i = $ greatest lower bound of values $f(x)$ for x in the interval $[x_i, x_{i+1}]$,

$M_i = $ least upper bound of values $f(x)$ for x in the interval $[x_i, x_{i+1}]$.

We then form the sum

$$L_a^b(P, f) = \sum_{i=0}^{n-1} m_i(x_{i+1} - x_i)$$

and similarly for the upper sum,

$$U_a^b(P, f) = \sum_{i=0}^{n-1} M_i(x_{i+1} - x_i).$$

Theorem 3 is still true for any bounded function f, and thus we can define the *lower integral*

$L_a^b(f)$ = least upper bound of all $L_a^b(P, f)$ for all partitions P.

The upper integral is then defined similarly. The function f is said to be *integrable* if

$$L_a^b(f) = U_a^b(f),$$

that is, if its lower integral is equal to its upper integral, in which case it is called simply the *integral* of f. We proved in the previous section that every continuous function is integrable. It can be shown that a bounded function which is continuous except at a finite number of points is integrable, but we shall leave it as an exercise. However, we prove:

Theorem 5. *Let f be an integrable function on $[a, b]$. Suppose that for each pair of numbers c, d with $a \leq c \leq d \leq b$ we have associated a number denoted by $I_c^d(f)$ satisfying the following properties:*

Property 1. If M, m are two numbers such that

$$m \leq f(x) \leq M$$

for all x in $[c, d]$ then

$$m(d - c) \leq I_c^d(f) \leq M(d - c).$$

Property 2. We have

$$I_a^c(f) + I_c^d(f) = I_a^d(f).$$

Then $I_a^b(f)$ is the integral of f on $[a, b]$.

Proof. Let P be a partition as before. Then

$$L_a^b(P, f) = \sum_{i=0}^{n-1} m_i(x_{i+1} - x_i) \leq \sum_{i=0}^{n-1} I_{x_i}^{x_{i+1}}(f) = I_a^b(f).$$

Similarly,

$$L_a^b(P, f) \leq I_a^b(f) \leq U_a^b(P, f).$$

Since f is integrable, $L_a^b(P, f)$ and $U_a^b(P, f)$ are arbitrarily close together for suitable partitions P, and hence the theorem follows.

EXERCISE

Prove that if f is bounded on $[a, b]$ and continuous except at a finite number of points, then f is integrable. [*Hint:* Let $c_1, \ldots, c_r$ be the points at which f is not continuous. Around each c_i, put an interval of radius δ. Consider partitions of $[a, b]$ which have the points $c_i - \delta$, c_i, $c_i + \delta$. Outside these small intervals, the upper and lower sums are close together because the function is continuous. Inside these intervals, the upper and lower sums are anyhow bounded by an expression of type $2\delta C r$ where C is a bound for f.]

Chapter X

Properties of the Integral

This is a short chapter. It shows how the integral combines with addition and inequalities. There is no good formula for the integral of a product. The closest thing is integration by parts, which is postponed to the next chapter.

Connecting the integral with the derivative is what allows us to compute integrals. The fact that two functions having the same derivative differ by a constant is again exploited to the hilt.

§1. FURTHER CONNECTION WITH THE DERIVATIVE

Let f be a continuous function on some interval. Let a, b be two points of the interval such that $a < b$, and let F be a function which is differentiable on the interval and whose derivative is f.

Then we know that there is a constant C such that

$$\int_a^x f = F(x) + C$$

for all x in the interval. If we put $x = a$, we get

$$0 = \int_a^a f = F(a) + C,$$

whence $C = -F(a)$. We also have

$$\int_a^b f = F(b) + C.$$

From this we obtain

$$\int_a^b f = F(b) - F(a).$$

This is extremely useful in practice, because we can usually guess the function F, and once we have guessed it, we can then compute the integral by means of this relation.

183

Furthermore, it is also practical to use the notation

$$F(x)\Big|_a^b$$

instead of $F(b) - F(a)$. Thus the integral

$$\int_0^\pi \sin x \, dx$$

is equal to

$$-\cos x\Big|_0^\pi,$$

which is $-\cos \pi - (-\cos 0) = 2$.

As another example, suppose we want to find

$$\int_1^3 x^2 \, dx.$$

Let $F(x) = x^3/3$. Then $F'(x) = x^2$. Hence our integral is equal to

$$\frac{x^3}{3}\Big|_1^3 = \frac{27}{3} - \frac{1}{3} = \frac{26}{3}.$$

Finally, we shall usually call the *indefinite integral* simply an *integral*, since the context makes clear what is meant. When we deal with a definite integral $\int_a^b$, the numbers a and b are sometimes called the *lower limit* and *upper limit*, respectively.

EXERCISES

Find the following integrals:

1. $\displaystyle\int_1^2 x^5 \, dx$ 2. $\displaystyle\int_{-1}^1 x^{1/3} \, dx$ 3. $\displaystyle\int_{-\pi}^\pi \sin x \, dx$ 4. $\displaystyle\int_0^\pi \cos x \, dx$

§2. SUMS

Let $f(x)$ and $g(x)$ be two functions defined over some interval, and let $F(x)$ and $G(x)$ be (indefinite) integrals for f and g, respectively. Since the derivative of a sum is the sum of the derivatives, we see that $F + G$ is an integral for $f + g$; in other words,

$$\int [f(x) + g(x)] \, dx = \int f(x) \, dx + \int g(x) \, dx.$$

Similarly, let c be a number. The derivative of $cF(x)$ is $cf(x)$. Hence

$$\int cf(x) \, dx = c \int f(x) \, dx.$$

A constant can be taken in and out of an integral.

Example 1. Find the integral of $\sin x + 3x^4$.

We have

$$\int (\sin x + 3x^4)\, dx = \int \sin x \, dx + \int 3x^4 \, dx$$

$$= -\cos x + 3x^5/5.$$

Any formula involving the indefinite integral yields a formula for the definite integral. Using the same notation as above, suppose we have to find

$$\int_a^b [f(x) + g(x)]\, dx.$$

We know that it is

$$[F(x) + G(x)]\Big|_a^b,$$

which is equal to

$$F(b) + G(b) - F(a) - G(a).$$

Thus we get the formula

$$\int_a^b [f(x) + g(x)]\, dx = \int_a^b f(x)\, dx + \int_a^b g(x)\, dx.$$

Similarly, for any constant c,

$$\int_a^b cf(x)\, dx = c\int_a^b f(x)\, dx.$$

Example 2. Find the integral

$$\int_0^\pi [\sin x + 3x^4]\, dx.$$

This (definite) integral is equal to

$$-\cos x + 3x^5/5\Big|_0^\pi = -\cos \pi + 3\pi^5/5 - (-\cos 0 + 0)$$

$$= 1 + 3\pi^5/5 + 1$$

$$= 2 + 3\pi^5/5.$$

In some applications, one meets a slightly wider class of functions than continuous ones. Let f be a function defined on an interval $[a, b]$. We shall say that f is *piecewise continuous* on $[a, b]$ if there exist numbers

$$a = a_0 < a_1 < \cdots < a_n = b$$

and on each interval $[a_{i-1}, a_i]$ there is a continuous function f_i such that $f(x) = f_i(x)$ for $a_{i-1} < x < a_i$. If this is the case, then we define the integral of f from a to b to be the sum

$$\int_a^b f = \int_{a_0}^{a_1} f_1 + \int_{a_1}^{a_2} f_2 + \cdots + \int_{a_{n-1}}^{a_n} f_n.$$

A piecewise continuous function may look like this:

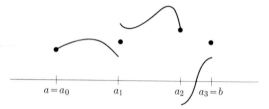

Example 3. Let f be the function defined on the interval $[0, 2]$ by the conditions:

$$f(x) = x \quad \text{if } 0 \leq x \leq 1$$
$$f(x) = 2 \quad \text{if } 1 < x \leq 2.$$

The graph of f looks like this:

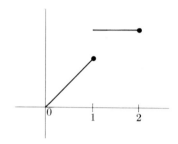

To find the integral of f between 0 and 2, we have

$$\int_0^2 f = \int_0^1 x \, dx + \int_1^2 2 \, dx = \frac{x^2}{2}\Big|_0^1 + 2x\Big|_1^2$$
$$= \frac{1}{2} + (4 - 2) = \frac{5}{2}.$$

We can also find $\int_0^x f(t) \, dt$ for $0 \leq x \leq 2$. If $0 \leq x \leq 1$:

$$\int_0^x f(t) \, dt = \int_0^x t \, dt = \frac{x^2}{2}.$$

If $1 \leq x \leq 2$:

$$\int_0^x f(t) \, dt = \int_0^1 f(t) \, dt + \int_1^x f(t) \, dt$$
$$= \frac{1}{2} + \int_1^x 2 \, dt = \frac{1}{2} + 2x - 2.$$

Example 4. Let $f(x)$ be defined for $0 \leq x \leq \pi$ by the formulas:

$$f(x) = \sin x \quad \text{if } 0 \leq x < \pi/2$$
$$f(x) = \cos x \quad \text{if } \pi/2 \leq x \leq \pi.$$

Then the integral of f from 0 to π is given by:

$$\int_0^\pi f = \int_0^{\pi/2} \sin x \, dx + \int_{\pi/2}^\pi \cos x \, dx$$

$$= -\cos x \Big|_0^{\pi/2} + \sin x \Big|_{\pi/2}^\pi$$

$$= 0.$$

The graph of f looks like this:

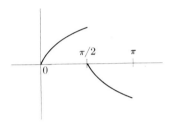

EXERCISES

Find the following integrals:

1. $\int 4x^3 \, dx$

2. $\int (3x^4 - x^5) \, dx$

3. $\int (2 \sin x + 3 \cos x) \, dx$

4. $\int (3x^{2/3} + 5 \cos x) \, dx$

5. $\int \left(5e^x + \frac{1}{x}\right) dx$

6. $\int_{-\pi}^{\pi} (\sin x + \cos x) \, dx$

7. $\int_{-1}^{1} 2x^5 \, dx$

8. $\int_{-1}^{2} e^x \, dx$

9. $\int_{-1}^{3} 4x_2 \, dx$

10. Find the area between the curves $y = x$ and $y = x^2$. [Sketch the curve. If $f(x)$ and $g(x)$ are two continuous functions such that $f(x) \geq g(x)$ on an interval $[a, b]$, then the area between the two curves, from a to b, is

$$\int_a^b (f(x) - g(x)) \, dx.$$

In this problem, the curves intersect at $x = 0$ and $x = 1$.]

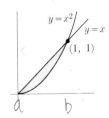

Hence the area is

$$\int_0^1 (x - x^2)\, dx = \frac{x^2}{2} - \frac{x^3}{3}\Big|_0^1 = \frac{1}{2} - \frac{1}{3}.$$

11. Find the area between the curves $y = x$ and $y = x^3$.

12. Find the area between the curves $y = x^2$ and $y = x^3$.

13. Find the area between the curve $y = (x - 1)(x - 2)(x - 3)$ and the x-axis. (Sketch the curve.)

14. Find the area between the curve $y = (x + 1)(x - 1)(x + 2)$ and the x-axis.

15. Find the area between the curves $y = \sin x$, $y = \cos x$, the y-axis, and the first point where these curves intersect for $x > 0$.

In each one of the following cases, find the integral of the function on the stated interval, and sketch the graph of the function.

16. On $[-1, 1]$, $f(x) = x$ if $-1 \leq x < 0$ and $f(x) = 5$ if $0 \leq x \leq 1$.

17. On $[-1, 1]$, $f(x) = x^2$ if $-1 \leq x \leq 0$ and $f(x) = -x$ if $0 < x \leq 1$.

18. On $[-1, 1]$, $f(x) = x - 1$ if $-1 \leq x < 0$ and $f(x) = x + 1$ if $0 \leq x \leq 1$.

19. On $[-\pi, \pi]$, $f(x) = \sin x$ if $-\pi \leq x \leq 0$, and $f(x) = x$ if $0 < x \leq \pi$.

20. On $[-\pi, \pi]$, $f(x) = |\sin x|$.   21. On $[-\pi, \pi]$, $f(x) = |\cos x|$.

22. On $[-1, 1]$, $f(x) = |x|$.   23. On $[-\pi, \pi]$, $f(x) = \sin x + |\cos x|$.

24. On $[-\pi, \pi]$, $f(x) = x - |x|$.   25. On $[-\pi, \pi]$, $f(x) = \sin x + |\sin x|$.

§3. INEQUALITIES

Theorem 1. *Let a, b be two numbers, with $a \leq b$. Let f, g be two continuous functions on the interval $[a, b]$ and assume that $f(x) \leq g(x)$ for all x in the interval. Then*

$$\int_a^b f(x)\, dx \leq \int_a^b g(x)\, dx.$$

Proof. Since $g(x) - f(x) \geq 0$, we can use the basic Property 1 of Chapter IX, §4 (with $m = 0$) to conclude that

$$\int_a^b (g - f) \geq 0.$$

But

$$\int_a^b (g - f) = \int_a^b g - \int_a^b f.$$

Transposing the second integral on the right in our inequality, we obtain

$$\int_a^b g \geq \int_a^b f,$$

as desired.

Theorem 1 will be used mostly when $g(x) = |f(x)|$. Since a negative number is always $\leq$ a positive number, we know that

$$f(x) \leq |f(x)|$$

and

$$-f(x) \leq |f(x)|.$$

Theorem 2. *Let a, b be two numbers, with $a \leq b$. Let f be a continuous function on the interval $[a, b]$. Then*

$$\left| \int_a^b f(x)\,dx \right| \leq \int_a^b |f(x)|\,dx.$$

Proof. We simply let $g(x) = |f(x)|$ in the preceding theorem. The absolute value of the integral on the left is equal to

$$\int_a^b f(x)\,dx \quad \text{or} \quad -\int_a^b f(x)\,dx.$$

We can apply Theorem 1 either to $f(x)$ or $-f(x)$ to get Theorem 2.

We make one other application of Theorem 2.

Theorem 3. *Let a, b be two numbers and f a continuous function on the closed interval between a and b. (We do not necessarily assume that $a < b$.) Let M be a number such that $|f(x)| \leq M$ for all x in the interval. Then*

$$\left| \int_a^b f(x)\,dx \right| \leq M|b - a|.$$

Proof. If $a \leq b$, we can use Theorem 2 to get

$$\left| \int_a^b f(x)\,dx \right| \leq \int_a^b M\,dx = M\int_a^b dx = M(b - a).$$

If $b < a$, then

$$\int_a^b f = -\int_b^a f.$$

Taking the absolute value gives us the estimate $M(a - b)$. Since $a - b = |b - a|$ in case $b < a$, we have proved our theorem.

Theorem 4. *Let f be a continuous function on the interval $[a, b]$ with $a < b$. Assume that $f(x) \geq 0$ for every x in this interval, and $f(x) > 0$ for some x in this interval. Then*

$$\int_a^b f(x)\,dx > 0.$$

Proof. Let c be a number of the interval such that $f(c) > 0$, and suppose for simplicity that $c \neq b$. Since f is continuous, there exists some number d close to c in the interval, with $c < d \leq b$ such that $f(x)$ is close to $f(c)$ for all x satisfying $c \leq x \leq d$. In particular, we have

$$f(x) \geq \frac{f(c)}{2}, \qquad\qquad c \leq x \leq d.$$

Then

$$\int_a^b f(x)\,dx = \int_a^c f + \int_c^d f + \int_d^b f$$

$$\geq \int_c^d f(x)\,dx \geq \int_c^d \frac{f(c)}{2}\,dx$$

$$= \frac{f(c)}{2}(d - c) > 0.$$

This proves our theorem if $c \neq b$. If $c = b$, we take $d < c$ and argue similarly.

Theorem 4 will not be used in the rest of this book except in a couple of exercises, but it is important in subsequent applications. The geometric idea behind the proof is quite simple, in terms of area. Since the function f is assumed ≥ 0 everywhere, and > 0 at the point c, then it is greater than some fixed positive number [taken to be $f(c)/2$, say] in some interval near c. This means that we can insert a small rectangle of height > 0 between the curve $y = f(x)$ and the x-axis. Then the area under the curve is at least equal to the area of this rectangle, which is > 0.

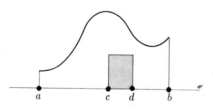

EXERCISES

1. Let a, b be numbers with $a < b$. If f, g are continuous functions on the interval $[a, b]$ let

$$\langle f, g \rangle = \int_a^b f(x)g(x)\,dx.$$

Show that the symbol $\langle f, g \rangle$ satisfies the following properties:
(a) If f_1, f_2, g are continuous on $[a, b]$ then

$$\langle f_1 + f_2, g \rangle = \langle f_1, g \rangle + \langle f_2, g \rangle.$$

If c is a number, then
$$\langle cf, g \rangle = c \langle f, g \rangle.$$

(b) We have $\langle f, g \rangle = \langle g, f \rangle$.

(c) We have $\langle f, f \rangle \geq 0$, and equality holds if and only if $f = 0$.

2. Let the notation be as in Exercise 1. For any number $p \geq 1$ define
$$\|f\|_p = \left[\int_a^b |f(x)|^p \, dx \right]^{1/p}.$$

Let q be such that $\dfrac{1}{p} + \dfrac{1}{q} = 1$. Prove that
$$|\langle f, g \rangle| \leq \|f\|_p \|g\|_q.$$

[*Hint:* If $\|f\|_p$ and $\|g\|_q \neq 0$ let $\alpha = |f|^p / \|f\|_p^p$ and $\beta = |g|^q / \|g\|_q^q$. Then use Exercise 13 of Chapter VIII, §3, and integrate both terms.]

3. Notation being as in the preceding exercise, prove that
$$\|f + g\|_p \leq \|f\|_p + \|g\|_p.$$

[*Hint:* Let I denote the integral. Show that
$$\|f + g\|_p^p \leq I(|f + g|^{p-1}|f|) + I(|f + g|^{p-1}|g|)$$

and apply Exercise 2.]

4. (a) Let f be an increasing continuous function, defined for all $x \geq 1$, such that $f(x) \geq 0$. Show that
$$f(1) + f(2) + \cdots + f(n-1) \leq \int_1^n f(x) \, dx \leq f(2) + \cdots + f(n).$$

(b) Let $F(x) = \int_1^x f(t) \, dt$. Assume that
$$\lim_{n \to \infty} \frac{f(n)}{F(n)} = 0.$$

Show that
$$\lim_{n \to \infty} \frac{f(1) + f(2) + \cdots + f(n)}{F(n)} = 1.$$

5. Evaluate the following limits, for $n \to \infty$.

(a) $\dfrac{1^{1/3} + 2^{1/3} + \cdots + n^{1/3}}{n^{4/3}}$

(b) $\dfrac{1^{1/4} + 2^{1/4} + \cdots + n^{1/4}}{n^{5/4}}$

(c) $n\left(\dfrac{1}{1^2} + \dfrac{1}{2^2} + \cdots + \dfrac{1}{n^2}\right)$

(d) $\dfrac{1 + 2^4 + \cdots + n^4}{n^5}$

(e) For a fixed integer $k \geq 1$,
$$\frac{1 + 2^k + \cdots + n^k}{n^{k+1}}.$$

6. Let f be a decreasing continuous function, defined for $x \geq 1$ and such that $f(x) \geq 0$. Show that

$$f(1) + f(2) + \cdots + f(n-1) \geq \int_1^n f(x)\,dx \geq f(2) + \cdots + f(n).$$

§4. IMPROPER INTEGRALS

We know that the area under the curve $1/x$ between 1 and x is $\log x$. Instead of taking $x > 1$, let us take $0 < x < 1$. As x approaches 0, $\log x$ becomes very large negative. The integral

$$\int_x^1 \frac{1}{t}\,dt = \log t \Big|_x^1 = -\log x$$

is therefore very large positive. We can interpret this by saying that the area becomes very large.

However, it is remarkable that an entirely different situation will occur when we consider the area under the curve $1/x^{1/2} = x^{-1/2}$. We take $x > 0$, of course, and compute the integral

$$\int_x^1 \frac{1}{t^{1/2}}\,dt = \frac{t^{1/2}}{1/2}\Big|_x^1 = 2 - 2x^{1/2}.$$

As x approaches 0, this approaches 2, in spite of the fact that our curve $y = x^{-1/2}$ gives rise to a chimney near the y-axis, and is not even defined for $x = 0$.

When that happens, we shall say that the integral

$$\int_0^1 t^{-1/2}\,dt$$

exists, or *converges* even though the function is not defined at 0 and is not continuous in the *closed* interval $[0, 1]$.

In general, suppose we have two numbers a, b with, say, $a < b$. Let f be a continuous function in the interval $a < x \leq b$. This means that for every positive number h (such that $a + h < b$), the function f is continuous on the interval

$$a + h \leq x \leq b.$$

We can then form our usual integral

$$\int_{a+h}^b f(x)\,dx.$$

If F is an indefinite integral for f over our interval, then the integral is equal to

$$F(b) - F(a + h).$$

If the limit

$$\lim_{h \to 0} F(a + h)$$

exists, then we say that the *improper integral*

$$\int_a^b f(x)\, dx$$

exists, and is equal to $F(b) - \lim_{h \to 0} F(a + h)$.

In our preceding examples, we can say that the improper integral

$$\int_0^1 \frac{1}{x}\, dx$$

does not exist, but that the improper integral

$$\int_0^1 x^{-1/2}\, dx$$

does exist. This second integral is equal to 2.

We make similar definitions when we deal with an interval $a \leq x < b$ and a function f which is continuous on this interval. If the limit

$$\lim_{\substack{h \to 0 \\ h > 0}} \int_a^{b-h} f(x)\, dx$$

exists, then we say that the improper integral exists, and it is equal to this limit.

Example 1. Show that the improper integral

$$\int_0^1 \frac{1}{x^2}\, dx$$

does not exist.

We consider

$$\int_h^1 x^{-2}\, dx = \frac{x^{-1}}{-1}\bigg|_h^1 = -1 - \left(-\frac{1}{h}\right) = -1 + \frac{1}{h}.$$

This does not approach a limit as h approaches 0 and hence the improper integral does not exist.

There is another type of improper integral, dealing with large values.

Let a be a number and f a continuous function defined for $x \geq a$. Consider the integral

$$\int_a^B f(x)\, dx$$

for some number $B > a$. If $F(x)$ is any indefinite integral of f, then our integral is equal to $F(B) - F(a)$. If it approaches a limit as B becomes very large, then we *define*

$$\int_a^\infty f(x)\, dx \quad \text{or} \quad \int_a^\infty f$$

to be this limit, and say that the *improper integral converges*.

Thus $\int_a^\infty f$ converges if

$$\lim_{B \to \infty} \int_a^B f$$

exists, and is equal to this limit. Otherwise, we say that the improper integral *does not converge*.

Example 2. Determine whether the improper integral $\displaystyle\int_1^\infty \frac{1}{x}\, dx$ converges, and if it does, find its value.

We have, for a large number B,

$$\int_1^B \frac{1}{x}\, dx = \log B - \log 1 = \log B.$$

As B becomes large, so does $\log B$, and hence the improper integral does not converge.

Let us look at the function $1/x^2$. Its graph looks like that in the next figure. At first sight, there seems to be no difference between this function and $1/x$, except that $1/x^2 < 1/x$ when $x > 1$. However, intuitively speaking, we shall find that $1/x^2$ approaches 0 sufficiently faster than $1/x$ to guarantee that the area under the curve between 1 and B approaches a limit as B becomes large.

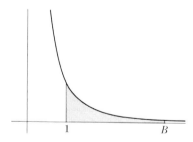

Example 3. Determine whether the improper integral

$$\int_1^\infty \frac{1}{x^2}\, dx$$

converges, and if it does, find its value.

For a large number B, we have

$$\int_1^B \frac{1}{x^2}\, dx = \frac{-1}{x}\Big|_1^B = -\frac{1}{B} + 1. \qquad \log(0)$$

As B becomes large, $1/B$ approaches 0. Hence the limit as B becomes large exists and is equal to 1, which is the value of our integral. We thus have by definition

$$\int_1^\infty \frac{1}{x^2}\, dx = 1.$$

It is frequently possible to determine whether an improper integral converges without computing it, by comparing it with another which is known to converge. We give such a criterion in the following theorem.

Theorem 5. *Let $f(x)$ and $g(x)$ be two continuous functions defined for $x \geq a$ and such that $f(x) \geq 0$ and $g(x) \geq 0$ for all $x \geq a$. Assume that $f(x) \leq g(x)$ and that the improper integral*

$$\int_a^\infty g(x)\, dx$$

converges. Then so does the improper integral

$$\int_a^\infty f(x)\, dx.$$

(Intuitively speaking, we visualize the theorem as saying that if the area under the graph of g is finite, then the area under the graph of f is also finite because it is smaller.)

Proof. Let B be a large number. Then according to the inequalities satisfied by the definite integral, we have

$$\int_a^B f \leq \int_a^B g.$$

As B becomes large, and increases, the integral on the right increases. But we know that it approaches a limit; call it L. This limit is a number, which is a bound for the integral of f between a and B, i.e.

$$\int_a^B f \leq L.$$

As B increases, this integral of f also increases (the area under the graph increases because f is ≥ 0) but stays below L for all B. There must be a least upper bound for such integrals of f, and this least upper bound is the desired limit.

Example 4. Determine whether the improper integral

$$\int_1^\infty \frac{x}{x^3 + 1}\, dx$$

converges.

We don't try to evaluate this, but observe that

$$x^3 \leq x^3 + 1$$

for $x \geq 1$, whence

$$\frac{x}{x^3 + 1} \leq \frac{x}{x^3} \leq \frac{1}{x^2}.$$

All the functions involved are ≥ 0 when $x \geq 1$. Using Example 3, we conclude that our improper integral converges.

Example 5. Note that Theorem 5 also applies to a finite interval. For instance, we wish to prove that the integral

$$\int_0^1 \frac{e^x}{\sqrt{x}}\, dx$$

converges. We use Exercise 8. There is some number $C > 0$ such that $e^x \leq C$ if $0 \leq x \leq 1$ and hence for $0 < x \leq 1$ we have $e^x/\sqrt{x} \leq C/\sqrt{x}$. By Exercise 8, the integral

$$\int_0^1 \frac{C}{\sqrt{x}}\, dx$$

converges. Hence by Theorem 5 our given integral $\int_0^1 e^x/\sqrt{x}\, dx$ converges.

EXERCISES

Determine whether the following improper integrals exist or not, and converge or not:

1. $\int_2^\infty \frac{1}{x^{3/2}}\, dx$ 2. $\int_1^\infty \frac{1}{x^{2/3}}\, dx$ 3. $\int_0^\infty \frac{1}{1 + x^2}\, dx$

4. $\int_0^5 \frac{1}{5 - x}\, dx$ 5. $\int_0^2 \frac{1}{x^2 - 2x}\, dx$ 6. $\int_1^\infty e^{-x}\, dx$

7. Let B be a number > 2. Find the area under the curve $y = e^{-2x}$ between 2 and B. Does this area approach a limit when B becomes very large? If so, what limit?

8. Let $0 < a < 1$. Does the integral

$$\int_a^1 \frac{1}{\sqrt{x}}\, dx$$

approach a limit as $a \to 0$? If so what limit?

9. Show that the integral

$$\int_0^1 \frac{1}{\sqrt{\sin x}}\, dx$$

exists.   [*Hint:* Get some lower bound for $\sin x$ in terms of cx for some constant c.]

10. Show that the integral

$$\int_0^1 \frac{1}{\sqrt{\tan x}}\, dx$$

exists.

11. Let s be a number < 1. Show that the improper integral

$$\int_0^1 \frac{1}{x^s}\, dx$$

exists.

12. (a) Show that $(\log x)x^{1/4}$ is bounded between 0 and 1.
    (b) Show that

$$\int_0^1 \frac{\log x}{x^{1/2}}\, dx$$

exists.

    (c) For any positive integer n, show that

$$\int_0^1 \frac{(\log x)^n}{\sqrt{x}}\, dx$$

exists.

Chapter XI

Techniques of Integration

The purpose of this chapter is to teach you certain basic tricks to find indefinite integrals. It is of course easier to look up integral tables, but you should have a minimum of training in standard techniques.

§1. SUBSTITUTION

We shall formulate the analogue of the chain rule for integration.

Suppose that we have a function $g(x)$ and another function f such that $f(g(x))$ is defined. (All these functions are supposed to be defined over suitable intervals.) We wish to evaluate an integral

$$\int f(g(x)) \frac{dg(x)}{dx} dx.$$

Let $F(u)$ be an indefinite integral for $f(u)$, so that

$$\int f(u)\, du = F(u), \quad \text{i.e.} \quad \frac{dF(u)}{du} = f(u).$$

Then we assert that $F(g(x))$ is an integral for $f(g(x)) \dfrac{dg}{dx}$, or symbolically, that

$$\boxed{\int f(g(x)) \frac{dg}{dx} dx = \int f(u)\, du.}$$

This follows at once from the chain rule, because

$$\frac{d(F \circ g)}{dx} = \frac{dF}{du} \frac{du}{dx} = f(u) \frac{du}{dx} = f(g(x)) \frac{dg(x)}{dx}.$$

Example 1. Find $\int (x^2 + 1)^3 (2x)\, dx$.

Put $u = x^2 + 1$. Then $du/dx = 2x$ and our integral is in the form

$$\int f(u) \frac{du}{dx} dx,$$

the function f being $f(u) = u^3$.

198

Therefore our integral is equal to

$$\int f(u)\, du = \int u^3\, du = \frac{u^4}{4} = \frac{(x^2 + 1)^4}{4}.$$

We can check this by differentiating the expression on the right, using the chain rule. We get $(x^2 + 1)^3(2x)$, as desired.

Example 2. Find $\int \sin (2x)(2)\, dx$.

Put $u = 2x$. Then $du/dx = 2$. Hence our integral is in the form

$$\int \sin u\, du = -\cos u = -\cos (2x).$$

Observe that

$$\int \sin (2x)\, dx \neq -\cos (2x).$$

If we differentiate $-\cos (2x)$, we get $\sin (2x) \cdot 2$.

The integral in Example 2 could also be written

$$\int 2 \sin (2x)\, dx.$$

It does not matter, of course, where we place the 2.

Example 3. Find $\int \cos (3x)\, dx$.

Let $u = 3x$. Then $du/dx = 3$. There is no extra 3 in our integral. However, we can take a constant in and out of an integral. Our integral is equal to

$$\tfrac{1}{3}\int 3 \cos (3x)\, dx,$$

and this integral is in the form

$$\tfrac{1}{3}\int \cos u\, du.$$

Thus our integral is equal to $\tfrac{1}{3} \sin u = \tfrac{1}{3} \sin (3x)$.

It is convenient to use a purely formal notation which allows us to make a substitution $u = g(x)$, as in the previous examples. Thus instead of writing

$$\frac{du}{dx} = 2x$$

in Example 1, we would write $du = 2x\, dx$. Similarly, in Example 2, we would write $du = 2\, dx$, and in Example 3 we would write $du = 3\, dx$. We do not attribute any meaning to this. It is merely a device of a type used in programming a computing machine. A machine does not think. One simply adjusts certain electric circuits so that the machine performs a certain operation and comes out with the right answer. The fact that writing

$$du = \frac{du}{dx}\,dx$$

makes us come out with the right answer was *proved* once and for all when we established the relationship

$$\int f(g(x))\frac{dg}{dx}\,dx = \int f(u)\,du.$$

The proof consisted in differentiating the answer and checking that it gives us the desired function.

Example 4. Find

$$\int (x^3 + x)^9 (3x^2 + 1)\,dx.$$

Let

$$u = x^3 + x.$$

Then

$$du = (3x^2 + 1)\,dx.$$

Hence our integral is of type $\int f(u)\,du$ and is equal to

$$\int u^9\,du = \frac{u^{10}}{10} = \frac{(x^3 + x)^{10}}{10}.$$

We should also observe that the formula for integration by substitution applies to the definite integral. We can state this formally as follows.

Let g be a differentiable function on the interval [a, b], whose derivative is continuous. Let f be a continuous function on an interval containing the values of g. Then

$$\int_a^b f(g(x))\frac{dg}{dx}\,dx = \int_{g(a)}^{g(b)} f(u)\,du.$$

The proof is immediate. If F is an indefinite integral for f, then $F \circ g$ is an indefinite integral for

$$f(g(x))\frac{dg}{dx}$$

by the chain rule. Hence the left-hand side of our formula is equal to

$$F(g(b)) - F(g(a)),$$

which is also the value of the right-hand side.

In Example 4, suppose that we consider the integral

$$\int_0^1 (x^3 + x)^9 (3x^2 + 1)\, dx,$$

with $u = x^3 + x$. When $x = 0$, $u = 0$, and when $x = 1$, $u = 2$. Thus our definite integral is equal to

$$\int_0^2 u^9\, du = \frac{2^{10}}{10}.$$

Example 5. Evaluate

$$\int_0^{\sqrt{\pi}} x \sin x^2\, dx.$$

We let $u = x^2$, $du = 2x\, dx$. When $x = 0$, $u = 0$. When $x = \sqrt{\pi}$, $u = \pi$. Thus our integral is equal to

$$\tfrac{1}{2}\int_0^\pi \sin u\, du = \tfrac{1}{2}(-\cos u)\Big|_0^\pi = \tfrac{1}{2}(-\cos \pi + \cos 0) = 1.$$

EXERCISES

Find the following integrals:

1. $\displaystyle\int xe^{x^2}\, dx$

2. $\displaystyle\int x^3 e^{-x^4}\, dx$

3. $\displaystyle\int x^2(1 + x^3)\, dx$

4. $\displaystyle\int \frac{\log x}{x}\, dx$

5. $\displaystyle\int \frac{1}{x(\log x)^n}\, dx \quad (n = \text{integer})$

6. $\displaystyle\int \frac{2x + 1}{x^2 + x + 1}\, dx$

7. $\displaystyle\int \frac{x}{x + 1}\, dx$

8. $\displaystyle\int \sin x \cos x\, dx$

9. $\displaystyle\int \sin^2 x \cos x\, dx$

10. $\displaystyle\int_0^\pi \sin^5 x \cos x\, dx$

11. $\displaystyle\int_0^\pi \cos^4 x \sin x\, dx$

12. $\displaystyle\int \frac{\sin x}{1 + \cos^2 x}\, dx$

13. $\displaystyle\int \frac{\arctan x}{1 + x^2}\, dx$

14. $\displaystyle\int_0^1 x^3\sqrt{1 - x^2}\, dx$

15. $\displaystyle\int_0^{\pi/2} x \sin (2x^2)\, dx$

16. Find the area under the curve $y = xe^{-x^2}$ between 0 and a number $B > 0$. Does this area approach a limit as B becomes very large? If so, what limit?

17. Find the area under the curve $y = x^2 e^{-x^3}$ between 0 and a number $B > 0$. Does this area approach a limit as B becomes very large? If so, what limit?

In some integrals involving e^x, one can sometimes find the integral by the substitution $u = e^x$, $x = \log u$, and $dx = (1/u)\,du$. You can combine this with the technique of §4 below to deal with the following integrals.

18. $\displaystyle\int \sqrt{1 + e^x}\,dx$

19. $\displaystyle\int \frac{1}{1 + e^x}\,dx$

20. $\displaystyle\int \frac{1}{e^x + e^{-x}}\,dx$

21. $\displaystyle\int \frac{1}{\sqrt{e^x + 1}}\,dx$

§2. INTEGRATION BY PARTS

If f, g are two differentiable functions of x, then

$$\frac{d(fg)}{dx} = f(x)\frac{dg}{dx} + g(x)\frac{df}{dx}.$$

Hence

$$f(x)\frac{dg}{dx} = \frac{d(fg)}{dx} - g(x)\frac{df}{dx}.$$

Using the formula for the integral of a sum, which is the sum of the integrals, we obtain

$$\int f(x)\frac{dg}{dx}\,dx = f(x)g(x) - \int g(x)\frac{df}{dx}\,dx,$$

which is called the formula for integrating by parts.

If we let $u = f(x)$ and $v = g(x)$, then the formula can be abbreviated in our shorthand notation as follows:

$$\boxed{\int u\,dv = uv - \int v\,du.}$$

Example 1. Find the integral $\int \log x\,dx$.

Let $u = \log x$ and $v = x$. Then $du = (1/x)\,dx$ and $dv = dx$. Hence our integral is in the form $\int u\,dv$ and is equal to

$$uv - \int v\,du = x\log x - \int 1\,dx$$
$$= x\log x - x.$$

Example 2. Find $\int e^x \sin x\,dx$.

Let $u = e^x$ and $dv = \sin x\,dx$. Then

$$du = e^x\,dx \quad\text{and}\quad v = -\cos x.$$

If we call our integral I, then

$$I = -e^x \cos x - \int -e^x \cos x$$
$$= -e^x \cos x + \int e^x \cos x \, dx.$$

This looks as if we were going around in circles. Don't lose heart. Rather, let $t = e^x$ and $dz = \cos x \, dx$. Then

$$dt = e^x \, dx \quad \text{and} \quad z = \sin x.$$

The second integral becomes

$$\int t \, dz = e^x \sin x - \int e^x \sin x \, dx.$$

We have come back to our integral I but with a minus sign! Thus

$$I = e^x \sin x - e^x \cos x - I.$$

Hence

$$2I = e^x \sin x - e^x \cos x,$$

and dividing by 2 gives us the value of I.

EXERCISES

Find the following integrals:

1. $\int \arcsin x \, dx$

2. $\int \arctan x \, dx$

3. $\int e^{2x} \sin 3x \, dx$

4. $\int e^{-4x} \cos 2x \, dx$

5. $\int (\log x)^2 \, dx$

6. $\int (\log x)^3 \, dx$

7. $\int x^2 e^x \, dx$

8. $\int x^2 e^{-x} \, dx$

9. $\int x \sin x \, dx$

10. $\int x \cos x \, dx$

11. $\int x^2 \sin x \, dx$

12. $\int x^2 \cos x \, dx$

13. $\int x^3 \cos x^2 \, dx$

14. $\int x^5 \sqrt{1 - x^2} \, dx$

15. $\int x^2 \log x \, dx$

16. $\int x^3 \log x \, dx$

17. $\int x^2 (\log x)^2 \, dx$

18. $\int x^3 e^{-x^2} \, dx$

19. $\displaystyle\int \frac{x^7}{(1 - x^4)^2}\, dx$ 20. $\displaystyle\int_{-\pi}^{\pi} x^2 \cos x\, dx$

21. Let B be a number > 0. Find the area under the curve $y = xe^{-x}$ between 0 and B. Does this area approach a limit as B becomes very large?

22. Does the improper integral $\int_1^\infty x^2 e^{-x}\, dx$ converge?

23. Does the improper integral $\int_1^\infty x^3 e^{-x}\, dx$ converge?

24. Let B be a number > 2. Find the area under the curve

$$y = \frac{1}{x(\log x)^2}$$

between 2 and B. Does this area approach a limit as B becomes very large? If so, what limit?

25. Does the improper integral

$$\int_3^\infty \frac{1}{x(\log x)^4}\, dx$$

converge? If yes, to what?

§3. TRIGONOMETRIC INTEGRALS

We shall investigate integrals involving sine and cosine. It will be useful to have the following formulas:

$$\sin^2 x = \frac{1 - \cos 2x}{2} \qquad \cos^2 x = \frac{1 + \cos 2x}{2}.$$

These are easily proved, using

$$\cos 2x = \cos^2 x - \sin^2 x \qquad \text{and} \qquad \sin^2 x + \cos^2 x = 1.$$

We can then integrate $\sin^2 x$, namely

$$\int \sin^2 x\, dx = \int \frac{1}{2}\, dx - \frac{1}{2}\int \cos 2x\, dx = \frac{x}{2} - \frac{1}{4}\sin 2x.$$

There is a general way in which one can integrate $\sin^n x$ for any positive integer n: integrating by parts. Let us take first an example.

Example 1. Find the integral $\int \sin^3 x\, dx$.

We write the integral in the form

$$\int \sin^2 x \sin x\, dx.$$

Let $u = \sin^2 x$ and $dv = \sin x\, dx$. Then

$$du = 2\sin x \cos x\, dx \qquad \text{and} \qquad v = -\cos x.$$

Thus our integral is equal to

$$-(\sin^2 x)(\cos x) - \int -\cos x(2 \sin x \cos x)\, dx$$
$$= -\sin^2 x \cos x + 2\int \cos^2 x \sin x\, dx.$$

This last integral could then be determined by substitution, for instance $t = \cos x$ and $dt = -\sin x\, dx$. The last integral becomes $-2\int t^2\, dt$, and hence

$$\int \sin^3 x\, dx = -\sin^2 x \cos x - \tfrac{2}{3} \cos^3 x.$$

To deal with an arbitrary positive integer n, we shall show how to reduce the integral $\int \sin^n x\, dx$ to the integral $\int \sin^{n-2} x\, dx$. Proceeding stepwise downwards will give a method for getting the full answer.

Theorem 1. *For any positive integer n, we have*

$$\int \sin^n x\, dx = -\frac{1}{n} \sin^{n-1} x \cos x + \frac{n-1}{n} \int \sin^{n-2} x\, dx.$$

Proof. We write the integral as

$$I_n = \int \sin^n x\, dx = \int \sin^{n-1} x \sin x\, dx.$$

Let $u = \sin^{n-1} x$ and $dv = \sin x\, dx$. Then

$$du = (n-1) \sin^{n-2} x \cos x\, dx \qquad \text{and} \qquad v = -\cos x.$$

Thus

$$I_n = -\sin^{n-1} x \cos x - \int -(n-1)\cos x \sin^{n-2} x \cos x\, dx$$
$$= -\sin^{n-1} x \cos x + (n-1)\int \sin^{n-2} x \cos^2 x\, dx.$$

We replace $\cos^2 x$ by $1 - \sin^2 x$ and get finally

$$I_n = -\sin^{n-1} x \cos x + (n-1)I_{n-2} - (n-1)I_n,$$

whence

$$nI_n = -\sin^{n-1} x \cos x + (n-1)I_{n-2}.$$

Dividing by n gives us our formula.

We leave the proof of the analogous formula for cosine as an exercise.

$$\int \cos^n x\, dx = \frac{1}{n} \cos^{n-1} x \sin x + \frac{n-1}{n} \int \cos^{n-2} x\, dx.$$

Integrals involving tangents can be done by a similar technique, because

$$\frac{d \tan x}{dx} = 1 + \tan^2 x.$$

These functions are less used than sine and cosine, and hence we don't write out the formulas, to lighten this printed page which would otherwise become oppressive.

It is also useful to remember the following trick:

$$\int \frac{1}{\cos x} \, dx = \int \sec x \, dx = \log (\sec x + \tan x).$$

This is done by substitution. We have

$$\frac{1}{\cos x} = \sec x = \frac{(\sec x)(\sec x + \tan x)}{\sec x + \tan x}.$$

Let $u = \sec x + \tan x$. Then the integral is in the form

$$\int \frac{1}{u} \, du.$$

(This is a good opportunity to emphasize that the formula we just obtained is valid on any interval such that $\cos x \neq 0$ and $\sec x + \tan x > 0$. Otherwise the symbols are meaningless. Determine such an interval as an exercise.)

One can integrate mixed powers of sine and cosine by replacing $\sin^2 x$ by $1 - \cos^2 x$, for instance.

Example 2. Find $\int \sin^2 x \cos^2 x \, dx$.

Replacing $\sin^2 x$ by $1 - \cos^2 x$, we see that our integral is equal to

$$\int \cos^2 x \, dx - \int \cos^4 x \, dx$$

and we know how to find each one of these integrals.

When we meet an integral involving a square root, we can frequently get rid of the square root by making a trigonometric substitution.

Example 3. Find the area of a circle of radius 3.

The equation of the circle is

$$x^2 + y^2 = 9,$$

and the portion of the circle in the first quadrant is described by the function

$$y = \sqrt{3^2 - x^2}.$$

One-fourth of the area is therefore given by the integral

$$\int_0^3 \sqrt{3^2 - x^2}\, dx.$$

Let $x = 3 \sin t$. Then $dx = 3 \cos t\, dt$ and our integral becomes

$$\int_0^{\pi/2} \sqrt{3^2 - 3^2 \sin^2 t}\; 3 \cos t\, dt = \int_0^{\pi/2} 9 \cos^2 t\, dt = \frac{9\pi}{4}.$$

(We see that $1 - \sin^2 t = \cos^2 t$ and $\sqrt{1 - \sin^2 t} = \cos t$ in the interval between 0 and $\pi/2$.) The total area of the circle is therefore 9π.

EXERCISES

Find the following integrals.

1. $\displaystyle\int \sin^4 x\, dx$ 2. $\displaystyle\int \cos^3 x\, dx$ 3. $\displaystyle\int \sin^2 x \cos^3 x\, dx$

Find the area of the region enclosed by the following curves:

4. $x^2 + \dfrac{y^2}{9} = 1$.   5. $\dfrac{x^2}{4} + \dfrac{y^2}{16} = 1$.   6. $\dfrac{x^2}{a^2} + \dfrac{y^2}{b^2} = 1$.

7. Find the area of a circle of radius $r > 0$.

8. For any two integers m, n prove the formulas:

$$\sin mx \sin nx = \tfrac{1}{2}[\cos (m - n)x - \cos (m + n)x]$$
$$\sin mx \cos nx = \tfrac{1}{2}[\sin (m + n)x + \sin (m - n)x]$$
$$\cos mx \cos nx = \tfrac{1}{2}[\cos (m + n)x + \cos (m - n)x].$$

9. Show that

$$\int_{-\pi}^{\pi} \sin 3x \cos 2x\, dx = 0.$$

10. Show that

$$\int_{-\pi}^{\pi} \cos 5x \cos 2x\, dx = 0.$$

11. Show in general that for any integers m, n we have

$$\int_{-\pi}^{\pi} \sin mx \cos nx\, dx = 0.$$

12. Show in general that

$$\int_{-\pi}^{\pi} \sin mx \sin nx\, dx = \begin{cases} 0 & \text{if } m \neq n, \\ \pi & \text{if } m = n. \end{cases}$$

13. Find $\int \tan x\, dx$.

Find the following integrals:

14. $\int \dfrac{1}{\sqrt{9 - x^2}}\, dx$

15. $\int \dfrac{1}{\sqrt{3 - x^2}}\, dx$

16. $\int \dfrac{1}{\sqrt{2 - 4x^2}}\, dx$

17. $\int \dfrac{1}{\sqrt{a^2 - b^2 x^2}}\, dx$

18. Let f be a continuous function on the interval $[-\pi, \pi]$. Define its *Fourier coefficients:*

$$c_0 = \frac{1}{2\pi} \int_{-\pi}^{\pi} f(x)\, dx,$$

$$a_n = \frac{1}{\pi} \int_{-\pi}^{\pi} f(x) \cos nx\, dx, \qquad b_n = \frac{1}{\pi} \int_{-\pi}^{\pi} f(x) \sin nx\, dx.$$

for n equal to an integer ≥ 1. Compute the Fourier coefficients of the following functions. (If you do 19 first, you might have less work.)

(a) $f(x) = x$ (b) $f(x) = x^2$ (c) $f(x) = |x|$
(d) $f(x) = \cos x$ (e) $f(x) = \sin x$ (f) $f(x) = \sin^2 x$
(g) $f(x) = \cos^2 x$ (h) $f(x) = |\sin x|$ (i) $f(x) = |\cos x|$
(j) $f(x) = 1$

19. (a) Let f be an even function [that is $f(x) = f(-x)$]. Show that its Fourier coefficients b_n are all equal to 0.
   (b) Let f be an odd function [that is $f(x) = -f(-x)$]. What can you say about its Fourier coefficients?

20. Let f be a continuous function, and assume that $f(x + 2\pi) = f(x)$ for all x. Show that for any numbers a, b, c we have

$$\int_{a+2\pi}^{b+2\pi} f(x)\, dx = \int_{a}^{b} f(x)\, dx \qquad \text{and} \qquad \int_{-\pi+c}^{\pi+c} f = \int_{-\pi}^{\pi} f.$$

[*Hint:* For the second integral, take the integral successively from the points $-\pi + c, -\pi, \pi, \pi + c$.]

§4. PARTIAL FRACTIONS

Let $f(x)$ and $g(x)$ be two polynomials. We want to investigate the integral

$$\int \frac{f(x)}{g(x)}\, dx.$$

Using long division, one can reduce the problem to the case when the degree of f is less than the degree of g. The following example illustrates this reduction.

Example 1. Consider the two polynomials $f(x) = x^3 - x + 1$ and $g(x) = x^2 + 1$. Dividing f by g (you should know how from high school) we obtain a quotient of x with remainder $-2x + 1$. Thus

$$x^3 - x + 1 = (x^2 + 1)x + (-2x + 1).$$

Hence

$$\frac{f(x)}{g(x)} = x + \frac{-2x + 1}{x^2 + 1}.$$

To find the integral of $f(x)/g(x)$ we integrate x, and the quotient on the right, which has the property that the degree of the numerator is less than the degree of the denominator.

From now on, *we assume throughout that when we consider a quotient $f(x)/g(x)$, the degree of f is less than the degree of g.* Factoring out a constant if necessary, we also assume that $g(x)$ can be written

$$g(x) = x^d + \text{lower terms}.$$

We shall begin by discussing special cases, and then describe afterwards how the general case can be reduced to these.

Case 1. If a is a number, find

$$\int \frac{1}{(x - a)^n} \, dx$$

if n is an integer ≥ 1.

This is an old story. We know how to do it. In fact, we have

$$\int \frac{1}{(x - a)^n} \, dx = \frac{1}{-n + 1} \frac{1}{(x - a)^{n-1}} \qquad \text{if} \quad n \neq 1$$

$$\int \frac{1}{(x - a)} \, dx = \log (x - a).$$

Case 2. If b is a number, find

$$\int \frac{1}{(x^2 + b^2)^n} \, dx.$$

This is new. Using the substitution $x = bz$, $dx = b \, dz$ reduces the integral to

$$\int \frac{1}{(x^2 + 1)^n} \, dx.$$

We shall now discuss how to find this integral. We use integration by parts when $n > 1$. (If $n = 1$, we get the arctangent.) Let the above integral be I_n. We shall start with I_{n-1} because our integration by parts will raise n instead of lowering n. We have

$$I_{n-1} = \int \frac{1}{(x^2 + 1)^{n-1}} \, dx.$$

Let $u = \dfrac{1}{(x^2 + 1)^{n-1}}$ and $dv = dx$. Then

$$du = -(n - 1)\frac{2x}{(x^2 + 1)^n}\,dx \quad \text{and} \quad v = x.$$

Thus

$$I_{n-1} = \frac{x}{(x^2 + 1)^{n-1}} + 2(n - 1)\int \frac{x^2}{(x^2 + 1)^n}\,dx.$$

We write $x^2 = x^2 + 1 - 1$. We obtain

$$I_{n-1} = \frac{x}{(x^2 + 1)^{n-1}} + 2(n - 1)\int \frac{1}{(x^2 + 1)^{n-1}}\,dx$$
$$- 2(n - 1)\int \frac{1}{(x^2 + 1)^n}\,dx$$

or in other words:

$$I_{n-1} = \frac{x}{(x^2 + 1)^{n-1}} + 2(n - 1)I_{n-1} - 2(n - 1)I_n.$$

Therefore

$$2(n - 1)I_n = \frac{x}{(x^2 + 1)^{n-1}} + (2n - 3)I_{n-1},$$

whence

$$\int \frac{1}{(x^2 + 1)^n}\,dx = \frac{1}{2(n - 1)}\frac{x}{(x^2 + 1)^{n-1}}$$
$$+ \frac{(2n - 3)}{2(n - 1)}\int \frac{1}{(x^2 + 1)^{n-1}}\,dx.$$

This gives us a recursion formula which lowers the exponent n in the denominator until we reach $n = 1$. In that case, we know that

$$\int \frac{1}{x^2 + 1}\,dx = \arctan x.$$

Case 3. Find the integral

$$\int \frac{x}{(x^2 + b^2)^n}\,dx.$$

This is an old story. We make the substitution

$$u = x^2 + b^2 \quad \text{and} \quad du = 2x\,dx.$$

The integral is then equal to

$$\frac{1}{2}\int \frac{1}{u^n}\,du,$$

which we know how to evaluate, and thus we find

$$\int \frac{x}{(x^2 + b^2)^n}\, dx = \begin{cases} \frac{1}{2} \log (x^2 + b^2) & \text{if } n = 1 \\[2mm] \dfrac{1}{2(-n + 1)} \dfrac{1}{(x^2 + b^2)^{n-1}} & \text{if } n \neq 1. \end{cases}$$

We shall now investigate a general quotient $f(x)/g(x)$.

If one is given a polynomial of type $x^2 + bx + c$, then one completes the square. The polynomial can thus be written in the form

$$(x - \alpha)(x - \beta) \qquad \text{or} \qquad (x - \alpha)^2 + \beta^2$$

with suitable numbers α, β. For instance,

$$x^2 - x - 6 = (x + 2)(x - 3)$$
$$x^2 - 2x + 5 = (x - 1)^2 + 2^2.$$

It can be shown that a polynomial $g(x)$ can always be written as a product of terms of type

$$(x - \alpha)^n \qquad \text{and} \qquad [(x - \beta)^2 + \gamma^2]^m,$$

n, m being integers ≥ 0. It can also be shown that a quotient $f(x)/g(x)$ can be written as a sum of terms of the following type:

$$\frac{c_1}{x - \alpha} + \frac{c_2}{(x - \alpha)^2} + \cdots + \frac{c_n}{(x - \alpha)^n}$$

$$+ \frac{d_1 + e_1 x}{(x - \beta)^2 + \gamma^2} + \cdots + \frac{d_m + e_m x}{[(x - \beta)^2 + \gamma^2]^m}$$

with suitable constants $c_1, c_2, \ldots, d_1, d_2, \ldots, e_1, e_2, \ldots$. The way one can determine these constants is to put the right-hand side over the common denominator $g(x)$, equate the numerator $f(x)$ with what is obtained on the right, and solve for the constants. We shall illustrate this by examples, and will not give the proofs of the preceding assertions, which are quite difficult.

Once the quotient $f(x)/g(x)$ is written as above, then Cases 1, 2, and 3 allow us to integrate each term. We then find that the integral involves functions of the following type:

A rational function

Log terms

Arctangent terms.

Example 2. Express the quotient

$$\frac{1}{(x - 2)(x - 3)}$$

as a sum of the previous type, and determine the integral.

This will be

$$\frac{c_1}{x-2} + \frac{c_2}{x-3}.$$

Putting this over the common denominator, we get the numerator

$$c_1(x-3) + c_2(x-2) = (c_1 + c_2)x - 3c_1 - 2c_2,$$

which must be equal to 1. Thus we must have

$$c_1 + c_2 = 0$$
$$-3c_1 - 2c_2 = 1.$$

Solving for c_1 and c_2 gives $c_2 = 1$ and $c_1 = -1$. Hence

$$\int \frac{1}{(x-2)(x-3)} \, dx = \int \frac{-1}{(x-2)} \, dx + \int \frac{1}{(x-3)} \, dx$$
$$= -\log(x-2) + \log(x-3).$$

Example 3. Express the quotient

$$\frac{x+1}{(x-1)^2(x-2)}$$

as a sum of the previous type, and find the integral.

We want to find numbers c_1, c_2, c_3 such that

$$\frac{x+1}{(x-1)^2(x-2)} = \frac{c_1}{x-1} + \frac{c_2}{(x-1)^2} + \frac{c_3}{x-2}.$$

Putting the right-hand side over the common denominator

$$(x-1)^2(x-2),$$

we get a numerator equal to

$$c_1(x-1)(x-2) + c_2(x-2) + c_3(x-1)^2.$$

This can be rewritten as

$$(c_1 + c_3)x^2 + (-3c_1 + c_2 - 2c_3)x + 2c_1 - 2c_2 + c_3,$$

and must be equal to $x + 1$. We equate the coefficients of x^2, x, and the constant terms. We get

$$c_1 \qquad\quad + c_3 = 0$$
$$-3c_1 + c_2 - 2c_3 = 1$$
$$2c_1 - 2c_2 + c_3 = 1.$$

This is a system of three linear equations in three unknowns, which you can solve to determine c_1, c_2, and c_3. One finds $c_1 = -3$, $c_2 = -2$, $c_3 = 3$. Hence

$$\int \frac{x+1}{(x-1)^2(x-2)}\,dx = \int \frac{-3}{x-1}\,dx + \int \frac{-2}{(x-1)^2}\,dx + \int \frac{3}{(x-2)}\,dx$$

$$= -3\log(x-1) + \frac{2}{x-1} + 3\log(x-2).$$

Example 4. Express the quotient

$$\frac{2x+5}{(x^2+1)^2(x-3)}$$

as a sum of the type described above, and find the integral.
  We can find numbers c_1, c_2, ... such that the quotient is equal to

$$\frac{c_1 + c_2 x}{x^2+1} + \frac{c_3 + c_4 x}{(x^2+1)^2} + \frac{c_5}{x-3}.$$

We put this over the common denominator $(x^2+1)^2(x-3)$. The numerator is equal to

$$(c_1 + c_2 x)(x^2+1)(x-3) + (c_3 + c_4 x)(x-3) + c_5(x^2+1)^2$$

and must be equal to $2x+5$. If we equate the coefficients of x^4, x^3, x^2, x and the respective constants, we get a system of five linear equations in five unknowns, which can be solved. It is tedious to do it here and we leave it as an exercise. For the integral, we then obtain:

$$\int \frac{2x+5}{(x^2+1)^2(x-3)}\,dx = c_1 \arctan x + \tfrac{1}{2}c_2 \log(x^2+1)$$

$$+ c_3 \int \frac{1}{(x^2+1)^2}\,dx + \tfrac{1}{2}c_4 \log(x^2+1) + c_5 \log(x-3).$$

The integral which we left standing is just that of Case 2. Find it explicitly as an exercise.

EXERCISES

1. Find the constants in Example 4.
2. Write out in full the integral

$$\int \frac{1}{(x^2+1)^2}\,dx.$$

Find the following integrals:

3. (a) $\displaystyle\int \frac{1}{(x-3)(x+2)}\,dx$ (b) $\displaystyle\int \frac{1}{(x+2)(x+1)}\,dx$

4. $\displaystyle\int \frac{x}{(x+1)(x+2)(x+3)}\,dx$

5. $\displaystyle\int \frac{x+2}{x^2+x}\,dx$

6. $\displaystyle\int \frac{x}{(x+1)^2}\,dx$

7. $\displaystyle\int \frac{x+1}{(x^2+9)^2}\,dx$

8. $\displaystyle\int \frac{4}{(x^2+16)^2}\,dx$

9. $\displaystyle\int \frac{x}{(x+1)(x+2)^2}\,dx$

10. $\displaystyle\int \frac{1}{(x^2+1)^3}\,dx$

11. $\displaystyle\int \frac{2x-3}{(x-1)(x+7)}\,dx$

12. $\displaystyle\int \frac{1}{x(x^2+x+1)}\,dx$

13. $\displaystyle\int \frac{1}{(x+1)(x^2+1)}\,dx$

14. $\displaystyle\int \frac{1}{(x^2+1)^2}\,dx$

15. $\displaystyle\int \frac{2x-3}{(x-1)(x-2)}\,dx$

16. $\displaystyle\int \frac{x}{x^4-1}\,dx$

17. $\displaystyle\int \frac{1}{x^4-1}\,dx$

18. $\displaystyle\int \frac{x^2-2x-2}{x^3-1}\,dx$

19. $\displaystyle\int \frac{x}{(x^2-3)^2}\,dx$

20. Let $a_1, \ldots, a_n$ be distinct numbers. Let

$$\frac{1}{(x-a_1)\cdots(x-a_n)} = \frac{c_1}{x-a_1} + \cdots + \frac{c_n}{x-a_n}.$$

Let $f(x) = (x-a_1)\cdots(x-a_n)$. Show that $c_1 = 1/f'(a_1)$.

21. If f is a function, define $L(f) = f'/f$. If f, g are functions, show that

$$L(fg) = L(f) + L(g), \quad \text{and} \quad L(cf) = L(f)$$

if c is a number. Compute $L(f)$ for the following functions:

(a) $(x-1)(x-2)$ (b) $(x-1)(x-2)(x-3)$
(c) $(x^2+5)(x^3-1)$ (d) $(x^2-1)/(x^2+1)$

Show that $L(1/f) = -L(f)$.

Supplementary Exercises

SUBSTITUTION

Find the following integrals.

1. $\displaystyle\int \frac{x^3}{x^4+2}\,dx$

2. $\displaystyle\int \sqrt{3x+1}\,dx$

3. $\displaystyle\int \sin^4 x \cos x\,dx$

4. $\displaystyle\int \frac{e^x-e^{-x}}{e^x+e^{-x}}\,dx$

5. $\displaystyle\int \frac{x}{\sqrt{x^2 - 1}}\, dx$

6. $\displaystyle\int x^3\sqrt{x^4 + 1}\, dx$

7. $\displaystyle\int \frac{x}{(3x^2 + 5)^2}\, dx$

8. $\displaystyle\int (x^2 + 3)^4 x^3\, dx$

$\times$ 9. $\displaystyle\int \frac{\cos x}{\sin^3 x}\, dx$

10. $\displaystyle\int e^x\sqrt{e^x + 1}\, dx$

11. $\displaystyle\int (x^3 + 1)^{7/5} x^5\, dx$

12. $\displaystyle\int \frac{x}{(x^2 - 4)^{3/2}}\, dx$

13. $\displaystyle\int \sin 3x\, dx$

14. $\displaystyle\int \cos 4x\, dx$

15. $\displaystyle\int e^x \sin e^x\, dx$

16. $\displaystyle\int x^2\sqrt{x^3 + 1}\, dx$

17. $\displaystyle\int \frac{1}{x \log x}\, dx$

18. $\displaystyle\int \frac{\sin x}{1 + \cos^2 x}\, dx$

19. $\displaystyle\int \frac{e^x}{e^x + 1}\, dx$

20. $\displaystyle\int \frac{(\log x)^4}{x}\, dx$

21. $\displaystyle\int_0^{\pi/2} \sin^3 x \cos x\, dx$

22. $\displaystyle\int_{-3}^{-1} \frac{1}{(x - 1)^2}\, dx$

23. $\displaystyle\int_0^1 \sqrt{2 - x}\, dx$

24. $\displaystyle\int_0^\pi \sin^2 x \cos x\, dx$

$\times$ 25. $\displaystyle\int_0^{\pi/2} \frac{\cos x}{1 + \sin^2 x}\, dx$

26. $\displaystyle\int_0^{2\pi} \frac{\sin x}{1 + \cos^2 x}\, dx$

$\times$ 27. $\displaystyle\int_0^{1/2} \frac{\arcsin x}{\sqrt{1 - x^2}}\, dx$

28. $\displaystyle\int_0^1 \frac{\arctan x}{1 + x^2}\, dx$

29. $\displaystyle\int_0^1 \frac{1 + e^{2x}}{e^x}\, dx$

30. $\displaystyle\int_0^{\pi/2} x \sin x^2\, dx$

31. $\displaystyle\int xe^{-\sqrt{x}}\, dx$

32. $\displaystyle\int \sqrt{x}\, e^{-\sqrt{x}}\, dx$

BY PARTS

Find the following integrals.

1. $\displaystyle\int x \arctan x\, dx$

2. $\displaystyle\int x \arcsin x\, dx$

3. $\displaystyle\int x \arccos x\, dx$

4. $\displaystyle\int x^3 e^{2x}\, dx$

5. $\int_{-1}^{0} \arcsin x \, dx$ 6. $\int_{1}^{2} x^3 \log x \, dx$

7. $\int_{0}^{1/2} x \arcsin 2x \, dx$ 8. $\int_{1}^{2} \sqrt{x} \log x \, dx$

9. $\int_{-1}^{1} x e^x \, dx$ 10. $\int_{0}^{1} x^3 \sqrt{1 - x^2} \, dx$

TRIGONOMETRIC INTEGRALS

Find the following integrals.

1. $\int \dfrac{\cos^3 x}{\sin x} \, dx$ 2. $\int \tan^2 x \, dx$

3. $\int e^x \sin e^x \, dx$ 4. $\int \dfrac{1}{1 - \cos x} \, dx$

5. $\int_{0}^{\pi/2} \cos^2 x \, dx$ 6. $\int_{0}^{\pi/3} \sin^6 x \, dx$

7. $\int_{-\pi}^{\pi} \sin^2 x \cos^2 x \, dx$ 8. $\int_{0}^{2\pi} \sin^3 2x \, dx$

9. $\int_{0}^{\pi/2} \sin^2 2x \cos^2 2x \, dx$ 10. $\int_{0}^{\pi/4} \cos^4 x \, dx$

11. $\int \dfrac{1}{x\sqrt{x^2 + 9}} \, dx$ 12. $\int \dfrac{1}{(x^2 + 1)^2} \, dx$

13. $\int_{0}^{1} \dfrac{1}{\sqrt{1 - x^2}} \, dx$ 14. $\int \dfrac{x^2}{\sqrt{x^2 + 4}} \, dx$

15. $\int \dfrac{x^3}{\sqrt{16 - x^2}}$ 16. $\int \dfrac{x^3}{\sqrt{1 + x^2}}$

17. $\int \dfrac{1}{x\sqrt{a^2 - x^2}} \, dx$ 18. $\int \dfrac{x^2}{\sqrt{a^2 - x^2}} \, dx$

19. $\int \dfrac{1}{x\sqrt{a^2 - x^2}} \, dx$ 20. $\int \dfrac{1}{x^2\sqrt{a^2 - x^2}} \, dx$

21. $\int \dfrac{1}{(1 + x^2)^{3/2}} \, dx$ 22. $\int \dfrac{\sqrt{a^2 - x^2}}{x^2} \, dx$

23. $\int \dfrac{x^2}{(a^2 - x^2)^{3/2}} \, dx$ 24. $\int \dfrac{\sqrt{a^2 + x^2}}{x} \, dx$

25. $\int_{0}^{4} \dfrac{1}{(16 + x^2)^2} \, dx$ 26. $\int_{0}^{a} x^4 \sqrt{a^2 - x^2} \, dx \quad (a > 0)$

MISCELLANEOUS

1. Show that for positive integers m, n we have

$$\int x^m (\log x)^n \, dx = \frac{x^{m+1}(\log x)^n}{m+1} - \frac{n}{m+1} \int x^m (\log x)^{n-1} \, dx.$$

6. Show by induction that

$$\int x^n e^x \, dx = x^n e^x - n \int x^{n-1} e^x \, dx.$$

3. Show that the improper integral

$$\int_0^1 \log x \, dx$$

exists and find its value.

4. By induction, find the value

$$\int_0^\infty x^n e^{-x} \, dx.$$

5. Evaluate

$$\int_0^\infty x^3 e^{-x^2} \, dx.$$

6. Show by induction that

$$\int_0^1 (1 - x^2)^n \, dx = \frac{2^{2n}(n!)^2}{(2n+1)!}.$$

7. Show that

$$\int_0^1 (1 - x^2)^n \, dx \geq \frac{1}{n+1}.$$

[*Hint:* Note that $1 - x^2 = (1 + x)(1 - x) \geq 1 - x$ if $0 \leq x \leq 1$.]

8. Let f be continuous on $[0, 1]$. Let

$$f_1(x) = \int_0^x f(t) \, dt$$

$$f_2(x) = \int_0^x f_1(t) \, dt$$

and in general,

$$f_n(x) = \int_0^x f_{n-1}(t) \, dt.$$

Show that

$$f_n(x) = \frac{1}{(n-1)!} \int_0^x f(t)(x - t)^{n-1} \, dt.$$

[*Note:* There are two possible choices for $u \, dv$, and one of them won't get you anywhere.]

9. A function f defined for all numbers is said to be *periodic* of period s if $f(x + s) = f(x)$ for all x. Assume that f is continuous and periodic. Show that

$$\int_a^b f = \int_{a+s}^{b+s} f \quad \text{and} \quad \int_a^{a+s} f = \int_0^s f.$$

10. Assume that $f(-x) = -f(x)$. Show that

$$\int_{-a}^a f(x)\, dx = 0.$$

11. Find the value of the integrals (a) $\int_0^{7\pi} |\sin x|\, dx$ (b) $\int_0^{7\pi} |\cos x|\, dx$. (c) For any positive integer n, $\int_0^{n\pi} |\sin x|\, dx$.

Chapter XII

Some Substantial Exercises

We shall not use the contents of this section until the chapter on series, and even then we use only the estimate of $(n!)^{1/n}$. Thus this chapter may be skipped entirely. We include it mostly for reference, and to provide some good exercises for those interested.

§1. AN ESTIMATE FOR $(n!)^{1/n}$

Let n be a positive integer. We define $n!$ (which we read n factorial) to be the product of the first n integers: Thus $1 \cdot 2 \cdot 3 \cdots n$. This is certainly less than n^n (the product of n with itself n times). We shall investigate to what extent it differs from n^n. (Not too much.)

In fact, what we shall prove first is that

$$n! = n^n e^{-n} d_n,$$

where d_n is a number such that $d_n^{1/n}$ approaches 1 as n becomes large. This is a weaker statement than the result stated in the next theorem, whose proof is very simple and very easy to remember. It is a nice application of the lower and upper sum techniques.

Theorem 1. *Let n be a positive integer. Then*

$$(n - 1)! \leqq n^n e^{-n} e \leqq n!$$

Proof. Exercise. Evaluate and compare the integral

$$\int_1^n \log x \, dx$$

with the upper and lower sum associated with the partition $(1, 2, \ldots, n)$ of the interval $[1, n]$. Then exponentiate.

Corollary. *As n becomes very large,*

$$\frac{(n!)^{1/n}}{n} = \left[\frac{n!}{n^n}\right]^{1/n}$$

approaches $1/e$.

Proof. Take the n-th root of the right inequality in our theorem. We get

$$ne^{-1}e^{1/n} \leqq (n!)^{1/n}.$$

Dividing by n yields

$$\frac{1}{e} e^{1/n} \leq \frac{(n!)^{1/n}}{n}.$$

On the other hand, multiply both sides of the inequality

$$(n - 1)! \leq n^n e^{-n} e$$

by n. We get $n! \leq n^n e^{-n} e n$. Take an n-th root:

$$(n!)^{1/n} \leq n e^{-1} e^{1/n} n^{1/n}.$$

Dividing by n yields

$$\frac{(n!)^{1/n}}{n} \leq \frac{1}{e} e^{1/n} n^{1/n}.$$

But we know that both $n^{1/n}$ and $e^{1/n}$ approach 1 as n becomes large. Thus our quotient is squeezed between two numbers approaching $1/e$, and must therefore approach $1/e$.

EXERCISES

1. Use the abbreviation $\lim_{n \to \infty}$ to mean: limit as n becomes very large. Prove that

(a) $\lim_{n \to \infty} \left[\frac{(3n)!}{n^{3n}} \right]^{1/n} = \frac{27}{e^3}$
  (b) $\lim_{n \to \infty} \left[\frac{(3n)!}{n! n^{2n}} \right]^{1/n} = \frac{27}{e^2}$

2. Find the limit:

(a) $\lim_{n \to \infty} \left[\frac{(2n)!}{n^{2n}} \right]^{1/n}$
  (b) $\lim_{n \to \infty} \left[\frac{(2n)!(5n)!}{n^{4n}(3n)!} \right]^{1/n}$

§2. STIRLING'S FORMULA

Using various refinements of the above method, one can prove the following theorem.

Theorem 2. *Let n be a positive integer. Then there is a number θ between 0 and 1 such that*

$$n! = \sqrt{2\pi n}\, n^n e^{-n} e^{\theta/12n}.$$

We shall present another proof giving the main steps, and leave the details to you as exercises.

1. Let $\varphi(x) = \frac{1}{2} \log \frac{1 + x}{1 - x} - x$. Show that

$$\varphi'(x) = \frac{x^2}{1 - x^2}.$$

2. Let $\psi(x) = \varphi(x) - \dfrac{x^3}{3(1 - x^2)}$ · Show that

$$\psi'(x) = \frac{-2x^4}{3(1 - x^2)^2}.$$

3. For $0 < x < 1$, conclude that $\varphi(x) > 0$ and $\psi(x) < 0$.

4. Deduce that for $0 \leqq x < 1$ we have

$$0 \leqq \tfrac{1}{2} \log \frac{1 + x}{1 - x} - x \leqq \frac{x^3}{3(1 - x^2)}.$$

5. Let $x = \dfrac{1}{2n + 1}$ · Then $\dfrac{1 + x}{1 - x} = \dfrac{n + 1}{n}$ and

$$\frac{x^3}{3(1 - x^2)} = \frac{1}{12(2n + 1)(n^2 + n)}.$$

6. Conclude that

$$0 \leqq \tfrac{1}{2} \log \frac{n + 1}{n} - \frac{1}{2n + 1} \leqq \frac{1}{12(2n + 1)(n^2 + n)}$$

$$0 \leqq (n + \tfrac{1}{2}) \log \frac{n + 1}{n} - 1 \leqq \frac{1}{12} \left(\frac{1}{n} - \frac{1}{n + 1} \right).$$

7. Let

$$a_n = \frac{n^{n+\frac{1}{2}} e^{-n}}{n!} \quad \text{and} \quad b_n = a_n e^{1/12n}.$$

Then $a_n \leqq b_n$. Show that

$$\frac{a_{n+1}}{a_n} \geqq 1 \quad \text{and} \quad \frac{b_{n+1}}{b_n} \leqq 1.$$

Thus the a_n are increasing and the b_n are decreasing. Hence there exists a unique number c such that

$$a_n \leqq c \leqq b_n$$

for all n.

8. Conclude that

$$n! = c^{-1} n^{n+\frac{1}{2}} e^{-n} e^{\theta/12n}$$

for some number θ between 0 and 1.

To get the value of the constant c, one has to use another argument, which will be described in the next section.

§3. WALLIS' PRODUCT

Our first aim is to obtain the following limit, known as the Wallis product.

Theorem 3. *We have*

$$\frac{\pi}{2} = \lim_{n \to \infty} \frac{2}{1} \frac{2}{3} \frac{4}{3} \frac{4}{5} \frac{6}{5} \frac{6}{7} \cdots \frac{2n}{2n-1} \frac{2n}{2n+1}.$$

Proof. The proof will again be presented as an exercise.

1. Using the recurrence formulas for the integrals of powers of the sine, prove that

$$\int_0^{\pi/2} \sin^{2n} x \, dx = \frac{2n-1}{2n} \frac{2n-3}{2n-2} \cdots \frac{1}{2} \frac{\pi}{2}$$

$$\int_0^{\pi/2} \sin^{2n+1} x \, dx = \frac{2n}{2n+1} \frac{2n-2}{2n-1} \cdots \frac{2}{3}.$$

2. Using the fact that powers of the sine are decreasing as $n = 1, 2, 3, \ldots$ and the second integral formula above, conclude that

$$1 \le \frac{\int_0^{\pi/2} \sin^{2n} x \, dx}{\int_0^{\pi/2} \sin^{2n+1} x \, dx} \le 1 + \frac{1}{2n}.$$

3. Taking the ratio of the integrals of $\sin^{2n} x$ and $\sin^{2n+1} x$ between 0 and $\pi/2$, deduce Wallis' product.

Corollary. *We have*

$$\lim_{n \to \infty} \frac{(n!)^2 2^{2n}}{(2n)! n^{1/2}} = \pi^{1/2}.$$

Proof. Rewrite the Wallis product into the form

$$\frac{\pi}{2} = \lim_{n \to \infty} \frac{2^2 4^2 \cdots (2n-2)^2}{3^2 5^2 \cdots (2n-1)^2} 2n.$$

Take the square root and find the limit stated in the corollary.

Finally, show that the constant c in Stirling's formula is $1/\sqrt{2\pi}$, by arguing as follows. (Justify all the steps.)

$$c = \lim_{n \to \infty} \frac{(2n)^{2n+\frac{1}{2}} e^{-2n}}{(2n)!}$$

$$= \lim_{n \to \infty} \frac{(n!)^2 2^{2n} \sqrt{2}}{(2n)! n^{1/2}} \left[\frac{n^{n+\frac{1}{2}} e^{-n}}{n!} \right]^2$$

$$= \sqrt{2\pi} \cdot c^2.$$

Thus $c = 1/\sqrt{2\pi}$.

Chapter XIII

Applications of Integration

Most of the applications are to physical concepts. The reader should read the appendix on physics and mathematics, to understand the point of view that what we try to find is a mathematical model for a given empirical notion. We shall do this in a number of cases for which the integral can be taken as a model. We shall use both the relation of the integral to Riemann sums, and its axiomatic characterization in Theorem 2 of Chapter IX, §4 to justify the interpretation of the integral in various physical contexts.

§1. LENGTH OF CURVES

Let $y = f(x)$ be a differentiable function over some interval $[a, b]$ (with $a < b$) and assume that its derivative f' is continuous. We wish to find a way to determine the length of the curve described by the graph. The main idea is to approximate the curve by small line segments and add these up.

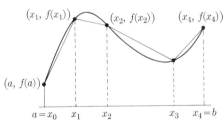

Consequently, we consider a partition of our interval:

$$a = x_0 \leqq x_1 \leqq \cdots \leqq x_n = b.$$

For each x_i we have the point $(x_i, f(x_i))$ on the curve $y = f(x)$. We draw the line segments between two successive points. The length of such a segment is the length of the line between

$$(x_i, f(x_i)) \quad \text{and} \quad (x_{i+1}, f(x_{i+1})),$$

and is equal to

$$\sqrt{(x_{i+1} - x_i)^2 + (f(x_{i+1}) - f(x_i))^2} \, .$$

223

length of line segment between pts $(x_i, f(x_i))$
and $(x_{i+1}, f(x_{i+1}))$

By the mean value theorem, we conclude that

$$f(x_{i+1}) - f(x_i) = (x_{i+1} - x_i)f'(c_i)$$

for some number c_i between x_i and x_{i+1}. Using this, we see that the length of our line segment is

$$\sqrt{(x_{i+1} - x_i)^2 + (x_{i+1} - x_i)^2 f'(c_i)^2}.$$

We can factor out $(x_{i+1} - x_i)^2$ and we see that the sum of the length of these line segments is

$$\sum_{i=0}^{n-1} \sqrt{1 + f'(c_i)^2}\, (x_{i+1} - x_i).$$

Let $G(x) = \sqrt{1 + f'(x)^2}$. Then $G(x)$ is continuous, and we see that the sum we have just written down is

$$\sum_{i=0}^{n-1} G(c_i)(x_{i+1} - x_i).$$

This is precisely a Riemann sum used to find the integral. It is therefore very reasonable to *define* the length of our curve between a and b to be

$$\int_a^b \sqrt{1 + f'(t)^2}\, dt.$$

Parametric Form

We shall now see what happens when the curve is given in parametric form.

Suppose that our curve is given by

$$x = f(t), \qquad y = g(t),$$

with $a \leqq t \leqq b$, and assume that both f, g have continuous derivatives.

As before, we cut our interval into a partition, say

$$a = t_0 \leqq t_1 \leqq \cdots \leqq t_n = b.$$

We then obtain points $(f(t_i), g(t_i))$ on the curve, and the distance between two successive points is

$$\sqrt{(f(t_{i+1}) - f(t_i))^2 + (g(t_{i+1}) - g(t_i))^2}.$$

We use the mean value theorem for f and g. There are numbers c_i and d_i between t_i and t_{i+1} such that

$$f(t_{i+1}) - f(t_i) = f'(c_i)(t_{i+1} - t_i)$$
$$g(t_{i+1}) - g(t_i) = g'(d_i)(t_{i+1} - t_i).$$

Substituting these values and factoring out $(t_{i+1} - t_i)$, we see that the sum of the lengths of our line segments is equal to

$$\sum_{i=0}^{n-1} \sqrt{f'(c_i)^2 + g'(d_i)^2} \, (t_{i+1} - t_i).$$

Let

$$G(t) = \sqrt{f'(t)^2 + g'(t)^2}.$$

Then our sum is almost equal to

$$\sum_{i=0}^{n-1} G(c_i)(t_{i+1} - t_i),$$

which would be a Riemann sum for G. It is not, because it is not necessarily true that $c_i = d_i$. Nevertheless, what we have done makes it very reasonable to *define* the length of our curve (in parametric form) to be

$$\boxed{\int_a^b \sqrt{f'(t)^2 + g'(t)^2} \, dt.}$$

(A complete justification that this integral is a limit, in a suitable sense, of our sums would require some additional theory, which is irrelevant anyway since we just want to make it reasonable that the above integral should represent what we mean physically by length.)

Observe that when $y = f(x)$ we can let $t = x = g(t)$ and $y = f(t)$. In that case, $g'(t) = 1$ and the formula for the length in parametric form is seen to be the same as the formula we obtained before for a curve $y = f(x)$.

Example. Find the length of the curve

$$x = \cos t, \qquad y = \sin t$$

between $t = 0$ and $t = \pi$. representative strip.
The length is the integral

$$\int_0^\pi \sqrt{(-\sin t)^2 + (\cos t)^2} \, dt.$$

$$\int_0^\pi \sqrt{f'(\cos t)^2 + f(\sin t)^2}$$

$$\int_0^\pi \sqrt{(-\sin t)^2 + (\cos t)^2}$$

$$\int_0^\pi \sqrt{(\sin t)^2 + (\cos t)^2} \, dt$$

$$\therefore \int_0^\pi 1 \cdot dt.$$

In view of the relation $(-\sin t)^2 = (\sin t)^2$ and a basic formula relating sine and cosine, we get

$$\int_0^\pi dt = \pi.$$

If we integrated between 0 and 2π we would get 2π. This is the length of the circle of radius 1. circle

Remark. We can also obtain the length of a curve by the axioms for the integral. If $f(t)$ and $g(t)$ are the coordinate functions of a curve given parametrically, i.e.

$$C(t) = \big(f(t), g(t)\big),$$

we view $C(t)$ as a point in the plane. We define the derivative

$$C'(t) = \big(f'(t), g'(t)\big),$$

differentiating componentwise. Then $C'(t)$ is interpreted as the velocity of the curve, and

$$v(t) = \sqrt{f'(t)^2 + g'(t)^2}$$

is interpreted as the speed of the curve. The length of a curve depends on its speed, and in fact: If the speed is constant, say M, over an interval of time $[a, b]$, then the length should be $M(b - a)$. Furthermore, if one curve has a greater speed than another, then its length should be greater. In particular, if

$$m \leqq v(t) \leqq M$$

for two constants M, $m \geqq 0$, and if we denote the length of the curve between a and b by $L_a^b(v)$, then

$$m(b - a) \leqq L_a^b(v) \leqq M(b - a).$$

Finally, the length of the curve should satisfy

$$L_a^c(v) = L_a^b(v) + L_b^c(v).$$

Thus, from the axioms for the integral given in Chapter IX, §4, there is only one way to define the length compatible with these properties, and that is

$$\int_a^b \sqrt{f'(t)^2 + g'(t)^2}\, dt$$

as we have done above.

Polar Coordinates

Let us now find a formula for the length of curves given in polar coordinates. Say the curve is

$$r = f(\theta),$$

with $\theta_1 \leqq \theta \leqq \theta_2$. We know that

$$x = r \cos \theta = f(\theta) \cos \theta$$

$$y = r \sin \theta = f(\theta) \sin \theta.$$

This puts the curve in parametric form, just as in the preceding considerations. Consequently we can apply the definition as before, and we see

that the length is
$$\int_{\theta_1}^{\theta_2} \sqrt{\left(\frac{dx}{d\theta}\right)^2 + \left(\frac{dy}{d\theta}\right)^2} \, d\theta.$$

You can compute $dx/d\theta$ and $dy/d\theta$ using the rule for the derivative of a product. If you do this, you will find that many terms cancel, and that the integral is equal to

$$\int_{\theta_1}^{\theta_2} \sqrt{f(\theta)^2 + f'(\theta)^2} \, d\theta.$$

(The computation is very easy, and is good practice in simple identities involving sine and cosine. We leave it to you as an exercise. Anyhow, working it out will make you remember the formula better.)

EXERCISES

1. Carry out the preceding computation.

2. Find the length of a circle of radius r.

3. Find the length of the curve $x = e^t \cos t$, $y = e^t \sin t$ between $t = 1$ and $t = 2$.

4. Find the length of the curve $x = \cos^3 t$, $y = \sin^3 t$ (a) between $t = 0$ and $t = \pi/4$, and (b) between $t = 0$ and $t = \pi$.

Find the lengths of the following curves:

5. $y = e^x$ between $x = 0$ and $x = 1$.

6. $y = x^{3/2}$ between $x = 1$ and $x = 3$.

7. $y = \frac{1}{2}(e^x + e^{-x})$ between $x = -1$ and $x = 1$.

8. Find the length of one loop of the curve $r = 1 + \cos \theta$ (polar coordinates).

9. Same, with $r = \cos \theta$, between $-\pi/2$ and $\pi/2$.

10. Find the length of the curve $r = 2/\cos \theta$ between $\theta = 0$ and $\theta = \pi/3$.

11. Find the length of the curve $r = |\sin \theta|$ from $\theta = 0$ to $\theta = 2\pi$.

12. Sketch the curve $r = e^\theta$ (in polar coordinates), and also the curve $r = e^{-\theta}$.

13. Find the length of the curve $r = e^\theta$ between $\theta = 1$ and $\theta = 2$.

14. In general, give the length of the curve $r = e^\theta$ between two values θ_1 and θ_2.

§2. AREA IN POLAR COORDINATES

Suppose we are given a continuous function

$$r = f(\theta)$$

which is defined in some interval $a \leq \theta \leq b$. We assume that $f(\theta) \geq 0$ and $b \leq a + 2\pi$.

We wish to find an integral expression for the area encompassed by the curve $r = f(\theta)$ between the two bounds a and b.

Let us take a partition of $[a, b]$, say

$$a = \theta_0 \leqq \theta_1 \leqq \cdots \leqq \theta_n = b.$$

The picture between θ_i and θ_{i+1} might look like this:

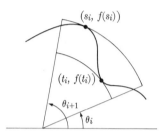

We let s_i be a number between θ_i and θ_{i+1} such that $f(s_i)$ is a maximum in that interval, and we let t_i be a number such that $f(t_i)$ is a minimum in that interval. In the picture, we have drawn the circles (or rather the sectors) of radius $f(s_i)$ and $f(t_i)$, respectively.

Then the area between θ_i, θ_{i+1} and the curve lies between the two sectors. Denote it by A_i. The area of a sector having angle $\theta_{i+1} - \theta_i$ and radius R is equal to the fraction

$$\frac{\theta_{i+1} - \theta_i}{2\pi}$$

of the total area of the circle of radius R, namely πR^2. Hence we get the inequality

$$\frac{\theta_{i+1} - \theta_i}{2\pi} \pi f(t_i)^2 \leqq A_i \leqq \frac{\theta_{i+1} - \theta_i}{2\pi} \pi f(s_i)^2.$$

Let $G(\theta) = \frac{1}{2} f(\theta)^2$. We see that the sum of the small pieces of area A_i satisfies the inequalities

$$\sum_{i=0}^{n-1} G(t_i)(\theta_{i+1} - \theta_i) \leqq \sum_{i=0}^{n-1} A_i \leqq \sum_{i=0}^{n-1} G(s_i)(\theta_{i+1} - \theta_i).$$

Thus the desired area lies between the upper sum and lower sum associated with the partition. Thus it is reasonable to define the *area* to be

$$\int_{\theta_1}^{\theta_2} \tfrac{1}{2} f(\theta)^2 \, d\theta.$$

Example. Find the area bounded by one loop of the curve

$$r^2 = 2a^2 \cos 2\theta \qquad (a > 0).$$

Between $-\dfrac{\pi}{4}$ and $\dfrac{\pi}{4}$ the cosine is ≥ 0. Thus we can write

$$r = \sqrt{2}\,a\sqrt{\cos 2\theta}.$$

The area is therefore

$$\int_{-\pi/4}^{\pi/4} \tfrac{1}{2}2a^2 \cos 2\theta\, d\theta = a^2.$$

EXERCISES

Find the area enclosed by the following curves:

1. $r = 2(1 + \cos\theta)$
2. $r^2 = a^2 \sin 2\theta \quad (a > 0)$
3. $r = 2a\cos\theta$
4. $r = \cos 3\theta,\ -\pi/6 \leq \theta \leq \pi/6$
5. $r = 1 + \sin\theta$
6. $r = 1 + \sin 2\theta$
7. $r = 2 + \cos\theta$
8. $r = 2\cos 3\theta,\ -\pi/6 \leq \theta \leq \pi/6$

§3. VOLUMES OF REVOLUTION

Let $y = f(x)$ be a continuous function of x on some interval $a \leq x \leq b$. Assume that $f(x) \geq 0$ in this interval. If we revolve the curve $y = f(x)$ around the x-axis, we obtain a solid, whose volume we wish to compute.

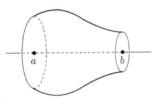

Take a partition of $[a, b]$, say

$$a = x_0 \leq x_1 \leq \cdots \leq x_n = b.$$

Let c_i be a minimum of f in the interval $[x_i, x_{i+1}]$ and let d_i be a maximum of f in that interval. Then the solid of revolution in that small interval lies between a small cylinder and a big cylinder. The width of these cylinders is $x_{i+1} - x_i$ and the radius is $f(c_i)$ for the small cylinder and $f(d_i)$ for the big one. Hence the volume of revolution, denoted by V, satisfies the inequalities

$$\sum_{i=0}^{n-1} \pi f(c_i)^2(x_{i+1} - x_i) \leq V \leq \sum_{i=0}^{n-1} \pi f(d_i)^2(x_{i+1} - x_i).$$

It is therefore reasonable to define this volume to be

$$\int_a^b \pi f(x)^2\, dx.$$

Example. Compute the volume of the sphere of radius 1.

We take the function $y = \sqrt{1 - x^2}$ between 0 and 1. If we rotate this curve around the x-axis, we shall get half the sphere. Its volume is therefore

$$\int_0^1 \pi(1 - x^2)\, dx = \tfrac{2}{3}\pi.$$

The volume of the full sphere is therefore $\tfrac{4}{3}\pi$.

One can also motivate the definition of the volume of revolution by the axioms for the integral given in Chapter IX, §4. One does this by considering the revolution of a rectangle, i.e. considering the case where f is constant, say M. Then one obtains the volume of a cylinder:

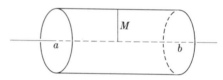

and this volume should be equal to $\pi M^2(b - a)$. Using the two properties of the integral which characterize it, we find once again that the volume should be given by the integral

$$\int_a^b \pi f(x)^2\, dx$$

which we wrote previously.

EXERCISES

1. Find the volume of a sphere of radius r.

Find the volumes of revolution of the following:

2. $y = 1/\cos x$ between $x = 0$ and $x = \pi/4$

3. $y = \sin x$ between $x = 0$ and $x = \pi/4$

4. $y = \cos x$ between $x = 0$ and $x = \pi/4$

5. The region between $y = x^2$ and $y = 5x$

6. $y = xe^{x/2}$ between $x = 0$ and $x = 1$

7. $y = x^{1/2}e^{x/2}$ between $x = 1$ and $x = 2$

8. $y = \log x$ between $x = 1$ and $x = 2$

9. $y = \sqrt{1 + x}$ between $x = 1$ and $x = 5$

10. (a) Let B be a number > 1. What is the volume of revolution of the curve $y = e^{-x}$ between 1 and B? Does this volume approach a limit as B becomes large? If so, what limit?

    (b) Same question for the curve $y = e^{-2x}$.

    (c) Same question for the curve $y = \sqrt{x}\, e^{-x^2}$.

11. Find the volume of a cone whose base has radius r, and of height h, by rotating a straight line passing through the origin around the x-axis.

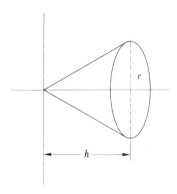

§4. WORK

Suppose a particle moves on a curve, and that the length of the curve is described by a variable u.

Let $f(u)$ be a function. We interpret f as a force acting on the particle, in the direction of the curve. We want to find an integral expression for the work done by the force between two points on the curve.

Whatever our expression will turn out to be, it is reasonable that the work done should satisfy the following properties:

If a, b, c are three numbers, with $a \leq b \leq c$, then the work done between a and c is equal to the work done between a and b, plus the work done between b and c. If we denote the work done between a and b by $W_a^b(f)$, then we should have

$$W_a^c(f) = W_a^b(f) + W_b^c(f).$$

Furthermore, if we have a constant force M acting on the particle, it is reasonable to expect that the work done between a and b is

$$M(b - a).$$

Finally, if g is a stronger force than f, say $f(u) \leq g(u)$, on the interval $[a, b]$, then we shall do more work with g than with f, meaning

$$W_a^b(f) \leq W_a^b(g).$$

In particular, if there are two constant forces m and M such that

$$m \leq f(u) \leq M$$

throughout the interval $[a, b]$, then

$$m(b - a) \leq W_a^b(f) \leq M(b - a).$$

But this condition, together with the first one expressed above, determines the integral uniquely! Hence there is only one reasonable way to associate a mathematical formula with work, compatible with physical requirements, and that is: The work done by the force f between a distance a and a distance b is

$$\int_a^b f(u)\, du.$$

If the particle or object happens to move along a straight line, say along the x-axis, then f is given as a function of x, and our integral is simply

$$\int_a^b f(x)\, dx.$$

Furthermore, if the length of the curve u is given as a function of time t (as it is in practice, cf. §1) we see that the force becomes a function of t by the chain rule, namely $f(u(t))$. Thus between time t_1 and t_2 the work done is equal to

$$\int_{t_1}^{t_2} f(u(t)) \frac{du}{dt}\, dt.$$

This is the most practical expression for the work, since curves and forces are most frequently expressed as functions of time.

Example. Find the work done in stretching a spring from its unstretched position to a length of 10 cm. You may assume that the force needed to stretch the spring is proportional to the increase in length.

We visualize the spring as being horizontal, on the x-axis. Thus there is a constant K such that the force is given by

$$f(x) = Kx.$$

The work done is therefore

$$\int_0^{10} Kx\, dx = \tfrac{1}{2}K(100)$$
$$= 50K.$$

§5. DENSITY AND MASS

Consider an interval $[a, b]$ with $0 \leqq a < b$. We think first of this interval as a rod, and let f be a continuous positive function defined on this interval. We interpret f as a density on the rod, so that $f(x)$ is the density at x. Given $a \leqq c \leqq d \leqq b$, we denote by $M_c^d(f)$ the mass of the rod between c and d, corresponding to the given density f. We wish to determine a mathematical notion to represent $M_c^d(f)$. If f is a constant density, with constant value $K \geqq 0$ on $[c, d]$, then the mass $M_c^d(f)$ should be $K(d - c)$. On the other hand, if g is another density such that

$$f(x) \leqq g(x),$$

then certainly we should have $M_c^d(f) \leqq M_c^d(g)$. In particular, if k, K are constants $\geqq 0$ such that

$$k \leqq f(x) \leqq K$$

for x in the interval $[c, d]$, then the mass should satisfy

$$k(d - c) \leqq M_c^d(f) \leqq K(d - c).$$

Finally, the mass should be additive, that is the mass of two disjoint pieces should be the sum of the mass of the pieces. In particular,

$$M_a^c(f) + M_c^d(f) = M_a^d(f).$$

We know from the basic properties of the integral that there is one and only one way to associate a number $M_c^d(f)$ to the density f compatible with the preceding requirements, and that is the integral, so that the mass is given by the integral:

$$M_a^b(f) = \int_a^b f.$$

§6. PROBABILITY

We have a very similar situation with probability densities. We are given an interval $[a, b]$ and a continuous function f, which we interpret as a probability density on this interval. We consider a function f such that $f(x) \geqq 0$ for all x in the interval and in addition assume that

$$\int_a^b f(x)\, dx = 1.$$

Such a function is called a *probability density* over the interval. We have a certain intuitive notion $P_c^d(f)$, which we think of as the probability that certain objects will fall within the interval $[c, d]$, given the probability density f. For instance, we may be shooting some particles along a slit above the interval, and we want a mathematical notion corresponding to the probability that a particle will fall in this interval $[c, d]$.

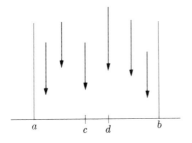

If we have a constant probability density over $[c, d]$, say K, then we want $P_c^d(K)$ to be a constant multiple of $K(d - c)$. In the special case where $K = 1/(b - a)$, we interpret this density as a uniform average density over the interval, and we wish its probability over $[c, d]$ to be the ratio $(d - c)/(b - a)$. From this we see that it is reasonable to require that in fact, $P_c^d(K) = K(d - c)$. Furthermore, if g is another probability density which is smaller than f, that is $g(x) \leq f(x)$ for all x, then we must have $P_c^d(g) \leq P_c^d(f)$. In particular, if k and K are two constants such that $k \leq f(x) \leq K$ for x in $[c, d]$, then

$$k(d - c) \leq P_c^d(f) \leq K(d - c).$$

Finally, the probability should be additive over disjoint intervals, so that in particular,

$$P_a^d(f) = P_a^c(f) + P_c^d(f).$$

We see that P_c^d satisfies the basic properties of the integral, and there is only one way to define probability compatible with these properties, that is

$$P_c^d(f) = \int_c^d f.$$

In particular,

$$P_a^b(f) = \int_a^b f.$$

Furthermore, under the present normalization, in order to have a probabilistic interpretation for $P_a^b(f)$, one must consider only those functions f such that

$$\int_a^b f = 1.$$

As a matter of terminology, we also say that $P_c^d(f)$ is the *probability that x lies within the interval* $[c, d]$.

Example 1. Consider a circle of radius 1 centered at the origin, and a needle which is given an initial push, rotates subject to friction, and comes to rest, pointing to some point of the circle as in the following diagram.

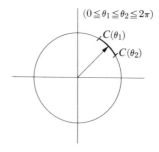

We want to know the probability that the point of the needle will lie in a given circular interval, as shown. We parametrize our circle in the usual way, letting $C(\theta) = (\cos \theta, \sin \theta)$ be a point of the circle, $0 \leq \theta \leq 2\pi$. The probability will of course depend on the probability density, which may be viewed as a function of θ. Assuming that this function is constant (which means that the needle is being slowed down by friction in a uniform way as it spins and no other force acts on it), let this constant be σ. Then we must have

$$1 = \int_0^{2\pi} \sigma \, d\theta = \sigma \int_0^{2\pi} d\theta = \sigma \cdot 2\pi.$$

Hence $\sigma = 1/2\pi$ is the constant probability density which can be taken as representing the physical situation under consideration. The probability that the needle comes to rest between $C(\theta_1)$ and $C(\theta_2)$ is then equal to $(\theta_2 - \theta_1)/2\pi$. Put another way, this is the probability that θ falls within the interval $[\theta_1, \theta_2]$.

Let us go back to the general case over the interval $[a, b]$. If F is an indefinite integral for f over the interval, then

$$\int_c^d f(x) \, dx = F(d) - F(c) \qquad \text{and} \qquad f(x) = F'(x).$$

The case when f is not constant may correspond empirically to a magnet on the interval, which varies in strength, and thus attracts more particles over certain regions than over others. Experimental data must then be used to determine the density function f, or its associated *probability function*, which we define to be the definite integral

$$F(x) = \int_a^x f(t) \, dt.$$

Example. A probability density on the interval $[-\pi, \pi]$ is given by the following conditions:

$$f(x) = 0 \qquad \text{if} \quad -\pi \leq x \leq -\pi/2$$
$$f(x) = a \cdot \cos x \qquad \text{if} \quad -\pi/2 \leq x \leq \pi/2$$
$$f(x) = 0 \qquad \text{if} \quad \pi/2 \leq x \leq \pi.$$

Here, a is some constant. Since we wish the probability associated with f over the whole interval to be equal to 1, we must have

$$a \int_{-\pi/2}^{\pi/2} \cos x \, dx = 1.$$

Integrating shows that $2a = 1$, so $a = 1/2$. If we let F be the probability function associated with f, so that

$$F(x) = \int_{-\pi/2}^{x} f(t)\, dt,$$

then a direct integration shows that

$$F(x) = \begin{cases} 0 & \text{if } -\pi \leqq x \leqq -\pi/2 \\ \dfrac{1 + \sin x}{2} & \text{if } -\pi/2 \leqq x \leqq \pi/2 \\ 2 & \text{if } \pi/2 \leqq x \leqq \pi. \end{cases}$$

The values between $-\pi/2$ and $\pi/2$ are given as the integral

$$F(x) = \tfrac{1}{2}\int_{-\pi/2}^{x} \cos t\, dt = \tfrac{1}{2}\sin t\,\Big|_{-\pi/2}^{x} = \tfrac{1}{2}(\sin x + 1).$$

The graphs of f and F look like this:

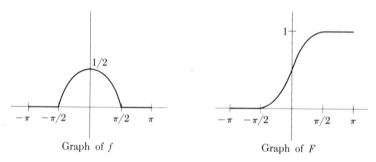

Graph of f Graph of F

In terms of the spinning needle, the probability density means that there is an increasingly vigorous attraction for the needle towards 0, and that the needle never comes to rest on the left side of the circle.

By definition, the probability that $0 \leqq x \leqq \pi/2$ is simply equal to the value

$$F(\pi/2) - F(0) = 1 - \tfrac{1}{2} = \tfrac{1}{2}.$$

EXERCISES

Each one of the following functions f represents a probability density over the interval $[0, 1]$. Determine the constant c, find the probability function F associated with f, and find the probability that $0 \leqq x \leqq 1/2$.

1. $f(x) = 1$ 2. $f(x) = cx$ 3. $f(x) = cx^4$

4. $f(x) = c \cdot \sin \pi x$ 5. $f(x) = c \cdot \sin^2 \pi x$

6. $f(x) = 3 - 2x$ 7. $f(x) = e - e^x$

Each one of the following functions f represents a probability density over the interval $[-\pi, \pi]$. In each case determine the constant c, find the probability function F associated with f, and find the probability that $0 \leq x \leq \pi/2$.

8. $f(x) = c|\cos x|$ 9. $f(x) = c|\sin x|$

10. $f(x) = c \cdot \cos^2 x$ 11. $f(x) = c \cdot \sin^2 x$

12. $f(x) = 0$ if $-\pi \leq x \leq 0$ and $f(x) = c(1 - \cos x)$ if $0 \leq x \leq \pi$.

§7. MOMENTS

We wish to describe the notion of "moment" (with respect to the origin), which arises in physics. "Moment" should have the following properties.

Suppose that we have a mass K concentrated at a point b on the x-axis. Then its moment is Kb.

Suppose that we have an interval $[a, b]$, with $a < b$ (which may be interpreted as a rod), and a constant density distribution C over the interval. Then the total mass is $C(b - a)$. The moment of our constant distribution, which we denote by M, should then satisfy the inequalities

$$Ca(b - a) \leq M \leq Cb(b - a).$$

If we think of the total mass $K = C(b - a)$ as being concentrated at the point b, then the right inequality states that the moment of our constant distribution is less than or equal to the moment of a total mass K placed at the point b. The left inequality states that the moment of our constant distribution is greater than or equal to that of a total mass K placed at the point a. If we assume $0 \leq a < b$ then these two inequalities state that the moment should be larger, the farther our total mass is from the origin. We shall assume $0 \leq a < b$ throughout our discussion.

Suppose that we have a variable density distribution over our interval $[a, b]$. This means that our distribution is represented by a function $f(x)$ on the interval. Let us denote its "moment" by $M_a^b(f)$. The following two properties should then be satisfied.

Property 1. If f is continuous on the interval $[a, b]$ and if there are two constants C_1, C_2 both ≥ 0 such that

$$C_1 \leq f(x) \leq C_2$$

for all x in our interval, then the moment of f satisfies the inequalities

$$C_1 a(b - a) \leq M_a^b(f) \leq C_2 b(b - a).$$

(In other words, the moment of f should lie between the moments determined by the constant distributions C_1 and C_2.)

Property 2. If f is continuous on the interval $[a, c]$, with $a \leq c$ and if b is a point such that $a \leq b \leq c$, then

$$M_a^c(f) = M_a^b(f) + M_b^c(f).$$

(In other words, the moment over the big interval is the sum of the moments over the first interval and the second interval.)

We shall now prove that there is one and only one way of obtaining a moment $M_a^b(f)$ satisfying the above two properties, and that is the integral

$$\int_a^b xf(x)\, dx.$$

To begin with, we note that the integral satisfies Property 2. This is an old result.

As to Property 1, assume that f lies between two constants C_1 and C_2 as above. For the interval $a \leq x \leq b$, we get

$$C_1 a \leq xf(x) \leq C_2 b,$$

and hence by Theorem 1 of Chapter XI, §3 we conclude that

$$C_1 a(b - a) \leq \int_a^b xf(x)\, dx \leq C_2 b(b - a).$$

Thus the integral certainly satisfies our two properties.

We shall now prove conversely that any $M_a^b(f)$ satisfying the two properties must be the integral written down above. This is done by our usual technique. We prove that the function $M_a^x(f)$ has a derivative, and that this derivative is $xf(x)$. Such a function must be the integral.

The Newton quotient is

$$\frac{M_a^{x+h}(f) - M_a^x(f)}{h}.$$

Using Property 2, we see that the Newton quotient is equal to

$$\frac{M_x^{x+h}(f)}{h}.$$

Let s be a maximum for f in the small interval between x and $x + h$ and let t be a minimum for f in that small interval. If, say, h is positive, then by Property 1 we conclude that

$$f(t)x(x + h - x) \leq M_x^{x+h}(f) \leq f(s)(x + h)(x + h - x),$$

or in other words that

$$f(t)xh \leq M_x^{x+h}(f) \leq f(s)(x + h)h.$$

Dividing by h yields

$$xf(t) \leqq \frac{M_x^{x+h}(f)}{h} \leqq (x + h)f(s).$$

As h approaches 0, both $f(t)$ and $f(s)$ approach $f(x)$ because s, t lie between x and $x + h$. The usual squeezing argument shows that the Newton quotient approaches $xf(x)$, as was to be shown. If h is negative, a similar argument can be applied as usual.

Consider now a density distribution on the interval $[a, b]$ represented by a continuous function f. We define the *total mass* (or simply *mass*) of this distribution over the interval to be the integral

$$\int_a^b f(x)\, dx.$$

Assume that $f(x) \geqq 0$ for all x in the interval, and that $f(x) \neq 0$ for some point in the interval. Then the total mass is positive. We define the *center of gravity* of our distribution over the interval to be that point c such that the moment of our total mass concentrated at the point c is equal to the moment of f over the interval. This can be expressed by the relation

$$c \cdot \int_a^b f(x)\, dx = \int_a^b xf(x)\, dx.$$

In other words,

$$c = \frac{\int_a^b xf(x)\, dx}{\int_a^b f(x)\, dx}.$$

If you study physics, you will recognize this as being the usual formula giving the center of gravity.

Supplementary Exercises

LENGTH OF CURVES

Find the length of the following curves in the indicated interval.

1. $y = x^{3/2}$, $\;0 \leqq x \leqq 4$
2. $y = \log x$, $\;\frac{1}{2} \leqq x \leqq 2$
3. $y = \log x$, $\;1 \leqq x \leqq e^2$
4. $y = 4 - x^2$, $\;-2 \leqq x \leqq 2$
5. $x = 2t + 1$, $\;y = t^2$, $\;0 \leqq t \leqq 2$
6. $x = 4 + 2t$, $\;y = \frac{1}{2}t^2 + 3$, $\;-2 \leqq t \leqq 2$
7. $x = 9t^2$, $\;y = 9t^3 - 3t$, $\;0 \leqq t \leqq 1/\sqrt{3}$
8. $x = 3t^2/2$, $\;y = t^3$, $\;0 \leqq t \leqq 1$

9. $y = \log (1 - x^2)$, $0 \leqq x \leqq \frac{3}{4}$

10. $y = \frac{1}{2}(e^x + e^{-x})$, $-1 \leqq x \leqq 0$

11. $y = \log \cos x$, $0 \leqq x \leqq \pi/3$

12. $x = 1 - \cos t$, $y = t - \sin t$, $0 \leqq t \leqq 2\pi$

13. $x = a(1 - \cos t)$, $y = a(t - \sin t)$, with $a > 0$, and $0 \leqq t \leqq \pi$.

Find the length of the following curves given in polar coordinates.

14. $r = 3\theta^2$ from $\theta = 1$ to $\theta = 2$

15. $r = e^{-4\theta}$, from $\theta = 1$ to $\theta = 2$

16. $r = 3 \cos \theta$, from $\theta = 0$ to $\theta = \pi/4$

17. $r = 2/\theta$ from $\theta = \frac{1}{2}$ to $\theta = 4$

18. $r = 1 + \cos \theta$ from $\theta = 0$ to $\theta = \pi/4$

19. $r = 1 - \cos \theta$ from $\theta = 0$ to $\theta = \pi$

20. $r = \sin^2 \dfrac{\theta}{2}$ from $\theta = 0$ to $\theta = \pi$

AREA

Find the areas of the following regions, bounded by the curve given in polar coordinates.

1. $r = 10 \cos \theta$	2. $r = 1 - \cos \theta$
3. $r = \sqrt{1 - \cos \theta}$	4. $r = 2 + \sin 2\theta$
5. $r = \sin^2 \theta$	6. $r = 1 - \sin \theta$
7. $r = 1 + 2 \sin \theta$	8. $r = 1 + \sin 2\theta$
9. $r = \cos 3\theta$	10. $r = 2 + \cos \theta$

Find the area between the following curves, given in rectangular coordinates.

11. $y = 4 - x^2, y = 0$,   between $x = -2$ and $x = 2$

12. $y = 4 - x^2, y = 8 - 2x^2$,   between $x = -2$ and $x = 2$

13. $y = x^3 + x^2, y = x^3 + 1$,   between $x = -1$ and $x = 1$

14. $y = x - x^2, y = -x$,   between $x = 0$ and $x = 2$

15. $y = x^2, y = x + 1$, between the two points where the two curves intersect.

16. $y = x^3$ and $y = x + 6$ between $x = 0$ and the value of $x > 0$ where the two curves intersect.

VOLUMES OF REVOLUTION

1. Find the volume of a cone of height h and radius of the circular side r, by rotating a straight line passing through the origin around the x-axis.

Find the volumes of the solid obtained by rotating each region as indicated, around the x-axis.

2. $y = x^2$, between $y = 0$ and $x = 2$

3. $y = \dfrac{4}{x + 1}$, $x = -5$, $x = -2$, $y = 0$

4. $y = \sqrt{x}$, the x-axis and $x = 2$

5. $y = 1/x$, $x = 1$, $x = 3$ and the x-axis

6. $y = \sqrt{x}$, $y = x^3$

7. The region bounded by the line $x + y = 1$ and the coordinate axes

8. The ellipse $a^2x^2 + b^2y^2 = a^2b^2$

9. $y = e^{-x}$, between $x = 1$ and $x = 5$

10. $y = \log x$, between $x = 1$ and $x = 2$

11. $y = \tan x$, $x = \pi/3$ and the x-axis

In the next problems, you are asked to find a volume of revolution of a region between certain bounds, and determine whether this volume approaches a limit when the bound B becomes very large. If it does, give this limit.

12. The region bounded by $1/x$, the x-axis, between $x = 1$ and $x = B$ for $B > 1$.

13. The region bounded by $1/x^2$ and the x-axis, between $x = 1$ and $x = B$ for $B > 1$.

14. The region bounded by $y = 1/\sqrt{x}$, the x-axis, between $x = 1$ and $x = B$ for $B > 1$.

In the next problems, find the volume of revolution, determined by bounds involving a number $a > 0$, and find whether this volume approaches a limit as a approaches 0. If it does, state what limit.

15. The region bounded by $y = 1/\sqrt{x}$, the x-axis, between $x = a$ and $x = 1$ for $0 < a < 1$.

16. The region bounded by $y = 1/x$, the x-axis, between $x = a$ and $x = 1$, with $0 < a < 1$.

17. The region bounded by $(\cos x)/\sqrt{\sin x}$, the x-axis, between $x = a$ and $x = \pi/4$, with $0 < a < \pi/4$.

WORK

1. A spring is 18 in. long, and a force of 10 lb is needed to compress it to a length of 16 in. If the force is given as $f(x) = kx$, where k is a constant, and x is the increase in length, what is the constant k? How much work is done in compressing the spring from 16 in. to 12 in.?

2. Assuming that the force is given as $k \sin (\pi x/18)$, in the spring compression problem, answer the two questions of the preceding problem for this force.

3. A particle at the origin attracts another particle with a force inversely proportional to the square of the distance between them. Let C be the proportionality constant. What work is done in moving the second particle along a straight line away from the origin, from a distance r_1 to a distance $r > r_1$ from the origin?

4. In the preceding exercise, determine whether the work approaches a limit as r becomes very large, and find this limit if it exists.

5. Two particles repel each other with a force inversely proportional to the cube of their distance. If one particle is fixed at the origin, what work is done in moving the other along the x-axis from a distance of 10 cm to a distance of 1 cm towards the origin?

6. Assuming that gravity, as usual, is a force inversely proportional to the square of the distance from the center of the earth, what work is done in lifting a weight of 1000 lb from the surface of the earth to a height of 4000 mi above the surface? (Assume the radius of the earth is 4000 mi.)

7. A bag of sand originally weighing 144 lb is lifted at a constant rate of 3 ft/min. The sand leaks out uniformly at such a rate that half of the sand is lost when the bag has been lifted 18 ft. Find the work done in lifting the bag this distance.

8. A metal bar has length L and cross section S. If it is stretched x units, then the force $f(x)$ required is given by

$$f(x) = \frac{ES}{L} x$$

where E is a constant. If a bar 12 in. long of uniform cross section 4 in^2 is stretched 1 in. find the work done (in terms of E).

Chapter XIV

Taylor's Formula

We finally come to the point where we develop a method which allows us to compute the values of the elementary functions like sine, exp, and log. The method is to approximate these functions by polynomials, with an error term which is easily estimated. This error term will be given by an integral, and our first task is to estimate integrals. We then go through the elementary functions systematically, and derive the approximating polynomials.

You should review the estimates of Chapter X, §3, which will be used to estimate our error terms.

§1. TAYLOR'S FORMULA

Let f be a function which is differentiable on some interval. We can then take its derivative f' on that interval. Suppose that this derivative is also differentiable. We need a notation for its derivative. We shall denote it by $f^{(2)}$. Similarly, if the derivative of the function $f^{(2)}$ exists, we denote it by $f^{(3)}$, and so forth. In this system, the first derivative is denoted by $f^{(1)}$. (Of course, we can also write $f^{(2)} = f''$.)

In the d/dx notation, we also write:

$$f^{(2)}(x) = \frac{d^2 f}{dx^2},$$

$$f^{(3)}(x) = \frac{d^3 f}{dx^3},$$

and so forth.

Taylor's formula gives us a polynomial which approximates the function, in terms of the derivatives of the function. Since these derivatives are usually easy to compute, there is no difficulty in computing these polynomials.

For instance, if $f(x) = \sin x$, then $f^{(1)}(x) = \cos x$, $f^{(2)}(x) = -\sin x$, $f^{(3)}(x) = -\cos x$, and $f^{(4)}(x) = \sin x$. From there on, we start all over again.

In the case of e^x, it is even easier, namely $f^{(n)}(x) = e^x$ for all positive integers n.

It is also customary to denote the function f itself by $f^{(0)}$. Thus $f(x) = f^{(0)}(x)$.

We need one more piece of notation before stating Taylor's formula. When we take successive derivatives of functions, the following numbers occur frequently:

$$1, \quad 2 \cdot 1, \quad 3 \cdot 2 \cdot 1, \quad 4 \cdot 3 \cdot 2 \cdot 1, \quad 5 \cdot 4 \cdot 3 \cdot 2 \cdot 1, \quad \text{etc.}$$

These numbers are denoted by

$$1! \quad 2! \quad 3! \quad 4! \quad 5! \quad \text{etc.}$$

Thus

$$1! = 1 \qquad\qquad 4! = 24$$
$$2! = 2 \qquad\qquad 5! = 120$$
$$3! = 6 \qquad\qquad 6! = 720$$

When n is a positive integer, the symbol $n!$ is read n *factorial*. Thus in general,

$$n! = n(n - 1)(n - 2) \cdots 2 \cdot 1$$

is the product of the first n integers from 1 to n.

It is also convenient to agree that $0! = 1$. This is the convention which makes certain formulas easiest to write.

We are now in a position to state Taylor's formula.

Theorem 1. *Let f be a function defined on a closed interval between two numbers a and b. Assume that the function has n derivatives on this interval, and that all of them are continuous functions. Then*

$$f(b) = f(a) + \frac{f^{(1)}(a)}{1!}(b - a) + \frac{f^{(2)}(a)}{2!}(b - a)^2 + \cdots$$
$$+ \frac{f^{(n-1)}(a)}{(n - 1)!}(b - a)^{n-1} + R_n,$$

where R_n (which is called the remainder term) is the integral

$$R_n = \int_a^b \frac{(b - t)^{n-1}}{(n - 1)!} f^{(n)}(t)\, dt.$$

The remainder term looks slightly complicated. In Theorem 2 we shall prove that R_n can be expressed in a form very similar to the other terms, namely

$$R_n = \frac{f^{(n)}(c)}{n!}(b - a)^n$$

for some number c between a and b. Taylor's formula with this form of the remainder is then very easy to memorize.

The most important case of Theorem 1 occurs when $a = 0$. In that case, the formula reads

$$f(b) = f(0) + \frac{f'(0)}{1!} b + \cdots + \frac{f^{(n-1)}(0)}{(n-1)!} b^{n-1} + R_n.$$

Furthermore, if x is any number between a and b, the same formula remains valid for this number x instead of b, simply by considering the interval between a and x instead of the interval between a and b. Thus the formula reads

$$f(x) = f(0) + \frac{f'(0)}{1!} x + \cdots + \frac{f^{(n-1)}(0)}{(n-1)!} x^{n-1} + R_n,$$

where R_n is the integral

$$R_n = \int_0^x \frac{(x-t)^{n-1}}{(n-1)!} f^{(n)}(t) \, dt.$$

Each derivative $f(0), f'(0), \ldots, f^{(n-1)}(0)$ is a number, and we see that the terms preceding R_n make up a polynomial in x. This is the approximating polynomial.

Of course, for the formula to be of any use, we have to estimate the remainder R_n and show that it becomes small when n becomes large, so that the polynomial does indeed approximate the function. We shall do this in the following sections for special functions. You may very well want to look at these sections before reading the proof, so as to familiarize yourselves with the symbols and nature of the theorem.

We shall now prove the theorem, for those of you who are interested in seeing the proof first. It is an application of integration by parts.

We proceed stepwise. We know that a function is the integral of its derivative. Thus when $n = 1$ we have

$$f(b) - f(a) = \int_a^b f'(t) \, dt.$$

Let $u = f'(t)$ and $dv = dt$. Then $du = f''(t) \, dt$. We are tempted to put $v = t$. This is one case where we choose another indefinite integral, namely $v = -(b - t)$, which differs from t by a constant. We still have $dv = dt$ (the minus signs cancel!). Integrating by parts, we get

$$\int_a^b u \, dv = uv \Big|_a^b - \int_a^b v \, du$$

$$= -f'(t)(b-t) \Big|_a^b - \int_a^b -(b-t) f^{(2)}(t) \, dt$$

$$= f'(a)(b-a) + \int_a^b (b-t) f^{(2)}(t) \, dt.$$

This is precisely the Taylor formula when $n = 2$.

We push it one step further, from 2 to 3. We rewrite the integral just obtained as

$$\int_a^b f^{(2)}(t)(b - t)\, dt.$$

Let $u = f^{(2)}(t)$ and $dv = (b - t)\, dt$. Then

$$du = f^{(3)}(t)\, dt \quad \text{and} \quad v = \frac{-(b - t)^2}{2}.$$

Thus, integrating by parts, we find that our integral, which is of the form $\int_a^b u\, dv$, is equal to

$$uv\Big|_a^b - \int_a^b v\, du = -f^{(2)}(t)\frac{(b - t)^2}{2}\Big|_a^b - \int_a^b -\frac{(b - t)^2}{2} f^{(3)}(t)\, dt$$

$$= f^{(2)}(a)\frac{(b - a)^2}{2} + R_3.$$

Here, R_3 is the desired remainder, and the term preceding it is just the proper term in the Taylor formula.

If you need it, do the next step yourself, from 3 to 4. We shall now show you how the general step goes, from n to $n + 1$.

Suppose that we have already obtained the first $n - 1$ terms of the Taylor formula, with a remainder term

$$R_n = \int_a^b \frac{(b - t)^{n-1}}{(n - 1)!} f^{(n)}(t)\, dt,$$

which we rewrite

$$R_n = \int_a^b f^{(n)}(t) \frac{(b - t)^{n-1}}{(n - 1)!}\, dt.$$

Let $u = f^{(n)}(t)$ and $dv = \dfrac{(b - t)^{n-1}}{(n - 1)!}\, dt$. Then

$$du = f^{(n+1)}(t)\, dt \quad \text{and} \quad v = \frac{-(b - t)^n}{n!}.$$

(Observe how, when we integrate dv, we get n in the denominator, to climb from $(n - 1)!$ to $n!$.)

Integrating by parts, we see that R_n is equal to

$$uv\Big|_a^b - \int_a^b v\, du = -f^{(n)}(t)\frac{(b - t)^n}{n!}\Big|_a^b - \int_a^b -\frac{(b - t)^n}{n!} f^{(n+1)}(t)\, dt$$

$$= f^{(n)}(a)\frac{(b - a)^n}{n!} + \int_a^b \frac{(b - t)^n}{n!} f^{(n+1)}(t)\, dt.$$

Thus we have split off one more term of the Taylor formula, and the new remainder is the desired R_{n+1}. This concludes the proof.

§2. ESTIMATE FOR THE REMAINDER

Theorem 2. *In Taylor's formula of Theorem 1, there exists a number c between a and b such that the remainder R_n is given by*

$$R_n = \frac{f^{(n)}(c)(b - a)^n}{n!}.$$

If M_n is a number such that $|f^{(n)}(x)| \leq M_n$ for all x in the interval, then

$$|R_n| \leq \frac{M_n|b - a|^n}{n!}.$$

Proof. The second assertion follows at once from the first, taking the absolute value of the product of the n-th derivative and the length of the interval.

Let us prove the first assertion. Since $f^{(n)}$ is continuous on the interval, there exists a point u in the interval such that $f^{(n)}(u)$ is a maximum, and a point v such that $f^{(n)}(v)$ is a minimum for all values of $f^{(n)}$ in our interval.

Let us assume that $a < b$. Then for any t in the interval, $b - t$ is ≥ 0, and hence

$$\frac{(b - t)^{n-1}}{(n - 1)!} f^{(n)}(v) \leq \frac{(b - t)^{n-1}}{(n - 1)!} f^{(n)}(t) \leq \frac{(b - t)^{n-1}}{(n - 1)!} f^{(n)}(u).$$

Using Theorem 1 of Chapter X, §3, we conclude that similar inequalities hold when we take the integral. However, $f^{(n)}(v)$ and $f^{(n)}(u)$ are now fixed numbers which can be taken out of the integral sign. Consequently, we obtain

$$f^{(n)}(v) \int_a^b \frac{(b - t)^{n-1}}{(n - 1)!} dt \leq R_n \leq f^{(n)}(u) \int_a^b \frac{(b - t)^{n-1}}{(n - 1)!} dt.$$

We now perform the integration, which is very easy, and get

$$f^{(n)}(v) \frac{(b - a)^n}{n!} \leq R_n \leq f^{(n)}(u) \frac{(b - a)^n}{n!}.$$

By the intermediate value theorem, the n-th derivative $f^{(n)}(t)$ takes on all values between its minimum and maximum in the interval. Hence

$$f^{(n)}(t) \frac{(b - a)^n}{n!}$$

takes on all values between *its* minimum and maximum in the interval.

Hence there is some point c in the interval such that

$$R_n = f^{(n)}(c) \frac{(b - a)^n}{n!},$$

which is what we wanted.

The proof in case $b < a$ is similar, except that certain inequalities get reversed. We leave it as an exercise. (*Hint:* Interchange the limits of integration, taking the integral from b to a.)

The estimate of the remainder is particularly useful when b is close to a. In that case, let us rewrite Taylor's formula by setting $b - a = h$. We obtain:

Theorem 3. *Assumptions being as in Theorem 1, we have*

$$f(a + h) = f(a) + f'(a)h + \cdots + f^{(n-1)}(a) \frac{h^{n-1}}{(n - 1)!} + R_n$$

with the estimate

$$|R_n| \leq M_n \frac{|h|^n}{n!},$$

where M_n is a bound for the absolute value of the n-th derivative of f between a and $a + h$.

In the following sections, we give several examples. Except in some exercises, we shall always take $a = 0$, so that we have

$$f(x) = f(0) + f'(0)x + \cdots + \frac{f^{(n-1)}(0)}{(n - 1)!} x^{n-1} + R_n$$

with the estimate

$$|R_n| \leq M_n \frac{|x|^n}{n!}$$

if M_n is a bound for the n-th derivative of f between 0 and x.

This means that we have expressed $f(x)$ in terms of a polynomial, and a remainder term, the polynomial being called the *Taylor polynomial*

$$P_n(x) = c_0 + c_1 x + \cdots + c_n x^n$$

where

$$c_k = \frac{f^{(k)}(0)}{k!}.$$

We call c_k the k-th *Taylor coefficient* of f.

Uniqueness Theorem. *Let b be a number > 0. Let f be a function having $n + 1$ continuous derivatives in the interval $-b < x < b$. Assume that there are numbers $a_0, \ldots, a_n$ such that we can write*

$$f(x) = a_0 + a_1 x + \cdots + a_n x^n + g(x),$$

where $g(x)$ is a function satisfying

$$|g(x)| \leqq C|x|^{n+1}$$

for some number $C > 0$ and all x in the interval. Then

$$a_k = \frac{f^{(k)}(0)}{k!}$$

is the k-th Taylor coefficient of f.

Proof. If c_k is the k-th Taylor coefficient of f as above, then we have

$$c_0 + c_1 x + \cdots + c_n x^n + R_{n+1}(x) = a_0 + a_1 x + \cdots + a_n x^n + g(x).$$

Letting $b_k = c_k - a_k$ and subtracting the polynomial on the right from that on the left, we obtain

$$b_0 + b_1 x + \cdots + b_n x^n = g(x) - R_{n+1}(x).$$

Letting $x = 0$ shows that $b_0 = 0$. Suppose by induction that we have shown $b_0 = b_1 = \cdots = b_{m-1} = 0$ for $0 \leqq m \leqq n$. Then

$$b_m x^m + \cdots + b_n x^n = g(x) - R_{n+1}(x).$$

Dividing by x^m for $x \neq 0$, we find

$$b_m + b_{m+1} x + \cdots + b_n x^{n-m} = \frac{g(x)}{x^m} - \frac{R_{n+1}(x)}{x^m}.$$

Now let x approach 0. The terms on the right approach 0, and all terms on the left (except possibly b_m) approach 0. Hence $b_m = 0$, thus proving our uniqueness theorem.

In some applications, we are able to construct an approximation to f by a polynomial using some other means than by computing the derivatives for the Taylor coefficients. If we can write f in the form given in the Uniqueness Theorem, then we know that in fact we have found the Taylor polynomial approximation of f to the n-th degree.

The estimate for the remainder being $\leqq C|x|^{n+1}$, it is useful to give an explicit name for such estimates. Thus, let f be a function defined on some open interval containing 0. We say that $f(x)$ is $O(x^n)$ for $x \to 0$ if there is a constant C such that for all x sufficiently small, we have

$$|f(x)| \leqq C|x|^n.$$

Example 1. The function f such that $f(x) = x^3$ is $O(x^2)$ for $x \to 0$. Indeed, for $|x| \leq 1$ we know that

$$|x^3| = |x|\,|x|^2 \leq |x|^2.$$

This can be generalized (cf. Exercise 4b).

Example 2. We have $\sin x = O(x)$ for $x \to 0$. This will come out of the Taylor formula for $\sin x$ in the next section, but we already know from previous work that

$$\sin x \leq x \qquad\qquad \text{for } 0 \leq x \leq 1.$$

Since

$$|\sin (-x)| = |-\sin x| = |\sin x| \leq |x|,$$

we see that $\sin x = O(x)$ for $x \to 0$.

EXERCISES

(The first exercises are to show you how to recover some classical forms of the remainder.)

1. Let $g(t)$ be a continuous function on an interval between two numbers a and b. Show that

$$\int_a^b g(t)\, dt$$

lies between $m(b - a)$ and $M(b - a)$ if m, M are minimum and maximum values of g over the interval.

2. Use the intermediate value theorem to conclude that there is a number c in the interval such that

$$\int_a^b g(t)\, dt = g(c)(b - a).$$

3. Apply this to the remainder term

$$R_n = \int_a^b \frac{(b - t)^{n-1}}{(n - 1)!} f^{(n)}(t)\, dt$$

to conclude that there exists a number c between a and b such that

$$R_n = \frac{(b - c)^{n-1}(b - a)}{(n - 1)!} f^{(n)}(c).$$

4. (a) If f and g are functions which are both $O(x^n)$ for $x \to 0$, show that $f + g$ is $O(x^n)$ for $x \to 0$. If K is a constant, show that Kf is $O(x^n)$ for $x \to 0$.
   (b) If $n \geq m$ show that $x^n = O(x^m)$ for $x \to 0$.
   (c) If $f(x) = O(x^n)$ and $g(x) = O(x^m)$ for $x \to 0$, show that

$$f(x)g(x) = O(x^{n+m}) \qquad\qquad \text{for } x \to 0.$$

(d) Let P, Q be polynomials of degree $\leq n$, and assume that

$$f(x) = P(x) + O(x^{n+1}), \qquad \text{for} \quad x \to 0,$$
$$g(x) = Q(x) + O(x^{n+1}), \qquad \text{for} \quad x \to 0.$$

Show that $f(x)g(x) = P(x)Q(x) + O(x^{n+1})$, for $x \to 0$.

5. Show that for $x \to 0$,

$$1 + 2x - 5x^2 = 1 + 2x + O(x^2).$$

6. Show that for $x \to 0$,

$$1 + 2x - 5x^2 + 2x^3 = 1 + 2x + O(x^2).$$

7. In general, let $a_0, \ldots, a_n$ be numbers, and let $k < n$. Show that

$$a_0 + a_1 x + \cdots + a_n x^n = a_0 + a_1 x + \cdots + a_k x^k + O(x^{k+1}).$$

Example. Suppose that two functions f and g have Taylor formulas giving

$$f(x) = x - 2x^3 + x^4 + O(x^5),$$
$$g(x) = 1 + x \qquad\quad + O(x^5),$$

for $x \to 0$. Then

$$(x - 2x^3 + x^4)(1 + x) = x + x^2 - x^4 + x^5$$

and hence

$$f(x)g(x) = x + x^2 - x^4 + O(x^5).$$

Thus $x + x^2 - x^4$ is the Taylor polynomial of fg of degree ≤ 4.

§3. TRIGONOMETRIC FUNCTIONS

Let $f(x) = \sin x$ and take $a = 0$ in Taylor's formula. We have already mentioned what the derivatives of $\sin x$ and $\cos x$ are. Thus

$$f(0) = 0, \qquad f^{(2)}(0) = 0$$
$$f'(0) = 1, \qquad f^{(3)}(0) = -1.$$

The Taylor formula for $\sin x$ is therefore as follows:

$$\sin x = x - \frac{x^3}{3!} + \frac{x^5}{5!} - \cdots + (-1)^{n-1} \frac{x^{2n-1}}{(2n-1)!} + R_{2n+1}.$$

We see that all the even terms are 0 because $\sin 0 = 0$.

We can estimate $\sin x$ and $\cos x$ very simply, because

$$|\sin x| \leq 1 \qquad \text{and} \qquad |\cos x| \leq 1$$

for all x. Thus we take the bound

$$M_n = 1$$

for all n, and

$$|R_n| \leq \frac{|x|^n}{n!}.$$

Thus if we look at all values of x such that $|x| \leq 1$, we see that R_n approaches 0 when n becomes very large.

Example 1. Compute sin (0.1) to 3 decimals.

Let us estimate R_3. We let $a = 0$, $b = a + 0.1$ in Taylor's formula. We get the estimate

$$|R_3| \leq \frac{(0.1)^3}{3!} = \frac{10^{-3}}{6}.$$

Such an error term would put us within the required range of accuracy. Hence we can just use the first term of Taylor's formula,

$$\sin (0.1) = 0.100,$$

with an error which does not exceed $\pm \frac{1}{6} 10^{-4}$.

We see how efficient this is for computing the sine for small values of x.

Example 2. Compute $\sin\left(\dfrac{\pi}{6} + 0.2\right)$ to an accuracy of 10^{-4}.

In this case, we take $a = \pi/6$. By trial and error, and guessing, we try for the remainder R_4. Thus

$$\sin (a + h) = \sin a + \cos (a) \frac{h}{1} - \sin (a) \frac{h^2}{2!} - \cos (a) \frac{h^3}{3!} + R_4$$

$$= \frac{1}{2} + \frac{\sqrt{3}}{2} (0.2) - \frac{1}{2} \frac{(0.2)^2}{2} - \frac{\sqrt{3}}{2} \frac{(0.2)^3}{6} + R_4.$$

For R_4 we have the estimate

$$|R_4| \leq \frac{(0.2)^4}{4!} = \frac{16 \cdot 10^{-4}}{24} \leq 10^{-4},$$

which is within the required bounds of accuracy. You do not need to carry out the actual decimal expansion of the first four terms, which are given just as an illustration.

Example 3. Find the limit

$$\lim_{x \to 0} \frac{\sin x - x + x^3/3!}{x^4}.$$

We have for $|x| \leq 1$:

$$\sin x - x + \frac{x^3}{3!} = R_5(x) \quad \text{and} \quad |R_5(x)| \leq \frac{|x|^5}{5!}.$$

Hence

$$\left| \frac{\sin x - x + x^3/3!}{x^4} \right| \leq \frac{|R_5(x)|}{|x^4|} \leq \frac{|x|}{5!}.$$

The desired limit is therefore equal to 0.

It is still true that the remainder term of the Taylor formula for $\sin x$ approaches 0 when n becomes large, even when x is > 1. For this we need:

Theorem 4. *Let c be any number. Then $c^n/n!$ approaches 0 as n becomes very large.*

Proof. Let n_0 be an integer such that $n_0 > 2c$. Thus $c < n_0/2$, and $c/n_0 < \frac{1}{2}$. We write

$$\frac{c^n}{n!} = \frac{c \cdot c \cdots c}{1 \cdot 2 \cdots n_0} \frac{c}{(n_0 + 1)(n_0 + 2)} \cdots \frac{c}{n}$$

$$\leq \frac{c^{n_0}}{n_0!} \left(\frac{1}{2}\right) \cdots \left(\frac{1}{2}\right)$$

$$= \frac{c^{n_0}}{n_0!} \left(\frac{1}{2}\right)^{n-n_0}$$

As n becomes large, $(1/2)^{n-n_0}$ becomes small and our fraction approaches 0. Take for instance $c = 10$. We write

$$\frac{10^n}{n!} = \frac{10 \cdots 10}{1 \cdot 2 \cdots 20} \frac{(10) \cdots (10)}{(21) \cdots (n)} < \frac{10^{20}}{20!} \left(\frac{1}{2}\right)^{n-20}$$

and $(1/2)^{n-20}$ approaches 0 as n becomes large.

From this we see that given a number $b > 0$, the remainder in Taylor's formula for $\sin x$ approaches 0, if $|x| \leq b$.

EXERCISES

1. Write down the first 5 terms of the Taylor formula for $\cos x$.

2. Give an estimate for the remainder similar to that for $\sin x$.

3. Compute $\cos (0.1)$ to 3 decimals.

4. Estimate the remainder R_3 in the Taylor formula for $\cos x$, for the value $x = 0.1$.

5. Estimate the remainder R_4 in the Taylor formula for $\sin x$, for the value $x = 0.2$.

6. Write down the terms of order ≤ 4 of the Taylor formula for $\tan x$.

7. Estimate the remainder R_4 in the Taylor formula for $\tan x$, for $0 \leq x \leq 0.2$.

8. Compute sine 31 degrees to 3 places.

Write down the terms of order ≤ 4 of the Taylor formula for the following functions:

9. $\sin^2 x$

10. $\cos^3 x$

11. $\dfrac{1}{\cos x}$

12. $\sin^3 x$

§4. EXPONENTIAL FUNCTION

All derivatives of e^x are equal to e^x and $e^0 = 1$. Hence the Taylor series for e^x is

$$e^x = 1 + x + \frac{x^2}{2!} + \cdots + \frac{x^{n-1}}{(n-1)!} + R_n.$$

Case 1. Look at values of x such that $x < 0$; then $e^x < 1$ and of course $e^x > 0$ for all x. Hence by Theorem 2, we get

$$|R_n| \leqq \frac{|x|^n}{n!},$$

which is the same estimate we obtained for $\sin x$.

Case 2. Look at values of $x > 0$, and say $x \leqq b$ for some number b. Since e^x is strictly increasing, we know that

$$e^x \leqq e^b$$

for any value of $x \leqq b$. Hence by Theorem 5, we get

$$|R_n| \leqq e^b \frac{b^n}{n!},$$

and we see again that this tends to 0 as n becomes large.

Example 1. Compute e to 3 decimals.

We have $e = e^1$. From Chapter VIII, §4 we know that $e < 4$. We estimate R_7:

$$|R_7| \leqq e \frac{1}{7!} \leqq 4 \frac{1}{5,040} \leqq 10^{-3}.$$

Thus

$$e = 1 + 1 + \frac{1}{2} + \cdots + \frac{1}{6!} + R_7$$
$$= 2.718\ldots.$$

Of course, the smaller x is, the fewer terms of the Taylor series do we need to approximate e^x.

Example 2. How many terms of the Taylor series do you need to compute $e^{1/10}$ to an accuracy of 10^{-3}?

We certainly have $e^{1/10} < 2$. Thus

$$|R_3| \leqq 2 \frac{(1/10)^3}{3!} < \frac{1}{2} 10^{-3}.$$

Hence we need just 3 terms (including the 0-th term).

EXERCISES

1. Write down the terms of order ≤ 4 of the Taylor formula e^{-x^2}.
2. Estimate the remainder R_3 in the Taylor series for e^x for $x = 1/2$.
3. Estimate the remainder R_4 for $x = 10^{-2}$.
4. Estimate the remainder R_3 for $x = 10^{-2}$.
5. Write down the terms of order ≤ 5 of the Taylor series for e^{-x}.
6. Compute $1/e$ to 3 decimals, and show which remainder would give you an accuracy of 10^{-3}.
7. Write down the first four terms of the Taylor series for the function f such that

$$f(x) = e^{-1/x^2}$$

when $x \neq 0$, and $f(0) = 0$. Can you say something about the other terms in the Taylor series?

§5. LOGARITHM

We leave it to you to derive the Taylor series for the logarithm. Take $a = 1$. We shall obtain an analogous result here by another method.

Let t be any number, and n an integer > 1. Then

$$\left(1 - t + t^2 - \cdots + (-1)^{n-1}t^{n-1}\right)(1 + t) = 1 + (-1)^{n-1}t^n.$$

This is trivially proved. We first multiply the big sum on the left by 1 and then by t, getting

$$1 - t + t^2 - \cdots + (-1)^{n-1}t^{n-1}$$
$$+ t - t^2 + \cdots - (-1)^{n-2}t^{n-1} + (-1)^{n-1}t^n,$$

and add, to obtain what we want.

Suppose that $t \neq -1$. Then we can divide by $1 + t$. Thus

$$\frac{1 + (-1)^{n-1}t^n}{1 + t} = \frac{1}{1 + t} + \frac{(-1)^{n-1}t^n}{1 + t}.$$

This yields

$$\boxed{\frac{1}{1 + t} = 1 - t + t^2 - \cdots + (-1)^{n-1}t^{n-1} + \frac{(-1)^n t^n}{1 + t}.}$$

Consider the interval $-1 < x \leq 1$, and take the integral from 0 to x (in this interval). The integrals of the powers of t are well known to you. The integral

$$\int_0^x \frac{1}{1 + t}\, dt = \log(1 + x)$$

is computed by the substitution $u = 1 + t$, $du = dt$. Thus we get:

Theorem 5. *For* $-1 < x \leq 1$, *we have*

$$\log (1 + x) = x - \frac{x^2}{2} + \frac{x^3}{3} - \cdots + (-1)^{n-1} \frac{x^n}{n} + R_{n+1},$$

where the remainder R_{n+1} *is the integral*

$$(-1)^n \int_0^x \frac{t^n}{1 + t} \, dt.$$

We shall now estimate the remainder term.

Case 1. Let a be a number with $0 < a \leq 1$, and consider the interval $0 \leq x \leq a$.

In that case, $1 + t \geq 1$. Thus

$$\frac{t^n}{1 + t} \leq t^n,$$

and our integral is bounded by $\int_0^x t^n \, dt$. Thus in that case,

$$|R_{n+1}| \leq \int_0^x t^n \, dt \leq \frac{x^{n+1}}{n + 1} \leq \frac{a^{n+1}}{n + 1}.$$

(We perform the integration and use the fact that $x \leq 1$.) In particular, the remainder approaches 0 as n becomes large.

Case 2. Let a be a number with $-1 < a < 0$ and consider the interval $a \leq x \leq 0$.

In that case, we see that $0 < 1 + a \leq 1 + t$ if t lies between x and 0.

Thus

$$\left| \frac{t^n}{1 + t} \right| = \frac{|t|^n}{1 + t} \leq \frac{(-t)^n}{1 + a}.$$

To estimate the absolute value of the integral, we can invert the limits (we do this because $x \leq 0$) and thus

$$|R_{n+1}| \leq \int_x^0 \frac{(-t)^n}{1 + a} \, dt$$

$$= \frac{(-x)^{n+1}}{(n + 1)(1 + a)} = \frac{|x|^{n+1}}{(n + 1)(1 + a)} \leq \frac{|a|^{n+1}}{(n + 1)(1 + a)}.$$

Therefore the remainder also approaches 0 in that case.

Example. Compute log 1.1 to three decimals.

To do this, i.e. compute $\log (1 + 0.1)$, we take $n = 2$, and $a = 0.1$ in Case 1. We find that

$$|R_3| \leq \tfrac{1}{3} \times 10^{-3}.$$

Hence

$$\log (1.1) = 0.1 - 0.005,$$

with an error not exceeding $\tfrac{1}{3} \times 10^{-3}$.

EXERCISES

1. Compute the following values up to an accuracy of 10^{-3}, estimating the remainder each time.

   (a) log 1.2   (b) log 0.9   (c) log 1.05
   (d) $\log \tfrac{9}{10}$ (e) $\log \tfrac{24}{25}$ (f) $\log \tfrac{26}{25}$

2. Show that the expression given in Theorem 5 for the log satisfies the conditions of the Uniqueness Theorem for the Taylor expansion.

§6. THE ARCTANGENT

We proceed as with the logarithm, except that we consider

$$\frac{1}{1 + t^2} = 1 - t^2 + t^4 - \cdots + (-1)^{n-1}t^{2n-2} + (-1)^n \frac{t^{2n}}{1 + t^2}.$$

After integration from 0 to any number x, we obtain:

Theorem 6. *The arctan has an expansion*

$$\arctan x = x - \frac{x^3}{3} + \frac{x^5}{5} - \cdots + (-1)^{n-1} \frac{x^{2n-1}}{2n - 1} + R_{2n},$$

where

$$R_{2n} = (-1)^n \int_0^x \frac{t^{2n}}{1 + t^2} \, dt.$$

If b is a positive number such that $|x| \leq b$ then

$$|R_{2n}| \leq \int_0^b t^{2n} \, dt \leq \frac{b^{2n+1}}{2n + 1}.$$

When $-1 \leq x \leq 1$, the remainder approaches 0 as n becomes large.

From our theorem, we get an expression for $\pi/4$:

$$\frac{\pi}{4} = 1 - \frac{1}{3} + \frac{1}{5} - \cdots$$

from the Taylor formula for arctan 1. However, it takes many terms to get a good approximation to $\pi/4$ by this expression. You will find a more clever approach in the exercises.

EXERCISES

1. Prove the addition formula for the tangent:

$$\tan (x + y) = \frac{\tan x + \tan y}{1 - \tan x \tan y}.$$

2. Prove that $\pi/4 = \arctan \frac{1}{2} + \arctan \frac{1}{3}$.

3. Verify that $\pi = 3.14159...$.

4. You will need even fewer terms if you prove that

$$\frac{\pi}{4} = 4 \arctan \frac{1}{5} - \arctan \frac{1}{239}.$$

Find the following limits as x approaches 0:

5. $\dfrac{e^x - 1}{x}$ 6. $\dfrac{\sin (x^2)}{(\sin x)^2}$ 7. $\dfrac{\tan x}{\sin x}$

8. $\dfrac{\arctan x}{x}$ 9. $\dfrac{\log (1 + x)}{x}$ 10. $\dfrac{\log (1 + 2x)}{x}$

11. $\dfrac{e^x - (1 + x)}{x^2}$ 12. $\dfrac{\sin x - x}{x^2}$ 13. $\dfrac{\cos x - 1}{x^2}$

14. $\dfrac{\log (1 + x^2)}{\sin (x^2)}$ 15. $\dfrac{\tan (x^2)}{(\sin x)^2}$ 16. $\dfrac{\log (1 + x^2)}{(\sin x)^2}$

17. Show that the polynomial approximation to the arctangent given in Theorem 6 satisfies the conditions of the Uniqueness Theorem. (Perform integrations just as we did for the logarithm.)

§7. THE BINOMIAL EXPANSION

Let us first consider a special case.

Let n be a positive integer, and consider the function

$$f(x) = (1 + x)^n.$$

We have no difficulty computing the derivatives:

$$f'(x) = n(1 + x)^{n-1}$$
$$f''(x) = n(n - 1)(1 + x)^{n-2}$$
$$\vdots$$
$$f^{(n)}(x) = n!$$
$$f^{(n+1)}(x) = 0.$$

Thus the Taylor formula has no remainder after the n-th term, and we get:

Theorem 7. *Let n be a positive integer. For any number x, we have*

$$(1 + x)^n = 1 + nx + \frac{n(n - 1)}{2!} x^2$$
$$+ \frac{n(n - 1)(n - 2)}{3!} x^3 + \cdots + x^n.$$

The coefficient of x^k is sometimes denoted by C_k^n or $\binom{n}{k}$ and is called a *binomial coefficient*. Thus:

$$\binom{n}{k} = \frac{n!}{k!(n - k)!}.$$

If we want an expression for $(a + b)^n$ with numbers a, b, then we let $x = b/a$. Then

$$\left(1 + \frac{b}{a}\right)^n = \frac{1}{a^n}(a + b)^n,$$

and from this we conclude at once that

$$(a + b)^n = \sum_{k=0}^{n} \binom{n}{k} a^k b^{n-k}.$$

We shall now consider the function $(1 + x)^s$ when s is not an integer. We define the *binomial coefficient*

$$\binom{s}{k} = \frac{s(s - 1) \cdots (s - k + 1)}{k!}.$$

Theorem 8. *Let s be any number and let x lie in the interval $-1 < x < 1$. Then we have*

$$(1 + x)^s = 1 + sx + \frac{s(s - 1)}{2!} x^2$$
$$+ \frac{s(s - 1)(s - 2)}{3!} x^3 + \cdots + \binom{s}{k} x^k + R_{k+1},$$

where the remainder term is equal to the usual integral. The remainder R_k approaches 0 as k becomes large.

Proof. The proof that the remainder approaches 0 is slightly more involved than our previous proofs, and will be omitted. There is of course no difficulty in verifying that when $f(x) = (1 + x)^s$ then

$$\frac{f^{(k)}(0)}{k!} = \binom{s}{k}$$

and you should definitely do this as an exercise.

What we shall do, however, is discuss the remainder R_2. Let

$$f(x) = (1 + x)^s,$$

where s is not an integer. We have

$$f^{(2)}(x) = s(s - 1)(1 + x)^{s-2}.$$

The Taylor formula gives

$$(1 + x)^s = 1 + sx + R_2.$$

For small x, this means that $1 + sx$ should be a good approximation to the s power of $1 + x$, if R_2 can be proved to be small. This we can do easily. We know that

$$|R_2| \leq \frac{M_2|x|^2}{2!} \leq \frac{|s(s - 1)|}{2}(1 + c)^{s-2}|x|^2,$$

where c is between 0 and x. By an easy estimate one sees, for instance, that $(1 + x)^{1/2}$ is approximately equal to $1 + \frac{1}{2}x$, and $(1 + x)^{1/3}$ is approximately equal to $1 + \frac{1}{3}x$, for small x.

Example 1. Find $\sqrt{1.2}$ to 2 decimals. We estimate R_2 with $s = \frac{1}{2}$, $x = 0.2$. Then $c \geq 0$ and $s - 2 = -3/2$. Hence

$$(1 + c)^{s-2} \leq 1.$$

Consequently

$$|R_2| \leq \tfrac{1}{8}(0.04) = 0.5 \times 10^{-2}.$$

Thus

$$\sqrt{1.2} = (1 + 0.2)^{1/2} = 1.10 \pm 0.5 \times 10^{-2},$$

which is within the desired accuracy.

EXERCISES

1. Compute the cube root of 126 to 4 decimals.
2. Compute $\sqrt{97}$ to 4 decimals.
3. Estimate R_2 in the remainder of $(1 + x)^{1/3}$ for x lying in the interval

$$-0.1 \leq x \leq 0.1.$$

4. Estimate the remainder R_2 in the Taylor series of $(1 + x)^{1/2}$ (a) when $x = -0.2$, (b) when $x = 0.1$.

5. Estimate the remainder R_2 in the Taylor series for $(1 + x)^{1/4}$ (a) when $x = 0.01$, (b) when $x = 0.2$, (c) when $x = 0.1$.

6. Estimate the remainder R_3 in the Taylor series for $(1 + x)^{1/2}$ (a) when $x = 0.2$, (b) when $x = -0.2$, (c) when $x = 0.1$.

Supplementary Exercises

Give the first four terms of the Taylor formula for the following functions:

1. $\dfrac{1}{1 + \sin x}$ 2. $\dfrac{1}{1 + \sin^2 x}$ 3. $\dfrac{1}{\cos^2 x}$

4. $\sin x \cos x$ 5. $\tan x$ 6. $\tan^2 x$

7. $\sin x - \cos x$ 8. $\sin x + \cos x$ 9. $(\sin x)e^x$

10. $(\cos x)e^x$ 11. $e^x + e^{-x}$ 12. $e^x - e^{-x}$

13. $\dfrac{1}{e^x + e^{-x}}$ 14. $1 + \pi x + 3x^2 + 2x^3$

15. Using Exercise 4(c) of §2, give the terms of degree ≤ 4 for the Taylor formula of the following functions:

(a) $(\sin x) \cos x$ (b) $(\sin x)e^x$ (c) $(\cos x)e^x$
(d) $(\arctan x) \sin x$ (e) $(\arctan x) \cos x$ (f) $(1 - x) \cos x$
(g) $(1 + x + x^2) \sin x$

16. (a) Verify the following formulas:

$$\log 2 = -7 \log \tfrac{9}{10} + 2 \log \tfrac{24}{25} + 3 \log \tfrac{81}{80}$$
$$\log 3 = -11 \log \tfrac{9}{10} + 3 \log \tfrac{24}{25} + 5 \log \tfrac{81}{80}$$

(b) Compute $\log 2$ and $\log 3$ to five decimals.

17. Compute $1/e^2$ to 4 decimals.

18. What are the first four terms of the Taylor series for

$$\log \frac{1 + x}{1 - x} \ ?$$

Estimate the remainder R_5.

Using the first few terms of the Taylor formula, and the estimate for the remainder, determine the following limits as x approaches 0.

19. $\dfrac{e^x - e^{-x}}{x}$ 20. $\dfrac{\sin x}{e^x - e^{-x}}$ 21. $\dfrac{\sin^2 x}{\sin x^2}$

22. $\dfrac{\tan x^2}{\sin^2 x}$ 23. $\dfrac{\log (1 - x)}{\sin x}$ 24. $\dfrac{e^x + e^{-x} - 2}{x^2}$

25. $\dfrac{e^x + e^{-x} - 2}{x \sin x}$ 26. $\dfrac{\sin x - x}{x^2}$ 27. $\dfrac{\sin x - x}{x^3}$

28. $\dfrac{e^x - 1 - x}{x}$
    29. $\dfrac{e^x - 1 - x}{x^2}$
    30. $\dfrac{\log (1 + x^2)}{x^2}$

31. $\dfrac{(1 + x)^{1/2} - 1 - \frac{1}{2}x}{x^2}$
    32. $\dfrac{(1 - x)^{1/3} - 1 - \frac{1}{3}x}{x^2}$

33. Let $f(x)$ be a function which has $n + 1$ continuous derivatives in an open interval containing the origin, and assume that the $(n + 1)$-th derivative is bounded by a constant M on this interval. Let $P_n(x)$ be the polynomial consisting of the terms whose degree is $\leq n$ in the Taylor formula for $f(x)$. What are the following limits?

(a) $\lim\limits_{x \to 0} \dfrac{f(x) - P_n(x)}{x^2}$ (assuming $n \geq 3$)

(b) $\lim\limits_{x \to 0} \dfrac{f(x) - P_n(x)}{x^n}$
    (c) $\lim\limits_{x \to 0} \dfrac{f(x) - P_n(x)}{x^{n-1}}$ (assuming $n \geq 2$)

Determine the following limits as x approaches 0.

34. $\dfrac{\sin x + \cos x - 1}{x}$
    35. $\dfrac{\sin x + \cos x - 1 - x}{x^2}$

36. $\dfrac{\sin x - x + x^3/3!}{x^4}$
    37. $\dfrac{\sin x - x + x^3/3!}{x^5}$

38. $\dfrac{\cos x - 1 - x^2/2!}{x}$
    39. $\dfrac{\cos x - 1 - x^2/2!}{x^2}$

40. $\dfrac{\cos x - 1 + x^2/2!}{x^3}$
    41. $\dfrac{\cos x - 1 + x^2/2!}{x^4}$

42. $\dfrac{\sin x + e^x - 1}{x}$
    43. $\dfrac{\sin x - e^x + 1}{x}$

44. $\dfrac{\sin x - e^x + 1}{x^2}$
    45. $\dfrac{\cos x - e^x}{x}$

46. Estimate the following integrals to three decimals.

(a) $\displaystyle\int_0^1 \dfrac{\sin x}{x}\, dx$
    (b) $\displaystyle\int_0^{0.1} \dfrac{\cos x - 1}{x}\, dx$

(c) $\displaystyle\int_0^{0.1} \dfrac{e^x - 1}{x}\, dx$
    (d) $\displaystyle\int_0^1 \dfrac{\sin x^2}{x}\, dx$

(e) $\displaystyle\int_0^1 \dfrac{\cos x^2}{x^2}\, dx$
    (f) $\displaystyle\int_0^1 \dfrac{\sin x^2}{x^2}\, dx$

(g) $\displaystyle\int_0^1 e^{-x^2}\, dx$
    (h) $\displaystyle\int_0^1 e^{x^2}\, dx$

(i) $\displaystyle\int_0^{0.1} e^{x^2}\, dx$
    (j) $\displaystyle\int_0^{0.1} e^{-x^2}\, dx$

We work out integral 46(a) as an example, to two decimals. We have:

$$\sin x = x - \frac{x^3}{3!} + R_5(x) \quad \text{and} \quad |R_5(x)| \leq \frac{|x|^5}{5!}.$$

Hence

$$\frac{\sin x}{x} = 1 - \frac{x^2}{3!} + \frac{R_5(x)}{x} \quad \text{and} \quad \left|\frac{R_5(x)}{x}\right| \leq \frac{|x|^4}{5!}.$$

Hence

$$\int_0^1 \frac{\sin x}{x}\,dx = x - \frac{x^3}{3\cdot 3!}\Big|_0^1 + \int_0^1 \frac{R_5(x)}{x}\,dx$$

and

$$\int_0^1 \left|\frac{R_5(x)}{x}\right|\,dx \leq \int_0^1 \frac{x^4}{5!}\,dx = \frac{x^5}{5\cdot 5!}\Big|_0^1 = \frac{1}{600}.$$

Hence up to two decimals, our integral has the value

$$x - \frac{x^3}{3\cdot 3!}\Big|_0^1 = 1 - \frac{1}{18} = \frac{17}{18}.$$

Chapter XV

Series

Series are a natural continuation of our study of functions. In the preceding chapter we found how to approximate our elementary functions by polynomials, with a certain error term. Conversely, one can define arbitrary functions by giving a series for them. We shall see how in the sections below.

In practice, very few tests are used to determine convergence of series. Essentially, the comparison test is the most frequent. Furthermore, the most important series are those which converge absolutely. Thus we shall put greater emphasis on these.

§1. CONVERGENT SERIES

Suppose that we are given a sequence of numbers

$$a_1, a_2, a_3, \ldots,$$

i.e. we are given a number a_n for each integer $n \geq 1$. (We picked the starting place to be 1, but we could have picked any integer.) We form the sums

$$s_n = a_1 + a_2 + \cdots + a_n.$$

It would be meaningless to form an infinite sum

$$a_1 + a_2 + a_3 + \cdots$$

because we do not know how to add infinitely many numbers. However, if our sums s_n approach a limit, as n becomes large, then we say that the sum of our sequence *converges*, and we now define its *sum* to be that limit.

The symbols

$$\sum_{n=1}^{\infty} a_n$$

will be called a *series*. We shall say that the *series converges* if the sums s_n approach a limit as n becomes large. Otherwise, we say that it does not converge, or *diverges*. If the series converges, we say that the value of the series is

$$\sum_{n=1}^{\infty} a_n = \lim_{n\to\infty} s_n = \lim_{n\to\infty} (a_1 + \cdots + a_n).$$

The symbols $\lim_{n\to\infty}$ are to be read: "The limit as n becomes large."

Example. Consider the sequence

$$1, \frac{1}{2}, \frac{1}{4}, \frac{1}{8}, \frac{1}{16}, \ldots,$$

and let us form the sums

$$1 + \frac{1}{2} + \frac{1}{4} + \cdots + \frac{1}{2^n}.$$

You probably know already that these sums approach a limit and that this limit is 2. To prove it, let $r = \frac{1}{2}$. Then

$$(1 + r + r^2 + \cdots + r^n) = \frac{1 - r^{n+1}}{1 - r} = \frac{1}{1 - r} - \frac{r^{n+1}}{1 - r}.$$

As n becomes large, r^{n+1} approaches 0, whence our sums approach

$$\frac{1}{1 - \frac{1}{2}} = 2.$$

Actually, the same argument works if we take for r any number such that

$$-1 < r < 1.$$

In that case, r^{n+1} approaches 0 as n becomes large, and consequently we can write

$$\sum_{n=0}^{\infty} r^n = \frac{1}{1 - r}.$$

In view of the fact that the limit of a sum is the sum of the limits, and other standard properties of limits, we get:

Theorem 1. *Let $\{a_n\}$ and $\{b_n\}$ $(n = 1, 2, \ldots)$ be two sequences and assume that the series*

$$\sum_{n=1}^{\infty} a_n \quad and \quad \sum_{n=1}^{\infty} b_n$$

converge. Then $\sum_{n=1}^{\infty} (a_n + b_n)$ also converges, and is equal to the sum of the two series. If c is a number, then

$$\sum_{n=1}^{\infty} ca = c \sum_{n=1}^{\infty} a_n.$$

Finally, if $s_n = a_1 + \cdots + a_n$ and $t_n = b_1 + \cdots + b_n$ then

$$\sum_{n=1}^{\infty} a_n \sum_{n=1}^{\infty} b_n = \lim_{n \to \infty} s_n t_n.$$

In particular, series can be added term by term. Of course, they cannot be multiplied term by term!

We also observe that a similar theorem holds for the difference of two series.

If a series $\sum a_n$ converges, then the numbers a_n must approach 0 as n becomes large. However, there are examples of sequences $\{a_n\}$ for which the series does not converge, and yet

$$\lim_{n \to \infty} a_n = 0.$$

Consider for instance

$$1 + \frac{1}{2} + \frac{1}{3} + \cdots + \frac{1}{n} + \cdots.$$

We contend that the partial sums s_n become very large when n becomes large. To see this, we look at partial sums as follows:

$$1 + \frac{1}{2} + \frac{1}{3} + \frac{1}{4} + \frac{1}{5} + \cdots + \frac{1}{8} + \frac{1}{9} + \cdots + \frac{1}{16} + \cdots.$$

In each bunch of terms as indicated, we replace each term by that farthest to the right. This makes our sums smaller. Thus our expression is

$$\geqq 1 + \frac{1}{2} + \frac{1}{4} + \frac{1}{4} + \frac{1}{8} + \cdots + \frac{1}{8} + \frac{1}{16} + \cdots + \frac{1}{16} + \cdots$$

$$\geqq 1 + \frac{1}{2} + \frac{1}{2} + \frac{1}{2} + \frac{1}{2} + \cdots$$

and therefore becomes arbitrarily large when n becomes large.

§2. SERIES WITH POSITIVE TERMS

Throughout this section, we shall assume that our numbers a_n are $\geqq 0$. Then the partial sums

$$s_n = a_1 + \cdots + a_n$$

are increasing, i.e.

$$s_1 \leqq s_2 \leqq s_3 \leqq \cdots \leqq s_n \leqq s_{n+1} \leqq \cdots.$$

If they are to approach a limit at all, they cannot become arbitrarily large.

Thus in that case there is a number B such that

$$s_n \leqq B$$

for all n. The collection of numbers $\{s_n\}$ has therefore a least upper bound, i.e. there is a smallest number S such that

$$s_n \leqq S$$

for all n. In that case, the partial sums s_n approach S as a limit. In other words, given any positive number $\epsilon > 0$, we have

$$S - \epsilon \leqq s_n \leqq S$$

for all n sufficiently large.

This simply expresses the fact that S is the least of all upper bounds for our collection of numbers s_n. We express this as a theorem.

Theorem 2. *Let $\{a_n\}$ $(n = 1, 2, \ldots)$ be a sequence of numbers $\geqq 0$ and let*

$$s_n = a_1 + \cdots + a_n.$$

If the sequence of numbers $\{s_n\}$ is bounded, then it approaches a limit S, which is its least upper bound.

Theorem 1 gives us a very useful criterion to determine when a series with positive terms converges:

Theorem 3. *Let*

$$\sum_{n=1}^{\infty} a_n \qquad and \qquad \sum_{n=1}^{\infty} b_n$$

be two series, with $a_n \geqq 0$ for all n and $b_n \geqq 0$ for all n. Assume that there is a number $C > 0$ such that

$$a_n \leqq C b_n$$

for all n, and that $\sum\limits_{n=1}^{\infty} b_n$ converges. Then $\sum\limits_{n=1}^{\infty} a_n$ converges, and

$$\sum_{n=1}^{\infty} a_n \leqq C \sum_{n=1}^{\infty} b_n.$$

Proof. We have

$$a_1 + \cdots + a_n \leqq C b_1 + \cdots + C b_n = C(b_1 + \cdots + b_n) \leqq C \sum_{n=1}^{\infty} b_n.$$

This means that $C \sum_{n=1}^{\infty} b_n$ is a bound for the partial sums

$$a_1 + \cdots + a_n.$$

The least upper bound of these sums is therefore $\leq C \sum_{n=1}^{\infty} b_n$, thereby proving our theorem.

Example 1. Prove that the series $\sum_{n=1}^{\infty} \frac{1}{n^2}$ converges.
Let us look at the series:

$$\frac{1}{1^2} + \frac{1}{2^2} + \frac{1}{3^2} + \frac{1}{4^2} + \cdots + \frac{1}{8^2} + \cdots + \frac{1}{16^2} + \cdots + \cdots.$$

We look at the groups of terms as indicated. In each group of terms, if we decrease the denominator in each term, then we increase the fraction. We replace 3 by 2, then 4, 5, 6, 7 by 4, then we replace the numbers from 8 to 15 by 8, and so forth. Our partial sums are therefore less than or equal to

$$1 + \frac{1}{2^2} + \frac{1}{2^2} + \frac{1}{4^2} + \cdots + \frac{1}{4^2} + \frac{1}{8^2} + \cdots + \frac{1}{8^2} + \cdots,$$

and we note that 2 occurs twice, 4 occurs four times, 8 occurs eight times, and so forth. Hence the partial sums are less than or equal to

$$1 + \frac{2}{2^2} + \frac{4}{4^2} + \frac{8}{8^2} + \cdots = 1 + \frac{1}{2} + \frac{1}{4} + \frac{1}{8} + \cdots.$$

Thus our partial sums are less than or equal to those of the geometric series and are bounded. Hence our series converges.

Theorem 3 has an analogue to show that a series does not converge.

Theorem 3'. *Let*

$$\sum_{n=1}^{\infty} a_n \qquad and \qquad \sum_{n=1}^{\infty} b_n$$

be two series, with a_n and $b_n \geq 0$ for all n. Assume that there is a number $C > 0$ such that

$$a_n \geq C b_n$$

for all n sufficiently large, and that $\sum_{n=1}^{\infty} b_n$ does not converge. Then $\sum_{n=1}^{\infty} a_n$ diverges.

Proof. Assume $a_n \geq C b_n$ for $n \geq n_0$.
Since $\sum b_n$ diverges, we can make the partial sums

$$\sum_{n=n_0}^{N} b_n = b_{n_0} + \cdots + b_N$$

arbitrarily large as N becomes arbitrarily large. But

$$\sum_{n=n_0}^{N} a_n \geq \sum_{n=n_0}^{N} Cb_n = C \sum_{n=n_0}^{N} b_n.$$

Hence the partial sums

$$\sum_{n=1}^{N} a_n = a_1 + \cdots + a_N$$

are arbitrarily large as N becomes arbitrarily large, and hence $\sum_{n=1}^{\infty} a_n$ diverges, as was to be shown.

Example 2. Determine whether the series

$$\sum_{n=1}^{\infty} \frac{n^2}{n^3 + 1}$$

converges.

We write

$$\frac{n^2}{n^3 + 1} = \frac{1}{n + 1/n^2} = \frac{1}{n}\left(\frac{1}{1 + 1/n^3}\right).$$

Then for n sufficiently large, we see that

$$\frac{n^2}{n^3 + 1} \geq \frac{1}{2n}.$$

Since $\sum 1/n$ does not converge, it follows that the series of Example 2 does not converge either.

EXERCISES

1. Show that the series $\displaystyle\sum_{n=1}^{\infty} \frac{1}{n^3}$ converges.

2. (a) Show that the series $\displaystyle\sum \frac{\log n}{n^3}$ converges. [*Hint:* Estimate $(\log n)/n$.]

   (b) Show that the series $\displaystyle\sum \frac{(\log n)^2}{n^3}$ converges.

Test the following series for convergence:

3. $\displaystyle\sum_{n=1}^{\infty} \frac{1}{n^{1/2}}$

4. $\displaystyle\sum_{n=1}^{\infty} \frac{n^2}{n^4 + n}$

5. $\displaystyle\sum_{n=1}^{\infty} \frac{n}{n + 1}$

6. $\displaystyle\sum_{n=1}^{\infty} \frac{n}{n + 5}$

7. $\displaystyle\sum_{n=1}^{\infty} \frac{n^2}{n^3 + n + 2}$

8. $\displaystyle\sum_{n=1}^{\infty} \frac{|\sin n|}{n^2 + 1}$

9. $\displaystyle\sum_{n=1}^{\infty} \frac{|\cos n|}{n^2 + n}$

§3. THE RATIO TEST

We continue to consider only series with terms ≥ 0. To compare such a series with a geometric series, the simplest test is given by the ratio test.

Ratio Test. *Let* $\sum\limits_{n=1}^{\infty} a_n$ *be a series with* $a_n > 0$ *for all* n. *Assume that there is a number* c *with* $0 < c < 1$ *such that*

$$\frac{a_{n+1}}{a_n} \leq c$$

for all n *sufficiently large. Then the series converges.*

Proof. Suppose that there exists some integer N such that $a_{n+1}/a_n \leq c$ if $n \geq N$. Then

$$a_{N+1} \leq ca_N$$
$$a_{N+2} \leq ca_{N+1} \leq c^2 a_N$$

and in general, by induction,

$$a_{N+k} \leq c^k a_N.$$

Thus

$$\sum_{n=N}^{N+k} a_n \leq a_N + ca_N + c^2 a_N + \cdots + c^k a_N$$

$$\leq a_N(1 + c + \cdots + c^k) \leq a_N \frac{1}{1-c}.$$

Thus in effect, we have compared our series with a geometric series, and we know that the partial sums are bounded. This implies that our series converges.

Example. Show that the series

$$\sum_{n=1}^{\infty} \frac{n}{3^n}$$

converges.

We let $a_n = n/3^n$. Then

$$\frac{a_{n+1}}{a_n} = \frac{n+1}{3^{n+1}} \frac{3^n}{n} = \frac{n+1}{n} \frac{1}{3}.$$

When n is large, then $(n+1)/n$ is close to 1, and $(n+1)/3n$ is close to $1/3$. In particular, if we take $1/3 < c < 1$, we see that $a_{n+1}/a_n < c$ for all n sufficiently large. Hence we can apply the theorem to see that our series converges.

EXERCISES

Determine whether the following series converge:

1. $\sum n2^{-n}$

2. $\sum n^2 2^{-n}$

3. $\sum \dfrac{1}{\log n}$

4. $\sum \dfrac{\log n}{n^2}$

5. $\sum \dfrac{\log n}{n}$

6. $\sum \dfrac{n^{10}}{3^n}$

7. $\sum \dfrac{1}{\sqrt{n(n+1)}}$

8. $\sum \dfrac{1}{\sqrt{n^3+1}}$

9. $\sum \dfrac{n+1}{\sqrt{n^4+n+1}}$

10. $\sum \dfrac{n+1}{2^n}$

11. $\sum \dfrac{n}{(4n-1)(n+15)}$

12. $\sum \dfrac{1+\cos(\pi n/2)}{e^n}$

13. $\sum \dfrac{1}{(\log n)^{10}}$

14. $\sum n^2 e^{-n^2}$

15. $\sum n^2 e^{-n^3}$

16. $\sum n^5 e^{-n^2}$

17. $\sum \dfrac{n!}{(n+2)!}$

18. $\sum \dfrac{n^n}{(n+1)!}$

19. Let $\{a_n\}$ be a sequence of positive numbers, and assume that

$$\frac{a_{n+1}}{a_n} \geqq 1 - \frac{1}{n}$$

for all n. Show that the series $\sum a_n$ diverges.

20. A ratio test can be applied in the opposite direction to determine when a series diverges. Prove the following statement: Let a_n be a sequence of positive numbers, and let $c \geqq 1$. If $a_{n+1}/a_n \geqq c$ for all n sufficiently large, then the series $\sum a_n$ diverges.

§4. THE INTEGRAL TEST

You must already have felt that there is an analogy between the convergence of an improper integral and the convergence of a series. We shall now make this precise.

Theorem 4. *Let f be a function which is defined and positive for all $x \geqq 1$, and decreasing. The series*

$$\sum_{n=1}^{\infty} f(n)$$

converges if and only if the improper integral

$$\int_1^{\infty} f(x)\, dx$$

converges.

We visualize the situation in the following diagram.

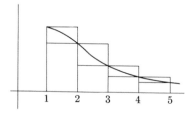

Consider the partial sums

$$f(2) + \cdots + f(n)$$

and assume that our improper integral converges. The area under the curve between 1 and 2 is greater than or equal to the area of the rectangle whose height is $f(2)$ and whose base is the interval between 1 and 2. This base has length 1. Thus

$$f(2) \leq \int_1^2 f(x)\, dx.$$

Again, since the function is decreasing, we have a similar estimate between 2 and 3:

$$f(3) \leq \int_2^3 f(x)\, dx.$$

We can continue up to n, and get

$$f(2) + f(3) + \cdots + f(n) \leq \int_1^n f(x)\, dx.$$

As n becomes large, we have assumed that the integral approaches a limit. This means that

$$f(2) + f(3) + \cdots + f(n) \leq \int_1^\infty f(x)\, dx.$$

Hence the partial sums are bounded, and hence by Theorem 2, they approach a limit. Therefore our series converges.

Conversely, assume that the partial sums

$$f(1) + \cdots + f(n)$$

approach a limit as n becomes large.

The area under the graph of f between 1 and n is less than or equal to the sum of the areas of the big rectangles. Thus

$$\int_1^2 f(x)\, dx \leq f(1)(2 - 1) = f(1)$$

and

$$\int_2^3 f(x)\, dx \leq f(2)(3 - 2) = f(2).$$

Proceeding stepwise, and taking the sum, we see that

$$\int_1^n f(x)\, dx \leqq f(1) + \cdots + f(n-1).$$

The partial sums on the right are less than or equal to their limit. Call this limit L. Then for all positive integers n, we have

$$\int_1^n f(x)\, dx \leqq L.$$

Given any number B, we can find an integer n such that $B \leqq n$. Then

$$\int_1^B f(x)\, dx \leqq \int_1^n f(x)\, dx \leqq L.$$

Hence the integral from 1 to B approaches a limit as B becomes large, and this limit is less than or equal to L. This proves our theorem.

Example. Prove that the series

$$\sum \frac{1}{n^2 + 1}$$

converges.

Let

$$f(x) = \frac{1}{x^2 + 1}.$$

Then f is decreasing, and

$$\int_1^B f(x)\, dx = \arctan B - \arctan 1 = \arctan B - \frac{\pi}{4}.$$

As B becomes large, $\arctan B$ approaches $\pi/2$ and therefore has a limit. Hence the integral converges. So does the series, by the theorem.

EXERCISES

1. Show that the following series diverges: $\displaystyle\sum_{n=2}^{\infty} \frac{1}{n \log n}$

2. Show that the following series converges: $\displaystyle\sum_{n=1}^{\infty} \frac{n+1}{(n+2)n!}$

Test for convergence:

3. $\displaystyle\sum_{n=1}^{\infty} n e^{-n^2}$

4. $\displaystyle\sum_{n=2}^{\infty} \frac{1}{n(\log n)^3}$

5. $\displaystyle\sum_{n=2}^{\infty} \frac{1}{n(\log n)^2}$

6. $\displaystyle\sum_{n=1}^{\infty} \frac{n!}{n^n}$

7. $\displaystyle\sum_{n=1}^{\infty} \frac{n}{e^n}$

8. $\displaystyle\sum_{n=1}^{\infty} \frac{n+1}{n^3 + 2}$

9. $\displaystyle\sum_{n=1}^{\infty} \frac{1}{n^2 + n - 1}$

10. $\displaystyle\sum_{n=1}^{\infty} \frac{n}{n^3 - n + 5}$

11. Let ϵ be a number > 0. Show that the series $\sum_{n=1}^{\infty} \dfrac{1}{n^{1+\epsilon}}$ converges.

12. Show that the following series converge.

(a) $\sum_{n=1}^{\infty} \dfrac{\log n}{n^2}$ (b) $\sum_{n=1}^{\infty} \dfrac{\log n}{n^{3/2}}$

(c) $\sum_{n=1}^{\infty} \dfrac{\log n}{n^{1+\epsilon}}$ if $\epsilon > 0$.

(d) $\sum_{n=1}^{\infty} \dfrac{(\log n)^2}{n^{3/2}}$ (e) $\sum_{n=1}^{\infty} \dfrac{(\log n)^3}{n^2}$

13. If $\epsilon > 0$ show that the series $\sum_{n=2}^{\infty} \dfrac{1}{n(\log n)^{1+\epsilon}}$ converges.

§5. ABSOLUTE AND ALTERNATING CONVERGENCE

We consider a series $\sum_{n=1}^{\infty} a_n$ in which we do not assume that the terms a_n are ≥ 0. We shall say that the series *converges absolutely* if the series

$$\sum_{n=1}^{\infty} |a_n|$$

formed with the absolute values of the terms a_n converges. This is now a series with terms ≥ 0, to which we can apply the tests for convergence given in the two preceding sections. This is important, because we have:

Theorem 5. *Let $\{a_n\}$ $(n = 1, 2, \ldots)$ be a sequence, and assume that the series*

$$\sum_{n=1}^{\infty} |a_n|$$

converges. Then so does the series $\sum_{n=1}^{\infty} a_n$.

Proof. Let a_n^+ be equal to 0 if $a_n < 0$ and equal to a_n itself if $a_n \geq 0$. Let a_n^- be equal to 0 if $a_n > 0$ and equal to $-a_n$ if $a_n \leq 0$. Then both a_n^+ and a_n^- are ≥ 0. By assumption and comparison with $\sum |a_n|$, we see that each one of the series

$$\sum_{n=1}^{\infty} a_n^+ \quad \text{and} \quad \sum_{n=1}^{\infty} a_n^-$$

converges. Hence so does their difference

$$\sum_{n=1}^{\infty} a_n^+ - \sum_{n=1}^{\infty} a_n^-,$$

which is equal to

$$\sum_{n=1}^{\infty} (a_n^+ - a_n^-),$$

which is none other than $\sum_{n=1}^{\infty} a_n$. This proves our theorem.

We shall use one more test for convergence of a series which may have positive and negative terms.

Theorem 6. *Let* $\sum_{n=1}^{\infty} a_n$ *be a series such that*

$$\lim_{n \to \infty} a_n = 0,$$

such that the terms a_n *are alternately positive and negative, and such that* $|a_{n+1}| \leq |a_n|$ *for* $n \geq 1$. *Then the series is convergent.*

Proof. Let us write the series in the form

$$b_1 - c_1 + b_2 - c_2 + b_3 - c_3 + \cdots,$$

with $b_n, c_n \geq 0$. Let

$$s_n = b_1 - c_1 + b_2 - c_2 + \cdots + b_n$$
$$t_n = b_1 - c_1 + b_2 - c_2 + \cdots + b_n - c_n.$$

Since the absolute values of the terms decrease, it follows that

$$s_1 \geq s_2 \geq s_3 \geq \cdots$$

and

$$t_1 \leq t_2 \leq t_3 \leq \cdots,$$

i.e. that the s_n are decreasing and the t_n are increasing. Indeed,

$$s_{n+1} = s_n - c_n + b_{n+1} \quad \text{and} \quad 0 \leq b_{n+1} \leq c_n.$$

Thus we subtract more from s_n by c_n than we add afterwards by b_{n+1}. Hence $s_n \geq s_{n+1}$. Furthermore, $s_n \geq t_n$. Hence we may visualize our sequences as follows:

$$s_n \geq s_{n+1} \geq \cdots \geq t_{n+1} \geq t_n.$$

Note that $s_n - t_n = c_n$, and that c_n approaches 0 as n becomes large. If we let L be the greatest lower bound for the sequence $\{s_n\}$, and M be the least upper bound for the sequence $\{t_n\}$, then

$$s_n \geq L \geq M \geq t_n$$

for all n. Since the difference $s_n - t_n$ becomes arbitrarily small, it follows that $L - M$ is arbitrarily small, and hence equal to 0. Thus $L = M$, and this proves that s_n and t_n approach L as a limit, whence our series $\sum a_n$ converges to L.

Example. The series

$$\sum_{n=1}^{\infty} (-1)^n \frac{1}{n}$$

is convergent, but not absolutely convergent.

EXERCISES

Determine whether the following series converge absolutely:

1. $\sum \dfrac{\sin n}{n^3}$

2. $\sum \dfrac{1 + \cos \pi n}{n!}$

3. $\sum \dfrac{\sin \pi n + \cos 2\pi n}{n^{3/2}}$

4. $\sum \dfrac{(-1)^n}{n^2 + 1}$

5. $\sum \dfrac{(-1)^n \sin n + \cos 3n}{n^2 + n}$

Which of the following series converge and which do not?

6. $\sum \dfrac{(-1)^n}{n}$

7. $\sum \dfrac{(-1)^n}{n^2}$

8. $\sum (-1)^n \dfrac{n}{n+1}$

9. $\sum \dfrac{(-1)^{n+1}}{\log (n + 2)}$

10. For each number x, show that the series $\sum \sin n^2 x / n^2$ converges absolutely. Let f be the function whose value at x is the above series. Show that f is continuous. Determine whether f is differentiable or not. (Remarkably enough, this was not known for a long time! Cf. J. P. Kahane, Bulletin of the American Mathematical Society, March 1964, p. 199. J. Gerver, a sophomore at Columbia College, has shown that the series is differentiable at π. Cf. his article in Am. J. Math., 1969.)

Determine whether the following series converge, and whether they converge absolutely.

11. $\sum \dfrac{(-1)^{n+1}}{\sqrt{n}}$

12. $\sum \dfrac{(-1)^{n+2}}{\log n}$

13. $\sum \dfrac{(-1)^n}{\sqrt[n]{n}}$

14. $\sum (-1)^n \dfrac{n^2}{n^2 + 1}$

15. $\sum (-1)^n \dfrac{n^2}{n^3 + 2}$

16. $\sum (-1)^{n+1} \dfrac{n^2 + 2}{n^3 + n - 1}$

17. $\sum (-1)^{n+1} \dfrac{\sqrt{n}}{n+2}$

18. $\sum \dfrac{(-1)^n}{n^{5/2}+n}$

19. $\sum (-1)^n \dfrac{n}{n^2+1}$

20. $\sum \dfrac{(-1)^n}{\sqrt{\log n}}$

§6. POWER SERIES

Perhaps the most important type of series are power series. Let x be any number and let $\{a_n\}$ $(n = 0, 1, \ldots)$ be a sequence of numbers. Then we can form the series

$$\sum_{n=0}^{\infty} a_n x^n.$$

The partial sums are

$$a_0 + a_1 x + a_2 x^2 + \cdots + a_n x^n.$$

We have already met such sums when we discussed Taylor's formula.

Example. The power series

$$\sum_{n=0}^{\infty} \frac{x^n}{n!}$$

converges for all x, absolutely. Indeed, given a number $R > 0$, it will suffice to prove that the above series converges for $0 < x \leq R$. We use the ratio test. Let

$$b_n = \frac{x^n}{n!}.$$

Then

$$\frac{b_{n+1}}{b_n} = \frac{x^{n+1}}{(n+1)!} \frac{n!}{x^n} = \frac{x}{n+1} \leq \frac{R}{n+1}.$$

When n is sufficiently large, it follows that $R/(n+1) < 1/2$, and we can apply the ratio test to prove our assertion.

Similarly, we could prove that the series

$$\sum_{n=0}^{\infty} (-1)^n \frac{x^{2n+1}}{(2n+1)!} \quad \text{and} \quad \sum_{n=0}^{\infty} (-1)^n \frac{x^{2n}}{(2n)!}$$

converge absolutely for all x, letting for instance

$$b_n = \frac{x^{2n+1}}{(2n+1)!}$$

for the first one. Then $b_{n+1}/b_n = x^2/(2n+3)$, and we can argue as before.

Theorem 7. *Assume that there is a number $r \geq 0$ such that the series*

$$\sum_{n=0}^{\infty} |a_n| r^n$$

converges. Then for all x such that $|x| \leq r$, the series

$$\sum_{n=0}^{\infty} a_n x^n$$

converges absolutely.

Proof. The absolute value of each term is

$$|a_n| |x|^n \leq |a_n| r^n.$$

Our assertion follows from the comparison Theorem 3.

The least upper bound of all numbers r for which we have the convergence stated in the theorem is called the *radius of convergence* of the series. If there is no upper bound for the numbers r such that the power series above converges, then we say that the radius of convergence is *infinity*. In this case, the series converges absolutely for all x.

Suppose that there is an upper bound for the numbers r above, and thus let s be the radius of convergence of the series. Then if $x > s$, the series

$$\sum_{n=0}^{\infty} |a_n| x^n$$

does *not* converge. Thus the radius of convergence s is the number such that the series converges absolutely if $0 < x < s$ but does not converge absolutely if $x > s$.

Theorem 7 allows us to define a function f; namely, for all numbers x such that $|x| < r$, we define

$$f(x) = \lim_{n \to \infty} (a_0 + a_1 x + \cdots + a_n x^n).$$

Our proofs that the remainder term in Taylor's formula approaches 0 for various functions now allow us to say that these functions are given by their Taylor series. Thus

$$\sin x = x - \frac{x^3}{3!} + \frac{x^5}{5!} - \cdots$$

$$e^x = 1 + x + \frac{x^2}{2!} + \cdots$$

for all x. Furthermore,

$$\log (1 + x) = x - \frac{x^2}{2} + \cdots$$

is valid for $-1 < x < 1$.

(Here we saw that the series converges for $x = 1$, but it does not converge absolutely, cf. §1.)

Root test. *Let $\sum a_n x^n$ be a power series and assume that*

$$\lim |a_n|^{1/n} = s,$$

where s is a number. If $s \neq 0$ then the radius of convergence of the series is equal to $1/s$. If $s = 0$, then the radius of convergence is infinity. If $|a_n|^{1/n}$ becomes arbitrarily large as n becomes large, then the radius of convergence is 0.

Proof. Without loss of generality, we may assume that $a_n \geq 0$ for all n. Suppose first that s is a number $\neq 0$, and let $0 \leq r < 1/s$. For small ϵ, the numbers $a_n^{1/n} r$ approach sr, and hence are $< 1 - \epsilon$ for all n sufficiently large. Hence the series $\sum a_n r^n$ converges by comparison with the geometric series. If on the other hand $r > 1/s$, then $a_n^{1/n} r$ approaches $sr > 1$, and hence we have

$$a_n^{1/n} r \geq 1 + \epsilon$$

for all n sufficiently large. Comparison from below shows that the series $\sum a_n r^n$ diverges. We leave the cases $s = 0$ or $s = \infty$ to the reader.

Example. The series $\sum x^n / n^2$ has a radius of convergence equal to 1, because

$$\lim \left(\frac{1}{n^2}\right)^{1/n} = \lim \frac{1}{n^{2/n}} = 1,$$

by Corollary 3 of Theorem 10, Chapter VIII, §4.

EXERCISES

Find the radius of convergence of the following series:

1. $\sum n^n x^n$

2. $\sum \dfrac{x^n}{n^n}$

3. $\sum \dfrac{(-1)^n}{n^2 + 1} x^n$

4. $\sum \dfrac{n}{n + 5} x^n$

5. $\sum (\log n) x^n$

6. $\sum \dfrac{1}{\log n} x^n$

7. $\sum (\log n)^2 x^n$

8. $\sum 2^n x^n$

9. $\sum 2^{-n} x^n$

10. $\sum (1 + n)^n x^n$

11. $\sum \dfrac{x^n}{n}$

12. $\sum \dfrac{x^n}{\sqrt{n}}$

13. $\sum (1 + (-2)^n)x^n$ 14. $\sum (1 + (-1)^n)x^n$ 15. $\sum_{n=1}^{\infty} \frac{(2n)!}{(n!)^2} x^n$

16. $\sum_{n=1}^{\infty} \frac{n^n}{n!} x^n$ 17. $\sum_{n=1}^{\infty} \frac{(n!)^3}{(3n)!} x^n$ 18. $\sum_{n=1}^{\infty} \frac{n^{5n}}{(2n)! n^{3n}} x^n$

19. $\sum_{n=1}^{\infty} \frac{(3n)!}{(n!)^2} x^n$ 20. $\sum_{n=1}^{\infty} \frac{\sin n\pi/2}{2^n} x^n$ 21. $\sum_{n=2}^{\infty} \frac{\log n}{2^n} x^n$

22. $\sum_{n=1}^{\infty} \frac{1 + \cos 2\pi n}{3^n} x^n$ 23. $\sum_{n=2}^{\infty} nx^n$ 24. $\sum_{n=1}^{\infty} \frac{\sin 2\pi n}{n!} x^n$

25. $\sum_{n=2}^{\infty} n^2 x^n$ 26. $\sum_{n=1}^{\infty} \frac{\cos^2 n}{n^n} x^n$ 27. $\sum_{n=2}^{\infty} \frac{n}{\log n} x^n$

28. $\sum_{n=2}^{\infty} \frac{(-1)^n}{n! - 1} x^n$ 29. $\sum_{n=1}^{\infty} \frac{n!}{n^n} x^n$ 30. $\sum_{n=1}^{\infty} \frac{(-1)^n + 1}{n!} x^n$

Note: For some of the above radii of convergence, recall that

$$\lim_{n \to \infty} \left(1 + \frac{1}{n}\right)^n = \lim_{n \to \infty} \left(\frac{1 + n}{n}\right)^n = e.$$

§7. DIFFERENTIATION AND INTEGRATION OF POWER SERIES

If we have a polynomial

$$a_0 + a_1 x + \cdots + a_n x^n$$

with numbers $a_0, a_1, \ldots, a_n$ as coefficients, then we know how to find its derivative. It is $a_1 + 2a_2 x + \cdots + na_n x^{n-1}$. We would like to say that the derivative of a series can be taken in the same way, and that the derivative converges whenever the series does.

Theorem 8. *Let r be a number > 0 and let $\sum a_n x^n$ be a series which converges absolutely for $|x| < r$. Then the series $\sum na_n x^{n-1}$ also converges absolutely for $|x| < r$.*

Proof. Since we are interested in the absolute convergence, we may assume that $a_n \geq 0$ for all n. Let $0 < x < r$, and let c be a number such that $x < c < r$. Recall that

$$\lim_{n \to \infty} n^{1/n} = 1.$$

We may write

$$na_n x^n = a_n(n^{1/n}x)^n.$$

Then for all n sufficiently large, we conclude that

$$n^{1/n}x < c$$

because $n^{1/n}x$ comes arbitrarily close to x. Hence for all n sufficiently large, we have

$$na_n x^n < a_n c^n.$$

We can then compare the series $\sum na_n x^n$ with $\sum a_n c^n$ to conclude that $\sum na_n x^n$ converges. Since

$$\sum na_n x^{n-1} = \frac{1}{x}\sum a_n x^n$$

we have proved Theorem 8.

A similar result holds for integration, but trivially. Indeed, if we have a series $\displaystyle\sum_{n=1}^{\infty} a_n x^n$ which converges absolutely for $|x| < r$, then the series

$$\sum_{n=1}^{\infty} \frac{a_n}{n+1} x^{n+1} = x \sum_{n=1}^{\infty} \frac{a_n}{n+1} x^n$$

has terms whose absolute value is smaller than in the original series.

The preceding results can be expressed by saying that an absolutely convergent power series can be integrated and differentiated term by term and still yield an absolutely convergent power series.

It is natural to expect that if

$$f(x) = \sum_{n=1}^{\infty} a_n x^n,$$

then f is differentiable and its derivative is given by differentiating the series term by term. The next theorem proves this.

Theorem 9. *Let*

$$f(x) = \sum_{n=1}^{\infty} a_n x^n$$

be a power series, which converges absolutely for $|x| < r$. Then f is differentiable for $|x| < r$, and

$$f'(x) = \sum_{n=1}^{\infty} na_n x^{n-1}.$$

Proof. Let $0 < b < r$. Let $\delta > 0$ be such that $b + \delta < r$. We consider values of x such that $|x| < b$ and values of h such that $|h| < \delta$.

We have the numerator of the Newton quotient:

$$f(x+h) - f(x) = \sum_{n=1}^{\infty} a_n(x+h)^n - \sum_{n=1}^{\infty} a_n x^n = \sum_{n=1}^{\infty} a_n[(x+h)^n - x^n].$$

By the mean value theorem, there exists a number x_n between x and $x + h$ such that

$$(x+h)^n - x^n = nx_n^{n-1}h$$

and consequently

$$f(x+h) - f(x) = \sum_{n=1}^{\infty} na_n x_n^{n-1}h.$$

Therefore

$$\frac{f(x+h) - f(x)}{h} = \sum_{n=1}^{\infty} na_n x_n^{n-1}.$$

We have to show that the Newton quotient above approaches the value of the series obtained by taking the derivative term by term. We have

$$\frac{f(x+h) - f(x)}{h} - \sum_{n=1}^{\infty} na_n x^{n-1} = \sum_{n=1}^{\infty} na_n x_n^{n-1} - \sum_{n=1}^{\infty} na_n x^{n-1}$$

$$= \sum_{n=1}^{\infty} na_n[x_n^{n-1} - x^{n-1}].$$

Using the mean value theorem again, there exists y_n between x_n and x such that the preceding expression is

$$\frac{f(x+h) - f(x)}{h} - \sum_{n=1}^{\infty} na_n x^{n-1} = \sum_{n=2}^{\infty} (n-1)na_n y_n^{n-2}(x_n - x).$$

We have $|y_n| \leq b + \delta < r$, and $|x_n - x| \leq |h|$. Consequently,

$$\left| \frac{f(x+h) - f(x)}{h} - \sum_{n=1}^{\infty} na_n x^{n-1} \right| \leq \sum_{n=2}^{\infty} (n-1)n|a_n| \, |y_n|^{n-2}|h|$$

$$\leq |h| \sum_{n=2}^{\infty} (n-1)n|a_n|(b+\delta)^{n-2}.$$

By Theorem 8 applied twice, we know that the series appearing on the right converges. It is equal to a fixed constant. As h approaches 0, it follows that the expression on the left also approaches 0. This proves that f is differentiable at x, and that its derivative is equal to $\sum_{n=1}^{\infty} na_n x^{n-1}$, for all x such that $|x| < b$. This is true for all b, $0 < b < r$, and therefore concludes the proof of our theorem.

Theorem 10. *Let* $f(x) = \sum\limits_{n=1}^{\infty} a_n x^n$ *be a power series, which converges absolutely for* $|x| < r$. *Then the relation*

$$\int f(x)\, dx = \sum_{n=1}^{\infty} \frac{a_n}{n+1} x^{n+1}$$

is valid in the interval $|x| < r$.

Proof. We know that the series for f integrated term by term converges absolutely in the interval. By the preceding theorem, its derivative term by term is the series for the derivative of the function, thereby proving our assertion.

Example. If we had never heard of the exponential function, we could define a function

$$f(x) = 1 + x + \frac{x^2}{2!} + \frac{x^3}{3!} + \cdots.$$

Taking the derivative term by term, we see that

$$f'(x) = f(x).$$

Hence by what we know from Chapter VIII, §2, Exercise 7, we conclude that

$$f(x) = Ke^x$$

for some constant K. Letting $x = 0$ shows that

$$1 = f(0) = K.$$

Thus $K = 1$ and $f(x) = e^x$.

Similarly, if we had never heard of sine and cosine, we could *define* functions

$$S(x) = x - \frac{x^3}{3!} + \frac{x^5}{5!} - \cdots, \qquad C(x) = 1 - \frac{x^2}{2!} + \frac{x^4}{4!} - \cdots.$$

Differentiating term by term shows that

$$S'(x) = C(x), \qquad C'(x) = -S(x).$$

Furthermore, $S(0) = 0$ and $C(0) = 1$. It can then be shown easily that any pair of functions $S(x)$ and $C(x)$ satisfying these properties must be the sine and cosine. This is actually carried out in an appendix.

Chapter XVI

Complex Numbers

One of the advantages of dealing with the real numbers instead of the rational numbers is that certain equations which do not have any solutions in the rational numbers have a solution in real numbers. For instance, $x^2 = 2$ is such an equation. However, we also know some equations having no solution in real numbers, for instance $x^2 = -1$, or $x^2 = -2$. In this chapter, we define a new kind of number where such equations have solutions. What we have simply called numbers in the preceding chapters will now be called *real* numbers. The new kind of numbers will be called *complex* numbers.

§1. DEFINITION

The complex numbers are a set of objects which can be added and multiplied, the sum and product of two complex numbers being also a complex number, and satisfy the following conditions.

1. Every real number is a complex number, and if α, β are real numbers, then their sum and product as complex numbers are the same as their sum and product as real numbers.
2. There is a complex number denoted by i such that $i^2 = -1$.
3. Every complex number can be written uniquely in the form $a + bi$ where a, b are real numbers.
4. The ordinary laws of arithmetic concerning addition and multiplication are satisfied. We list these laws:

If α, β, γ are complex numbers, then $(\alpha\beta)\gamma = \alpha(\beta\gamma)$, and

$$(\alpha + \beta) + \gamma = \alpha + (\beta + \gamma).$$

We have $\alpha(\beta + \gamma) = \alpha\beta + \alpha\gamma$, and $(\beta + \gamma)\alpha = \beta\alpha + \gamma\alpha$.
We have $\alpha\beta = \beta\alpha$, and $\alpha + \beta = \beta + \alpha$.
If 1 is the real number one, then $1\alpha = \alpha$.
If 0 is the real number zero, then $0\alpha = 0$.
We have $\alpha + (-1)\alpha = 0$.

We shall now draw consequences of these properties. With each complex number $a + bi$, we associate the point (a, b) in the plane.

284

Let $\alpha = a_1 + a_2 i$ and $\beta = b_1 + b_2 i$ be two complex numbers. Then

$$\alpha + \beta = a_1 + b_1 + (a_2 + b_2)i.$$

Hence addition of complex numbers is carried out "componentwise". For example, $(2 + 3i) + (-1 + 5i) = 1 + 8i$.

In multiplying complex numbers, we use the rule $i^2 = -1$ to simplify a product and to put it in the form $a + bi$. For instance, let $\alpha = 2 + 3i$ and $\beta = 1 - i$. Then

$$\begin{aligned}
\alpha\beta = (2 + 3i)(1 - i) &= 2(1 - i) + 3i(1 - i) \\
&= 2 - 2i + 3i - 3i^2 \\
&= 2 + i - 3(-1) \\
&= 2 + 3 + i \\
&= 5 + i.
\end{aligned}$$

Let $\alpha = a + bi$ be a complex number. We define $\bar{\alpha}$ to be $a - bi$. Thus if $\alpha = 2 + 3i$, then $\bar{\alpha} = 2 - 3i$. The complex number $\bar{\alpha}$ is called the *conjugate* of α. We see at once that

$$\alpha\bar{\alpha} = a^2 + b^2.$$

With the vector interpretation of complex numbers, we see that $\alpha\bar{\alpha}$ is the square of the distance of the point (a, b) from the origin.

We now have one more important property of complex numbers, which will allow us to divide by complex numbers other than 0.

If $\alpha = a + bi$ is a complex number $\neq 0$, and if we let

$$\lambda = \frac{\bar{\alpha}}{a^2 + b^2}$$

then $\alpha\lambda = \lambda\alpha = 1$.

The proof of this property is an immediate consequence of the law of multiplication of complex numbers, because

$$\alpha\frac{\bar{\alpha}}{a^2 + b^2} = \frac{\alpha\bar{\alpha}}{a^2 + b^2} = 1.$$

The number λ above is called the *inverse* of α, and is denoted by α^{-1} or $1/\alpha$. If α, β are complex numbers, we often write β/α instead of $\alpha^{-1}\beta$ (or $\beta\alpha^{-1}$), just as we did with real numbers. We see that we can divide by complex numbers $\neq 0$.

Example. To find the inverse of $(1 + i)$ we note that the conjugate of $1 + i$ is $1 - i$ and that $(1 + i)(1 - i) = 2$. Hence

$$(1 + i)^{-1} = \frac{1 - i}{2}.$$

Theorem 1. *Let* α, β *be complex numbers. Then*

$$\overline{\alpha\beta} = \bar{\alpha}\bar{\beta}, \qquad \overline{\alpha + \beta} = \bar{\alpha} + \bar{\beta}, \qquad \bar{\bar{\alpha}} = \alpha.$$

Proof. The proofs follow immediately from the definitions of addition, multiplication, and the complex conjugate. We leave them as exercises (Exercises 3 and 4).

Let $\alpha = a + bi$ be a complex number, where a, b are real. We shall call a the *real part* of α, and denote it by $\text{Re}(\alpha)$. Thus

$$\alpha + \bar{\alpha} = 2a = 2\,\text{Re}(\alpha).$$

We define the *absolute value* of a complex number $\alpha = a_1 + ia_2$ (where a_1, a_2 are real) to be

$$|\alpha| = \sqrt{a_1^2 + a_2^2}.$$

If we think of α as a point in the plane (a_1, a_2), then $|\alpha|$ is the length of the line segment from the origin to α.

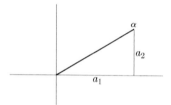

In terms of the absolute value, we can write

$$\alpha^{-1} = \frac{\bar{\alpha}}{|\alpha|^2}$$

provided $\alpha \neq 0$. Indeed, we observe that $|\alpha|^2 = \alpha\bar{\alpha}$.

If $\alpha = a_1 + ia_2$, we note that

$$|\alpha| = |\bar{\alpha}|$$

because $(-a_2)^2 = a_2^2$, so $\sqrt{a_1^2 + a_2^2} = \sqrt{a_1^2 + (-a_2)^2}$.

Theorem 2. *The absolute value of a complex number satisfies the following properties. If* α, β *are complex numbers, then*

$$|\alpha\beta| = |\alpha|\,|\beta|$$
$$|\alpha + \beta| \leq |\alpha| + |\beta|.$$

Proof. We have:

$$|\alpha\beta|^2 = \alpha\beta\overline{\alpha\beta} = \alpha\bar{\alpha}\beta\bar{\beta} = |\alpha|^2|\beta|^2.$$

Taking the square root, we conclude that $|\alpha|\,|\beta| = |\alpha\beta|$, thus proving the first assertion. As for the second, we have

$$|\alpha + \beta|^2 = (\alpha + \beta)\overline{(\alpha + \beta)} = (\alpha + \beta)(\bar{\alpha} + \bar{\beta})$$
$$= \alpha\bar{\alpha} + \beta\bar{\alpha} + \alpha\bar{\beta} + \beta\bar{\beta}$$
$$= |\alpha|^2 + 2\,\mathrm{Re}(\beta\bar{\alpha}) + |\beta|^2$$

because $\alpha\bar{\beta} = \overline{\beta\bar{\alpha}}$. However, we have

$$2\,\mathrm{Re}(\beta\bar{\alpha}) \le 2|\beta\bar{\alpha}|$$

because the real part of a complex number is $\le$ its absolute value. Hence

$$|\alpha + \beta|^2 \le |\alpha|^2 + 2|\beta\bar{\alpha}| + |\beta|^2$$
$$\le |\alpha|^2 + 2|\beta|\,|\alpha| + |\beta|^2$$
$$= (|\alpha| + |\beta|)^2.$$

Taking the square root yields the second assertion of the theorem.

EXERCISES

1. Express the following complex numbers in the form $x + iy$, where x, y are real numbers.

   (a) $(-1 + 3i)^{-1}$ 　　　　　　　(b) $(1 + i)(1 - i)$
   (c) $(1 + i)i(2 - i)$ 　　　　　　　(d) $(i - 1)(2 - i)$
   (e) $(7 + \pi i)(\pi + i)$ 　　　　　　(f) $(2i + 1)\pi i$
   (g) $(\sqrt{2}\,i)(\pi + 3i)$ 　　　　　(h) $(i + 1)(i - 2)(i + 3)$

2. Express the following complex numbers in the form $x + iy$, where x, y are real numbers.

   (a) $(1 + i)^{-1}$ 　(b) $\dfrac{1}{3 + i}$ 　(c) $\dfrac{2 + i}{2 - i}$ 　(d) $\dfrac{1}{2 - i}$

   (e) $\dfrac{1 + i}{i}$ 　(f) $\dfrac{i}{1 + i}$ 　(g) $\dfrac{2i}{3 - i}$ 　(h) $\dfrac{1}{-1 + i}$

3. Let α be a complex number $\ne 0$. What is the absolute value of $\alpha/\bar{\alpha}$? What is $\bar{\bar{\alpha}}$?

4. Let α, β be two complex numbers. Show that $\overline{\alpha\beta} = \bar{\alpha}\bar{\beta}$ and that

$$\overline{\alpha + \beta} = \bar{\alpha} + \bar{\beta}.$$

5. Justify the assertion made in the proof of Theorem 2, that the real part of a complex number is $\le$ its absolute value.

6. If $\alpha = a + ib$ with a, b real, then b is called the *imaginary* part of α and we write $b = \mathrm{Im}(\alpha)$. Show that $\alpha - \bar{\alpha} = 2\,\mathrm{Im}(\alpha)$. Show that

$$\mathrm{Im}(\alpha) \le |\mathrm{Im}(\alpha)| \le |\alpha|.$$

§2. POLAR FORM

Let $(x, y) = x + iy$ be a complex number. We know that any point in the plane can be represented by polar coordinates (r, θ). We shall now see how to write our complex number in terms of such polar coordinates.

Let θ be a real number. We define the expression $e^{i\theta}$ to be

$$e^{i\theta} = \cos \theta + i \sin \theta.$$

Thus $e^{i\theta}$ is a complex number.

For example, if $\theta = \pi$, then $e^{i\pi} = -1$. Also, $e^{2\pi i} = 1$, and $e^{i\pi/2} = i$. Furthermore, $e^{i(\theta+2\pi)} = e^{i\theta}$ for any real θ.

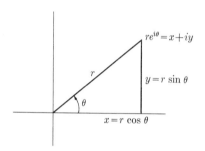

Let x, y be real numbers and $x + iy$ a complex number. Let

$$r = \sqrt{x^2 + y^2}.$$

If (r, θ) are the polar coordinates of the point (x, y) in the plane, then

$$x = r \cos \theta \qquad \text{and} \qquad y = r \sin \theta.$$

Hence

$$x + iy = r \cos \theta + ir \sin \theta = re^{i\theta}.$$

The expression $re^{i\theta}$ is called the *polar form* of the complex number $x + iy$.

The most important property of this polar form is given in Theorem 3. It will allow us to have a very good geometric interpretation for the product of two complex numbers.

Theorem 3. *Let θ, φ be two real numbers. Then*

$$e^{i\theta+i\varphi} = e^{i\theta}e^{i\varphi}.$$

Proof. By definition, we have

$$e^{i\theta+i\varphi} = e^{i(\theta+\varphi)} = \cos (\theta + \varphi) + i \sin (\theta + \varphi).$$

Using the addition formula for sine and cosine, we see that the preceding expression is equal to

$$\cos\theta\cos\varphi - \sin\theta\sin\varphi + i(\sin\theta\cos\varphi + \sin\varphi\cos\theta).$$

This is exactly the same expression as the one we obtain by multiplying out

$$(\cos\theta + i\sin\theta)(\cos\varphi + i\sin\varphi).$$

Our theorem is proved.

Theorem 3 justifies our notation, by showing that the exponential of complex numbers satisfies the same formal rule as the exponential of real numbers.

Let $\alpha = a_1 + ia_2$ be a complex number. We define e^α to be

$$e^{a_1}e^{ia_2}.$$

For instance, let $\alpha = 2 + 3i$. Then $e^\alpha = e^2 e^{3i}$.

Theorem 4. *Let α, β be complex numbers. Then*

$$e^{\alpha+\beta} = e^\alpha e^\beta.$$

Proof. Let $\alpha = a_1 + ia_2$ and $\beta = b_1 + ib_2$. Then

$$e^{\alpha+\beta} = e^{(a_1+b_1)+i(a_2+b_2)} = e^{a_1+b_1}e^{i(a_2+b_2)}$$
$$= e^{a_1}e^{b_1}e^{ia_2+ib_2}.$$

Using Theorem 3, we see that this last expression is equal to

$$e^{a_1}e^{b_1}e^{ia_2}e^{ib_2} = e^{a_1}e^{ia_2}e^{b_1}e^{ib_2}.$$

By definition, this is equal to $e^\alpha e^\beta$, thereby proving our theorem.

Theorem 4 is very useful in dealing with complex numbers. We shall now consider several examples to illustrate it.

Example 1. Find a complex number whose square is $4e^{i\pi/2}$.
Let $z = 2e^{i\pi/4}$. Using the rule for exponentials, we see that $z^2 = 4e^{i\pi/2}$.

Example 2. Let n be a positive integer. Find a complex number w such that $w^n = e^{i\pi/2}$.
It is clear that the complex number $w = e^{i\pi/2n}$ satisfies our requirement.
In other words, we may express Theorem 4 as follows. Let $z_1 = r_1 e^{i\theta_1}$ and $z_2 = r_2 e^{i\theta_2}$ be two complex numbers. To find the product $z_1 z_2$, we multiply the absolute values and add the angles. Thus

$$z_1 z_2 = r_1 r_2 e^{i(\theta_1+\theta_2)}.$$

In many cases, this way of visualizing the product of complex numbers is more useful than that coming out of the definition.

EXERCISES

1. Put the following complex numbers in polar form.
   (a) $1 + i$ (b) $1 + i\sqrt{2}$ (c) -3 (d) $4i$
   (e) $1 - i\sqrt{2}$ (f) $-5i$ (g) -7 (h) $-1 - i$

2. Put the following complex numbers in the ordinary form $x + iy$.
   (a) $e^{3i\pi}$ (b) $e^{2i\pi/3}$ (c) $3e^{i\pi/4}$ (d) $\pi e^{-i\pi/3}$
   (e) $e^{2\pi i/6}$ (f) $e^{-i\pi/2}$ (g) $e^{-i\pi}$ (h) $e^{-5i\pi/4}$

3. Let α be a complex number $\neq 0$. Show that there are two distinct complex numbers whose square is α.

4. Let α be a complex number $\neq 0$. Let n be a positive integer. Show that there are n distinct complex numbers z such that $z^n = \alpha$. Write these complex numbers in polar form.

5. Let $\alpha = 1$ in Exercise 4. Plot all the complex numbers z such that $z^n = 1$ on a sheet of graph paper, for $n = 2, 3, 4,$ and 5.

6. Let $a + bi$ be a complex number. Find real numbers x, y such that $(x + iy)^2 = a + bi$, expressing x, y in terms of a and b.

7. Let w be a complex number and suppose that z is a complex number such that $e^z = w$. Describe all complex numbers u such that $e^u = w$.

8. What are the complex numbers z such that $e^z = 1$?

9. If θ is real, show that

$$\cos \theta = \frac{e^{i\theta} + e^{-i\theta}}{2} \quad \text{and} \quad \sin \theta = \frac{e^{i\theta} - e^{-i\theta}}{2}.$$

§3. COMPLEX VALUED FUNCTIONS

Let S be a collection of real numbers. An association which to each element of S associates a complex number is called a *complex valued function*. For instance, the association

$$\theta \mapsto e^{i\theta}$$

is a complex valued function, defined for all real numbers θ.

Let F be a complex valued function defined on some open interval. We can write F in the form

$$F(t) = f(t) + ig(t),$$

where f and g are real valued functions. If $F(\theta) = e^{i\theta}$, then $f(\theta) = \cos \theta$ and $g(\theta) = \sin \theta$. We call f the *real part* of F, and g its *imaginary part*.

For example, the real part of the complex valued function

$$t \mapsto t^2 + 1 + i(\cos t + e^t)$$

is the function $t \mapsto t^2 + 1$.

If both the real part and imaginary part of F are differentiable, then we say that F is differentiable, and we define

$$F'(t) = f'(t) + ig'(t),$$

thus differentiating componentwise. For example, if

$$F(t) = t^2 + 1 + i(\cos t + e^t)$$

then

$$F'(t) = 2t + i(-\sin t + e^t).$$

We shall also write

$$\frac{dF(t)}{dt}$$

for the derivative, instead of $F'(t)$.

The following rules for the derivative of complex valued functions are easily verified:

(a) Let F, G be complex valued functions defined on the same interval, and differentiable. Then $F + G$ is differentiable, and $(F + G)' = F' + G'$, or in other words,

$$\frac{d(F + G)}{dt} = \frac{dF}{dt} + \frac{dG}{dt}.$$

If α is a complex number, then $(\alpha F)' = \alpha F'$, i.e.

$$\frac{d(\alpha F)}{dt} = \alpha \frac{dF}{dt}.$$

(b) Let F, G be as above. Then FG is differentiable and

$$(FG)' = FG' + F'G,$$

or in other words,

$$\frac{d(FG)}{dt} = F \frac{dG}{dt} + \frac{dF}{dt} G.$$

We shall leave the first assertion as an exercise. To prove the second, let $F(t) = f_1(t) + if_2(t)$, $G(t) = g_1(t) + ig_2(t)$. Then

$$FG = f_1 g_1 - f_2 g_2 + i(f_1 g_2 + f_2 g_1),$$

whence

$$(FG)' = f_1 g_1' + f_1' g_1 - f_2 g_2' - f_2' g_2$$
$$+ i(f_1 g_2' + f_1' g_2 + f_2 g_1' + f_2' g_1).$$

If one expands out $F'G + FG'$ according to the rule of multiplication of complex numbers, one finds precisely the same expression that we just found for $(FG)'$, as was to be shown.

We define the integral also componentwise. We say that a complex valued function

$$F(t) = f(t) + ig(t)$$

is continuous if both f and g are continuous. In this case, we define the indefinite integral

$$\int F(t)\, dt = \int f(t)\, dt + i \int g(t)\, dt,$$

and similarly, if f, g are continuous over the closed interval $[a, b]$ we define

$$\int_a^b F(t)\, dt = \int_a^b f(t)\, dt + i \int_a^b g(t)\, dt.$$

As with real valued functions, if F, G are complex valued functions on an interval such that $F' = G'$, then there is a complex number C such that $F = G + C$. Thus an indefinite integral is again determined up to a constant (complex, of course). This is seen immediately by applying the known result to the real and imaginary parts of F and G.

EXERCISES

1. Let F be a differentiable complex valued function. Show that

$$\frac{d(e^{F(t)})}{dt} = F'(t)e^{F(t)}.$$

2. Let α be a complex number $\neq 0$. Show that

$$\int e^{\alpha t}\, dt = \frac{e^{\alpha t}}{\alpha}.$$

3. Let n be an integer $\neq 0$. Find

$$\int_0^1 e^{2\pi i n t}\, dt.$$

4. Let F be a differentiable complex valued function defined on an interval. If $F' = 0$ show that F is constant. Also prove in detail the last assertion of the section.

Appendix 1

ϵ *and* δ

This appendix is intended to show how the notions of limits and the properties of limits can be explained and proved in terms of the notions and properties of numbers. We therefore assume the latter and carry out the proofs from there.

There remains the problem of showing how the real numbers can be defined in terms of the rational numbers, and the rational numbers in terms of integers. This takes too long to be included in this book.

Aside from the ordinary rules for addition, multiplication, subtraction, division (by non-zero numbers), ordering, positivity, and inequalities, there is one more basic property satisfied by the real numbers. This property is stated in §1. Our proofs then use only these properties.

§1. LEAST UPPER BOUND

We meet again the problem of where to jump into the theory. It would be long and tedious to jump in too early. Hence we assume known the contents of Chapter I, §1 and §2. These involve the ordinary operations of addition and multiplication, and the notion of ordering, positivity, negative numbers, and inequalities. Those who are interested in seeing the logical development of these notions are referred to books on analysis.

A collection of numbers will simply be called a *set* of numbers. This is shorter and is the usual terminology. If a set has at least one number in it, we say that it is *non-empty*. A set S' is called a *subset* of S if every element of S' is an element of S. In other words, if S' is part of S.

Let S be a non-empty set of numbers. We shall say that S is *bounded from above* if there exists a number B such that

$$x \leq B$$

for all x in our set S. We then call B an *upper bound* for S.

A *least upper bound* for S is an upper bound L such that any upper bound B for S satisfies the inequality $B \geq L$. If M is another least upper bound, then we have $M \geq L$ and $L \geq M$, whence $L = M$. Consequently, a least upper bound is unique.

Similarly, we define the notions of bounded from below, and of greatest lower bound. (Do it yourself.)

The real numbers satisfy a property which is not satisfied by the set of rational numbers, namely:

Fundamental Property. *Every non-empty set S of numbers which is bounded from above has a least upper bound. Every non-empty set of numbers S which is bounded from below has a greatest lower bound.*

Proposition 1. *Let a be a number such that*

$$0 \leq a < \frac{1}{n}$$

for every positive integer n. Then a = 0. There is no number b such that b ≥ n for every positive integer n.

Proof. Suppose there is a number $a \neq 0$ such that $a < 1/n$ for every positive integer n. Then $n < 1/a$ for every positive integer n. Thus to prove both our assertions, it will suffice to prove the second.

Suppose there is a number b such that $b \geq n$ for every positive integer n. Let S be the set of positive integers. Then S is bounded, and hence has a least upper bound. Let C be this least upper bound. No number strictly less than C can be an upper bound. Since $0 < 1$, we have $C < C + 1$, whence $C - 1 < C$. Hence there is a positive integer n such that

$$C - 1 < n.$$

This implies that $C < n + 1$ and $n + 1$ is a positive integer. We have contradicted our assumption that C is an upper bound for the set of positive integers, so no such upper bound can exist.

§2. LIMITS

Let S be a set of numbers and let f be a function defined for all numbers in S. Let x_0 be a number. We shall assume that S is *arbitrarily close to* x_0, i.e. given $\epsilon > 0$ there exists an element x of S such that $|x - x_0| < \epsilon$. Let L be a number. We shall say that $f(x)$ *approaches the limit L as x approaches* x_0 if the following condition is satisfied:

Given a number $\epsilon > 0$, there exists a number $\delta > 0$ such that for all x in S satisfying

$$|x - x_0| < \delta$$

we have

$$|f(x) - L| < \epsilon.$$

If that is the case, then we write

$$\lim_{x \to x_0} f(x) = L.$$

We could also rephrase this as follows. We write

$$\lim_{h \to 0} f(x_0 + h) = L$$

and say that *the limit of $f(x_0 + h)$ is L as h approaches 0* if the following condition is satisfied:

Given $\epsilon > 0$, there exists $\delta > 0$ such that whenever h is a number with $|h| < \delta$ and $x_0 + h$ in S, then

$$|f(x_0 + h) - L| < \epsilon.$$

We note that our definition of limit depends on the set S on which f is defined. Thus we should say "limit with respect to S". The next proposition shows that this is really unnecessary.

Proposition 2. *Let S be a set of numbers arbitrarily close to x_0 and let S' be a subset of S, also arbitrarily close to x_0. Let f be a function defined on S. If*

$$\lim_{x \to x_0} f(x) = L \qquad \text{(with respect to S)}$$

$$\lim_{x \to x_0} f(x) = M \qquad \text{(with respect to S')}$$

then $L = M$. In particular, the limit is unique.

Proof. Given $\epsilon > 0$, there exists $\delta_1 > 0$ such that whenever x is in S' and $|x - x_0| < \delta_1$ we have

$$|f(x) - L| < \frac{\epsilon}{2},$$

and there exists $\delta_2 > 0$ such that whenever $|x - x_0| < \delta_2$ then

$$|f(x) - M| < \frac{\epsilon}{2}.$$

Let $\delta = \min(\delta_1, \delta_2)$. If $|x - x_0| < \delta$ then

$$|L - M| \leqq |L - f(x) + f(x) - M| < \frac{\epsilon}{2} + \frac{\epsilon}{2} = \epsilon.$$

Hence $|L - M|$ is less than any $\epsilon > 0$, and by Proposition 1 of §1, we must have $|L - M| = 0$, whence

$$L - M = 0$$

and

$$L = M.$$

In practice from now on, we omit to state that x is an element of S. The context makes it clear each time.

Furthermore, in many subsequent proofs, we shall need several simultaneous inequalities to be satisfied, just as in the preceding proof we had inequalities with δ_1 and δ_2. In each case, we use a similar trick, letting δ be the minimum of $\delta_1, \delta_2, \delta_3, \ldots$ needed to make each desired inequality valid. Thus in writing down the proofs, we omit the intermediate $\delta_1, \delta_2, \delta_3 \ldots$.

Remark. Suppose that $\lim_{x \to x_0} f(x) = L$. Then there exists $\delta > 0$ such that whenever $|x - x_0| < \delta$ we have

$$|f(x)| < |L| + 1.$$

Indeed, given $1 > 0$ there exists δ such that whenever $|x - x_0| < \delta$ we have

$$|f(x) - L| < 1,$$

so that our assertion follows from standard properties of inequalities.

Also, note that we have trivially

$$\lim_{x \to x_0} C = C$$

for any number C, viewed as a constant function on S. Indeed, given $\epsilon > 0$,

$$|C - C| < \epsilon.$$

Remark. We mention a word about limits "*when x becomes large*". Let a be a number and f a function defined for all numbers $x \geq a$. Let L be a number. We shall say that $f(x)$ *approaches L as x becomes large*, and we write

$$\lim_{x \to \infty} f(x) = L$$

if the following condition is satisfied. Given $\epsilon > 0$ there exists a number A such that whenever $x > A$ we have

$$|f(x) - L| < \epsilon.$$

In practice, instead of saying "when x becomes large", we sometimes say "when x approaches ∞". We leave it to you to define the analogous notion "when x becomes large negative", or "x approaches $-\infty$".

In the definition of $\lim_{x \to \infty}$ we took a function f defined for $x \geq a$. If $a_1 > a$, and we restrict the function to all numbers $\geq a_1$, then the limit as x becomes very large will be the same.

Let us suppose that $a \geq 1$. Define a function g for values of x such that

$$0 < x \leq 1/a$$

by the rule

$$g(x) = f(1/x).$$

Then a second's thought will allow you to prove that

$$\lim_{x \to 0} g(x)$$

exists if and only if

$$\lim_{x \to \infty} f(x)$$

exists, and that they are equal.

Consequently all properties which we prove concerning limits as x approaches 0 (or a number) immediately give rise to similar properties concerning limits as x becomes very large. We leave their formulations to you.

The next theorems, concerning the basic properties of limits, describe limits of sums, products, quotients, inequalities, and composite functions.

Theorem 1. *Let S be a set of numbers, and f, g two functions defined for all numbers in S. Let x_0 be a number. If*

$$\lim_{x \to x_0} f(x) = L$$

and

$$\lim_{x \to x_0} g(x) = M,$$

then $\lim_{x \to x_0} (f + g)(x)$ *exists and is equal to* $L + M$.

Proof. Given $\epsilon > 0$, there exists $\delta > 0$ such that, whenever $|x - x_0| < \delta$ (and x is in S), we have

$$|f(x) - L| < \frac{\epsilon}{2}$$

$$|g(x) - M| < \frac{\epsilon}{2}.$$

We observe that

$$|f(x) + g(x) - L - M| \leqq |f(x) - L| + |g(x) - M| < \epsilon.$$

This proves that $L + M$ is the limit of $(f + g)(x)$ as x approaches x_0.

Theorem 2. *Let S be a set of numbers, and f, g two functions defined for all numbers in S. Let x_0 be a number. If*

$$\lim_{x \to x_0} f(x) = L$$

and

$$\lim_{x \to x_0} g(x) = M,$$

then $\lim_{x \to x_0} f(x)g(x)$ *exists and is equal to* LM.

Proof. Given $\epsilon > 0$ there exists $\delta > 0$ such that, whenever $|x - x_0| < \delta$, we have

$$|f(x) - L| < \frac{1}{2} \frac{\epsilon}{|M| + 1}$$

$$|g(x) - M| < \frac{1}{2} \frac{\epsilon}{|L| + 1}$$

$$|f(x)| < |L| + 1.$$

We have

$$\begin{aligned}
|f(x)g(x) - LM| &= |f(x)g(x) - f(x)M + f(x)M - LM| \\
&\leq |f(x)g(x) - f(x)M| + |f(x)M - LM| \\
&\leq |f(x)| \, |g(x) - M| + |f(x) - L| \, |M| \\
&< (|L| + 1)\frac{1}{2} \frac{\epsilon}{|L| + 1} + \frac{1}{2} \frac{\epsilon}{|M| + 1} |M| \\
&\leq \frac{\epsilon}{2} + \frac{\epsilon}{2} \\
&\leq \epsilon.
\end{aligned}$$

Corollary 1. *Let C be a number and let the assumptions be as in the theorem. Then*

$$\lim_{x \to x_0} Cf(x) = CL.$$

Proof. Clear.

Corollary 2. *Let the notation be as in Theorem 2. Then*

$$\lim_{x \to x_0} [f(x) - g(x)] = L - M.$$

Proof. Clear.

Theorem 3. *Let S be a set of numbers, and f a function defined for all numbers in S. Let x_0 be a number. If*

$$\lim_{x \to x_0} f(x) = L$$

and $L \neq 0$, then the limit

$$\lim_{x \to x_0} \frac{1}{f(x)}$$

exists and is equal to $1/L$.

Proof. Given $\epsilon > 0$, there exists $\delta > 0$ such that whenever $|x - x_0| < \delta$ we have

$$|f(x) - L| < \frac{|L|}{2}$$

and also

$$|f(x) - L| < \frac{\epsilon|L|^2}{2}.$$

From the first inequality, we get

$$|f(x)| \geq |L| - \frac{|L|}{2} = \frac{|L|}{2}.$$

In particular, $f(x) \neq 0$ when $|x - x_0| < \delta$. For such x we get

$$\left|\frac{1}{f(x)} - \frac{1}{L}\right| = \frac{|L - f(x)|}{|f(x)L|}$$

$$\leq \frac{2}{|L|}\frac{|L - f(x)|}{|L|}$$

$$< \frac{2}{|L|^2}\frac{\epsilon|L|^2}{2} = \epsilon.$$

Corollary. *Let the hypotheses be as in Theorem 2, and assume that $L \neq 0$. Then*

$$\lim_{x \to x_0} \frac{g(x)}{f(x)}$$

exists and is equal to M/L.

Proof. Use Theorem 2 and Theorem 3.

Theorem 4. *Let S be a set of numbers, and f a function on S. Let x_0 be a number. Let g be a function on S such that $g(x) \leq f(x)$ for all x in S. Assume that*

$$\lim_{x \to x_0} f(x) = L \quad and \quad \lim_{x \to x_0} g(x) = M.$$

Then $M \leq L$.

Proof. Let $\varphi(x) = f(x) - g(x)$. Then $\varphi(x) \geq 0$ for all x in S. Also,

$$\lim_{x \to x_0} \varphi(x) = L - M$$

by Corollary 2 of Theorem 2. Let K be this limit. We must show $K \geq 0$. Suppose $K < 0$. Then $-K > 0$ and $|K| = -K$. Given $\epsilon > 0$ there exists $\delta > 0$ such that whenever $|x - x_0| < \delta$ we have

$$|\varphi(x) - K| < \epsilon,$$

whence

$$|\varphi(x)| - K < \epsilon.$$

Since $\varphi(x) \geq 0$, we get $-K < \epsilon$ for all $\epsilon > 0$. In particular, for all positive integers n we get $-K < 1/n$. But $-K > 0$. This contradicts Proposition 1 of §1.

Theorem 5. *Let the notation be as in Theorem 4 and assume that* $M = L$. *Let* ψ *be a function on S such that*

$$g(x) \leqq \psi(x) \leqq f(x)$$

for all x in S. Then

$$\lim_{x \to x_0} \psi(x)$$

exists and is equal to L (or M).

Proof. Given $\epsilon > 0$ there exists $\delta > 0$ such that whenever $|x - x_0| < \delta$ we have

$$|g(x) - L| < \frac{\epsilon}{4}$$

$$|f(x) - L| < \frac{\epsilon}{4}.$$

We also have

$$\begin{aligned}
|f(x) - \psi(x)| &\leqq |f(x) - g(x)| \\
&\leqq |f(x) - L + L - g(x)| \\
&\leqq |f(x) - L| + |L - g(x)| \\
&< \frac{\epsilon}{2}.
\end{aligned}$$

But

$$\begin{aligned}
|L - \psi(x)| &\leqq |L - f(x)| + |f(x) - \psi(x)| \\
&< \frac{\epsilon}{2} + \frac{\epsilon}{2} = \epsilon.
\end{aligned}$$

Theorem 6. *Let S, T be sets of numbers, and let f, g be functions defined on S and T respectively. Let* x_0 *be arbitrarily close to S. Assume that for all x in S we have f(x) in T, so that* $g \circ f$ *is defined. Assume that*

$$\lim_{x \to x_0} f(x)$$

exists and is equal to a number y_0 *arbitrarily close to T. Assume that*

$$\lim_{y \to y_0} g(y)$$

exists and equals L. Then

$$\lim_{x \to x_0} g(f(x)) = L.$$

Proof. Given ϵ there exists δ such that whenever y is in T and

$$|y - y_0| < \delta$$

we have

$$|g(y) - L| < \epsilon.$$

With the above δ being given, there exists δ_1 such that whenever x is in S

and $|x - x_0| < \delta_1$ we have $|f(x) - y_0| < \delta$. From this it follows that

$$|g(f(x)) - L| < \epsilon$$

whence proving our assertion.

[*Note:* Theorem 6 justifies the limit procedure used to prove the chain rule.]

This completely proves all the statements about limits we made in Chapter III.

§3. POINTS OF ACCUMULATION

A *sequence* is a function defined on a set of integers ≥ 0. Usually, this set consists of all positive integers. In that case, a sequence amounts to giving numbers

$$a_1, a_2, a_3, \ldots$$

for each positive integer, and we denote the sequence by $\{a_n\}$ $(n = 1, 2, \ldots)$.

If the set consists of all integers ≥ 0, then we denote the sequence by $\{a_n\}$ $(n = 0, 1, 2, \ldots)$.

Let $\{a_n\}$ $(n = 1, 2, \ldots)$ be a sequence. Let C be a number. We say that C is a *point of accumulation* of the sequence if given $\epsilon > 0$ there exist infinitely many integers n such that

$$|a_n - C| < \epsilon.$$

Let $\{a_n\}$ $(n = 1, 2, \ldots)$ be a sequence, and L a number. We shall say that L is a *limit of the sequence* if given $\epsilon > 0$ there exists an integer N such that for all $n > N$ we have

$$|a_n - L| < \epsilon.$$

The limit is then unique (same type of proof as we had for limits of functions).

We shall say that the sequence $\{a_n\}$ $(n = 1, 2, \ldots)$ is *increasing* if $a_n \leq a_{n+1}$ for all positive integers n.

Theorem 7. *Let* $\{a_n\}$ $(n = 1, 2, \ldots)$ *be an increasing sequence, and assume that it is bounded from above. Then the least upper bound L is a limit of the sequence.*

Proof. Given $\epsilon > 0$ the number $L - (\epsilon/2)$ is not an upper bound for the sequence. Hence there exists some number a_N such that

$$L - (\epsilon/2) \leq a_N.$$

This inequality is also satisfied for all $n > N$, since the sequence is increasing. But

$$a_n \leqq L$$

because L is an upper bound. Thus

$$|L - a_n| = L - a_n \leqq \frac{\epsilon}{2} < \epsilon$$

for all $n > N$, thereby proving our assertion.

Corollary. *Let* $\{a_n\}$ $(n = 1, 2, \ldots)$ *be a sequence, and let* A, B *be two numbers such that* $A \leqq a_n \leqq B$ *for all positive integers* n. *Then there exists a point of accumulation* C *of the sequence between* A *and* B.

Proof. For each integer n we let b_n be the greatest lower bound of the set of numbers $\{a_n, a_{n+1}, a_{n+2}, \ldots\}$. Then $b_n \leqq b_{n+1} \leqq \cdots$, i.e. $\{b_n\}$ $(n = 1, 2, \ldots)$ is an increasing sequence. Let L be its limit, as in Theorem 7. We leave it to you as an exercise to prove that this limit is a point of accumulation.

One can reduce the notion of limit of a sequence to that of limits defined previously.

Let S be the set of numbers

$$1, \quad \frac{1}{2}, \quad \frac{1}{3}, \quad \ldots, \quad \frac{1}{n}, \quad \ldots,$$

i.e. the set of numbers which can be written as $1/n$, where n is a positive integer.

If $\{a_n\}$ $(n = 1, 2, \ldots)$ is a sequence, we let f be a function defined on S by the rule

$$f(1/n) = a_n.$$

Then you will verify immediately that

$$\lim_{n \to \infty} a_n$$

exists if and only if

$$\lim_{h \to 0} f(h) \qquad \cdot$$

exists, and in that case the two limits are equal. We say that a sequence $\{a_n\}$ *approaches a number* L *when n becomes large if*

$$L = \lim_{n \to \infty} a_n.$$

Thus properties concerning limits in the sense of §2 immediately give rise to properties concerning limits of sequences (for instance limits of sums, products, quotients). We leave their translations to you.

§4. CONTINUOUS FUNCTIONS

Let f be a function defined on a set of numbers S. Let x_0 be a number in S. Then S is arbitrarily close to x_0. We say that f is *continuous* at x_0 if

$$\lim_{x \to x_0} f(x) = f(x_0).$$

Note that there may be two numbers a, b with $a < x_0 < b$ such that x_0 is the only point which is in the interval and lies also in S. (In this case, one could say that x_0 is an *isolated* point of S.)

It follows at once from our definition that if $\{a_n\}$ ($n = 1, 2, \ldots$) is a sequence of numbers in S such that

$$\lim_{n \to \infty} a_n = x_0$$

and f is continuous at x_0, then

$$\lim_{n \to \infty} f(a_n) = f(x_0).$$

It is immediate that the sum, product, quotient of continuous functions are again continuous. (In the quotient, we have to assume that $f(x_0) \neq 0$, of course.) Every constant function is continuous. The function $f(x) = x$ is continuous for all x. This is trivially verified. From the quotient theorem, we see that the function $f(x) = 1/x$ (defined for $x \neq 0$) is continuous.

Theorem 8. *Let f and g be continuous functions such that the values of f are contained in the domain of definition of g. Then $g \circ f$ is continuous.*

Proof. Let x_0 be a number at which f is defined, and let

$$y_0 = f(x_0).$$

Given $\epsilon > 0$, since g is continuous at y_0, there exists $\delta_1 > 0$ such that if $|y - y_0| < \delta_1$, then

$$|g(y) - g(y_0)| < \epsilon.$$

Now with the above δ_1 being given, there exists $\delta > 0$ such that if $|x - x_0| < \delta$ then

$$|f(x) - f(x_0)| < \delta_1.$$

Hence

$$|g(f(x)) - g(f(x_0))| < \epsilon,$$

thus proving our theorem.

Theorem 9. *Let f be a continuous function on a closed interval $a \leq x \leq b$. Then there exists a point c in the interval such that $f(c)$ is a maximum, and there exists a point d in the interval such that $f(d)$ is a minimum.*

Proof. We shall first prove that f is bounded, i.e. that there exists a number M such that $|f(x)| \leq M$ for all x in the interval.

If f is not bounded, then for every positive integer n we can find a number x_n in the interval such that $|f(x_n)| > n$. The sequence of such x_n has a point of accumulation C in the interval. We have

$$|f(x_n) - f(C)| \geq |f(x_n)| - |f(C)|$$
$$\geq n - f(C).$$

Given $\epsilon > 0$, there exists a $\delta > 0$ such that, whenever

$$|x_n - C| < \delta$$

we have $|f(x_n) - f(C)| < \epsilon$. This has to happen for infinitely many n, since C is an accumulation point. Our statements are contradictory, and we therefore conclude that the function is bounded.

Let β be the least upper bound of the set of values $f(x)$ for all x in the interval. Then given a positive integer n, we can find a number z_n in the interval such that

$$|f(z_n) - \beta| < \frac{1}{n}.$$

Let c be a point of accumulation of the sequence of numbers $\{z_n\}$ $(n = 1, 2, \ldots)$. Then $f(c) \leq \beta$. We contend that

$$f(c) = \beta$$

(this will prove our theorem).

Given $\epsilon > 0$, there exists $\delta > 0$ such that whenever $|z_n - c| < \delta$ we have

$$|f(z_n) - f(c)| < \epsilon.$$

This happens for infinitely many n, since c is a point of accumulation of the sequence $\{z_n\}$. But

$$|f(c) - \beta| \leq |f(c) - f(z_n)| + |f(z_n) - \beta|$$
$$< \epsilon + \frac{1}{n}.$$

This is true for every ϵ and infinitely many positive integers n. Hence $|f(c) - \beta| = 0$ and $f(c) = \beta$.

The proof for the minimum is similar and will be left as an exercise.

Theorem 10. *Let f be a continuous function on a closed interval $a \leq x \leq b$. Let $\alpha = f(a)$ and $\beta = f(b)$. Let γ be a number such that $\alpha < \gamma < \beta$. Then there exists a number c between a and b such that $f(c) = \gamma$.*

Proof. Let S be the set of numbers x in the interval such that $f(x) \leq \gamma$. Then S is not empty because a is in it, and b is an upper bound for S. Let c be its least upper bound. Then c is in our interval. We contend that $f(c) = \gamma$. If $f(c) < \gamma$, then $c \neq b$, and $f(x) < \gamma$ for all $x > c$ sufficiently close to c, because f is continuous at c. This contradicts the fact that c is an upper bound for S. If $f(c) > \gamma$, then $c \neq a$, and $f(x) > \gamma$ for all $x < c$ sufficiently close to c, again because f is continuous at c. This contradicts the fact that c is a least upper bound for S. We conclude that $f(c) = \gamma$, as was to be shown.

Appendix 2

Induction

In the course of several proofs, we have given a "stepwise" argument. One can formalize this type of argument, which is called *induction*. It is a property of integers which is assumed, and is stated as follows.

Suppose that we wish to prove a certain assertion concerning positive integers n. Let $A(n)$ denote the assertion concerning the integer n. To prove it for all n, it suffices to prove the following.

1. The assertion $A(1)$ is true (i.e. the assertion concerning the integer 1 is true).

2. Assuming the assertion proved for all positive integers $\leq n$, prove it for $n + 1$, i.e. prove $A(n + 1)$.

Step 2 is the procedure which allows us to proceed from one integer to the next, and step 1 gives us a starting point. We shall now give examples.

Example 1. For all integers $n \geq 1$, we have

$$1 + 2 + \cdots + n = \frac{n(n + 1)}{2}.$$

Proof. By induction. The assertion $A(n)$ is the assertion of the theorem. When $n = 1$, it simply states that

$$1 = \frac{1(1 + 1)}{2},$$

and is clearly true. Assume now that the assertion is true for n. Then:

$$1 + 2 + \cdots + n + (n + 1) = \frac{n(n + 1)}{2} + (n + 1).$$

Putting the expression on the right of the equality sign over a common denominator 2, we see that it is equal to

$$\frac{n^2 + n + 2n + 2}{2} = \frac{(n + 1)(n + 2)}{2}.$$

Hence assuming $A(n)$, we have shown that

$$1 + 2 + \cdots + (n + 1) = \frac{(n + 1)(n + 2)}{2},$$

which is none other than assertion $A(n + 1)$. This proves our theorem.

Example 2. Assume that there is a function f such that

$$f(x + y) = f(x)f(y).$$

We let $f(1) = e$, and we want to prove that $f(n) = e^n$ for all positive integers n. This is true for $n = 1$. By induction, assume the result for an integer $n \geq 1$. Then

$$f(n + 1) = f(n)f(1) = e^n e = e^{n+1},$$

thereby proving our assertion.

Example 3. We shall use induction to prove that

$$\frac{d(x^n)}{dx} = nx^{n-1}$$

for all integers $n \geq 1$. We assume known the rule for differentiating a product, namely $(fg)' = f'g + fg'$, and we also assume that we have proved the special case

$$\frac{dx}{dx} = 1.$$

Thus we have assumed the result when $n = 1$. By induction, assume the result proved for some integer $n \geq 1$. Let $f(x) = x^n$ and $g(x) = x$. Then $(fg)(x) = x^{n+1}$. Hence

$$\begin{aligned}
(fg)'(x) &= f'(x)g(x) + f(x)g'(x) \\
&= nx^{n-1}x + x^n \\
&= nx^n + x^n \\
&= (n + 1)x^n,
\end{aligned}$$

thus proving what we wanted.

EXERCISES

1. Prove that for all integers $n \geq 1$,

$$1 + 3 + 5 + \cdots + (2n - 1) = n^2.$$

2. Prove that for all integers $n \geq 1$,

(a) $1^2 + 2^2 + 3^2 + \cdots + n^2 = \frac{1}{6}n(n + 1)(2n + 1)$;

(b) $1^3 + 2^3 + 3^3 + \cdots + n^3 = \left[\dfrac{n(n+1)}{2}\right]^2$.

3. Prove that

$$1^2 + 3^2 + 5^2 + \cdots + (2n-1)^2 = \tfrac{1}{3}(4n^3 - n).$$

4. Prove that $n(n^2 + 5)$ is divisible by 6 for all integers $n \geq 1$.

5. Prove that

$$(1 + x)(1 + x^2)(1 + x^4) \cdots (1 + x^{2^n}) = \dfrac{1 - x^{2^{n+1}}}{1 - x}.$$

6. If $f_1, \ldots, f_n$ are differentiable functions, prove by induction that

$$(f_1 \cdots f_n)' = f_1' f_2 \cdots f_n + f_1 f_2' \cdots f_n + \cdots + f_1 \cdots f_{n-1} f_n'.$$

7. (a) Let f be a function such that $f(xy) = f(x) + f(y)$. Show that

$$f(a^n) = nf(a)$$

for all positive integers n.

(b) Let f be a function such that $f(x + y) = f(x) + f(y)$. Show that $f(na) = nf(a)$ for all positive integers n.

(c) Let f be a function such that $f(xy) = f(x)f(y)$. Show that $f(a^n) = f(a)^n$ for all positive integers n.

8. Let $\dbinom{n}{k}$ denote the binomial coefficient, $\dbinom{n}{k} = \dfrac{n!}{k!(n-k)!}$, where n, k are integers ≥ 0, $0 \leq k \leq n$, and 0! is defined to be equal to 1. Prove the following assertions.

(a) $\dbinom{n}{k} = \dbinom{n}{n-k}$ (b) $\dbinom{n}{k-1} + \dbinom{n}{k} = \dbinom{n+1}{k}$ (for $k > 0$)

9. Prove by induction that

$$(x + y)^n = \sum_{k=0}^{n} \binom{n}{k} x^k y^{n-k}.$$

Appendix 3

Sine and Cosine

In our course in calculus, we gave geometric definitions for the sine and cosine, and geometric proofs for the theorems concerning their derivatives, and the limit

$$\lim_{h \to 0} \frac{\sin h}{h} = 1$$

on which these proofs were based, drawing pictures. For the other functions, we showed how to give definitions in terms involving only properties of (real) numbers. Such definitions are called *analytic*. There is of course nothing wrong about using pictures, and it would be insane to have inhibitions about them, but it is reasonable to ask whether it is possible to develop the theory of the sine and cosine without appeal to geometric intuition, i.e. give for these notions purely analytic definitions, and prove their properties purely analytically.

In fact, in Chapter XV, we have already proved that by using suitable series, we can find functions f and g such that

$$f' = g \qquad \text{and} \qquad g' = -f,$$

and $f(0) = 0$, $g(0) = 1$. Using only the properties just stated, we shall develop the entire theory of sine and cosine, based only on the use of the mean value theorem and its applications (to increasing and decreasing functions), and on the intermediate value theorem proved in Appendix 1. Thus what follows gives an interesting theoretical application of the mean value theorem.

To begin with, we have a standard relation,

$$f(x)^2 + g(x)^2 = 1$$

for all x. This is proved by differentiating the left-hand side. We obtain

$$2ff' + 2gg' = 2fg - 2gf = 0.$$

Hence the left-hand side is constant, and substituting $x = 0$ we see that this constant is equal to 1, as desired.

Proposition 1. *There exists only one pair of functions f, g which are differentiable, satisfying*

$$f' = g \quad and \quad g' = -f,$$

and such that $f(0) = 0$, $g(0) = 1$. .

Proof. Let f_1, g_1 be functions such that

$$f_1' = g_1 \quad and \quad g_1' = -f_1.$$

Differentiating the functions $fg_1 - f_1g$ and $ff_1 + gg_1$ we find 0, in each case. Hence there exist numbers a, b such that

$$fg_1 - f_1g = a$$
$$ff_1 + gg_1 = b.$$

We multiply the first equation by f, the second by g and add. We multiply the second equation by f, the first equation by g and subtract. Using $f^2 + g^2 = 1$, we find

(*)
$$g_1 = af + bg$$
$$f_1 = bf - ag.$$

If we assume that $f_1(0) = 0$ and $g_1(0) = 1$, then we find the values $a = 0$ and $b = 1$. This proves that $f_1 = f$ and $g_1 = g$, as was to be shown.

In view of Proposition 1, we define the functions f and g in that proposition to be the *sine* and *cosine* functions respectively, and denote them by sin and cos.

Proposition 2. *For all numbers x, y we have:*

(1) $\sin^2 x + \cos^2 x = 1$,
(2) $\sin(-x) = -\sin x$,
(3) $\cos(-x) = \cos x$,
(4) $\sin(x + y) = \sin x \cos y + \cos x \sin y$,
(5) $\cos(x + y) = \cos x \cos y - \sin x \sin y$.

Proof. The first formula has already been proved. To prove each pair of succeeding formulas, we make a suitable choice of functions f_1, g_1 and apply equations (*) of the proof of uniqueness. For instance, to prove (2) and (3), we let

$$f_1(x) = \cos(-x) \quad and \quad g_1(x) = \sin(-x).$$

Then we find numbers a, b as in the uniqueness proof such that equations (*) are satisfied. Taking the values of these functions at 0, we now find that $b = 0$ and $a = -1$. This proves what we want. To prove (4) and (5), we let y be a fixed number, and let

$$f_1(x) = \sin(x + y) \qquad \text{and} \qquad g_1(x) = \cos(x + y).$$

We determine the constants a, b as before, in equations (*), and find $a = -\sin y$, $b = \cos y$. Formulas (4) and (5) then drop out.

Since the functions sin and cos are differentiable, and since their derivatives are expressed in terms of each other, it follows that they are infinitely differentiable. In particular, they are continuous.

Since $\sin^2 x + \cos^2 x = 1$ for all x, it follows that the values of sin and cos lie between -1 and 1. Of course, we do not yet know that sin and cos take on all such values. This will be proved later.

Since the derivative of $\sin x$ at 0 is equal to 1, and since this derivative is continuous, it follows that the derivative of $\sin x$ (which is $\cos x$) is > 0 for all numbers x in some open interval containing 0. Hence sin is strictly increasing in such an interval, and is strictly positive for all $x > 0$ in such an interval.

We shall now prove that there is a number $x > 0$ such that $\sin x = 1$. In view of the relation between sin and cos, this amounts to proving that there exists a number $x > 0$ such that $\cos x = 0$.

Suppose that no such number exists. Since cos is continuous, we conclude that $\cos x$ cannot be negative for any value of $x > 0$ (by the intermediate value theorem). Hence sin is strictly increasing for all $x > 0$, and cos is strictly decreasing for all $x > 0$. Let $a > 0$. Then

$$0 < \cos 2a = \cos^2 a - \sin^2 a < \cos^2 a.$$

By induction, one sees that $\cos(2^n a) < (\cos a)^{2^n}$ for all integers $n > 0$. Hence $\cos(2^n a)$ approaches 0 as n becomes large, because $0 < \cos a < 1$. Since cos is strictly decreasing for $x > 0$, it follows that $\cos x$ approaches 0 as x becomes large, and hence $\sin x$ approaches 1. In particular, there exists a number $b > 0$ such that

$$\cos b < \tfrac{1}{4} \qquad \text{and} \qquad \sin b > \tfrac{1}{2}.$$

Then $\cos 2b = \cos^2 b - \sin^2 b < (\tfrac{1}{4})^2 - (\tfrac{1}{2})^2 < 0$, contradiction, proving that there is a number $x > 0$ such that $\sin x = 1$, $\cos x = 0$.

The set of numbers $x > 0$ such that $\cos x = 0$ (or equivalently, $\sin x = 1$) is non-empty, bounded from below. Let c be its greatest lower bound. By continuity, we must have $\cos c = 0$. We *define* π to be the number $2c$. Thus $c = \pi/2$. (We follow the Greeks. Unfortunately, it would be more practical to define π as being equal to $4c$. This would get rid of an extraneous factor of 2 appearing in almost all formulas in mathematics involving π. However, it is too late in history to change the notation.) It is clear that $c > 0$, and by definition of the greatest lower bound, there is no number x such that

$$0 \leq x < \pi/2$$

and such that $\cos x = 0$, or $\sin x = 1$.

By the intermediate value theorem, it follows that for $0 \leq x < \pi/2$ we have $0 \leq \sin x < 1$ and $0 \leq \cos x < 1$. However, by definition,

$$\cos \frac{\pi}{2} = 0 \qquad \text{and} \qquad \sin \frac{\pi}{2} = 1.$$

Using the addition formula, we can now find

$$\sin \pi = 0, \qquad \cos \pi = -1, \qquad \sin 2\pi = 0, \qquad \cos 2\pi = 1.$$

For instance,

$$\sin \pi = \sin \left(\frac{\pi}{2} + \frac{\pi}{2} \right) = 2 \sin \frac{\pi}{2} \cos \frac{\pi}{2} = 0.$$

The others are proved similarly.

Proposition 3. *For all x we have:*

$$\sin \left(x + \frac{\pi}{2} \right) = \cos x \qquad\qquad \cos \left(x + \frac{\pi}{2} \right) = -\sin x$$

$$\sin (x + \pi) = -\sin x \qquad\qquad \cos (x + \pi) = -\cos x$$

$$\sin (x + 2\pi) = \sin x \qquad\qquad \cos (x + 2\pi) = \cos x.$$

Proof. Use (4) and (5) in Proposition 2, together with the values we have found above.

We shall now use systematically these relations in investigating the behavior of sin and cos between 0 and 2π.

Proposition 4. *The functions* sin *and* cos *behave as described in the following table. We use* "s.i." *and* "s.d." *to abbreviate* "strictly increasing" *and* "strictly decreasing" *respectively.*

	$0 \leq x \leq \dfrac{\pi}{2}$	$\dfrac{\pi}{2} \leq x \leq \pi$	$\pi \leq x \leq \dfrac{3\pi}{2}$	$\dfrac{3\pi}{2} \leq x \leq 2\pi$
sin	s.i. *from* 0 *to* 1	s.d. *from* 1 *to* 0	s.d. *from* 0 *to* -1	s.i. *from* -1 *to* 0
cos	s.d. *from* 1 *to* 0	s.d. *from* 0 *to* -1	s.i. *from* -1 *to* 0	s.i. *from* 0 *to* 1.

Proof. The behavior in the first column has already been proved in the course of our discussion concerning the definition of $\pi/2$. Consider the second column. The behavior of sin in the indicated interval comes from Proposition 3 (it is the same as the behavior of cos in the preceding column). In that interval, the derivative of cos is therefore negative, and cos is strictly decreasing. Furthermore, cos decreases from 0 to -1, since we must always have $\sin^2 x + \cos^2 x = 1$.

To determine the behavior in the third and fourth columns, we can use the relations of Proposition 3, namely

$$\sin (x + \pi) = -\sin x \qquad \text{and} \qquad \cos (x + \pi) = -\cos x.$$

We see that the graph of the functions sin and cos in the third and fourth columns are similar to those of the first and second, except that they are flipped over the x-axis.

A function f is called *periodic* and a number s is called a period, if $f(x + s) = f(x)$ for all numbers x. From Proposition 3, we see that 2π is a period for sin and cos.

Proposition 5. *The functions* sin *and* cos *are periodic. The numbers* $2n\pi$ *(n equal to an integer) are periods, and every period is equal to* $2n\pi$ *for some integer n.*

Proof. Let s_1, s_2 be periods for the function f. Then

$$f(x + s_1 + s_2) = f(x + s_1) = f(x)$$

so that $s_1 + s_2$ is a period. If s is a period, then

$$f(x) = f(x - s + s) = f(x - s),$$

so that $-s$ is also a period. Since 2π is a period, it follows by induction that $2n\pi$ is also a period for all integers $n \geq 1$, and then also for all integers n.

Let s be a period for sin. Consider the set of integers m such that $2m\pi \leq s$. Taking m sufficiently large negative shows that this set is not empty, and is bounded from above by $s/2\pi$. Let n be its least upper bound. Then n is an integer, and $2n\pi \leq s$ but $2(n + 1)\pi > s$. Let $t = s - 2n\pi$. Then t is a period, and $0 \leq t < 2\pi$. We must have

$$\sin (0 + t) = \sin 0 = 0,$$

$$\cos (0 + t) = \cos 0 = 1.$$

From the table in Proposition 4, we see that this is possible only if $t = 0$, as was to be shown.

The preceding propositions give us all the usual properties of sin and cos.

We recall that a point (a, b) in 2-space is said to lie on the unit circle if $a^2 + b^2 = 1$. We see that for any number x, the point $(\cos x, \sin x)$ lies on the unit circle.

Proposition 6. *Given a point (a, b) on the unit circle in 2-space, there exists a unique number t such that $0 \leq t < 2\pi$ and such that $a = \cos t$, $b = \sin t$.*

Proof. We consider four different cases, according as a, b are ≥ 0 or ≤ 0. In any case, both a and b are between -1 and 1.

Consider for instance the case where $-1 \leq a \leq 0$ and $0 \leq b \leq 1$. From the table in Proposition 4, we see that there is only one possible column in which we could find a value of t satisfying our requirements, and that is the second column.

By the intermediate value theorem, we know that there is one number t such that

$$\frac{\pi}{2} \leq t \leq \pi$$

and $\sin t = b$. Since $\cos^2 x = 1 - \sin^2 x = 1 - b^2 = a^2$, and since both $\cos x$ and a are ≤ 0 in this interval, it follows that we must also have $\cos t = a$. This proves what we want.

The other cases are treated in an entirely similar way, and can be left to the reader.

This essentially concludes our theory of sine and cosine. Note that we have parametrized the circle in the usual way, i.e. we have an association

$$t \mapsto (\cos t, \sin t)$$

which to each number t associates a point on the circle of radius 1 centered at the origin in the plane. In terms of complex numbers, this is nothing else but the association

$$t \mapsto e^{it}$$

discussed in the text.

As to the limit of $(\sin h)/h$, observe that it is nothing but the limit of the Newton quotient,

$$\lim_{h \to 0} \frac{\sin h - \sin 0}{h} = \lim_{h \to 0} \frac{\sin h}{h},$$

and since the sine is differentiable, we know that this limit is equal to

$$\sin'(0) = \cos 0 = 1.$$

Thus we recover this limit in a particularly easy way.

Appendix 4

Physics and Mathematics

Mathematics consists in discovering and describing certain objects and structures. It is essentially impossible to give an all-encompassing description of these. Hence, instead of such a definition, we simply state that the objects of study of mathematics as we know it are those which you will find described in the mathematical journals of the past two centuries, and leave it at that. There are many reasons for studying these objects, among which are aesthetic reasons (some people like them), and practical reasons (some mathematics can be applied).

Physics, on the other hand, consists in describing the empirical world by means of mathematical structures. The empirical world is the world with which we come into contact through our senses, through experiments, measurements, etc. What makes a good physicist is the ability to choose, among many mathematical structures and objects, the ones which can be used to describe the empirical world. I should of course immediately qualify the above assertion in two ways: First, the description of physical situations by mathematical structures can only be done within the degree of accuracy provided by the experimental apparatus. Second, the description should satisfy certain aesthetic criteria (simplicity, elegance). After all, a complete listing of all results of all experiments performed is a description of the physical world, but is quite a distinct thing from giving at one single stroke a general principle which will account simultaneously for the results of all these experiments.

For psychological reasons, it is impossible (for most people) to learn certain mathematical theories without seeing first a geometric or physical interpretation. Hence in this book, before introducing a mathematical notion, we frequently introduce one of its geometric or physical interpretations. These two, however, should not be confused. Thus we might make two columns, as shown on the following page.

As far as the logical development of our course is concerned, we could omit the second column entirely. The second column is used, however, for many purposes: To motivate the first column (because our brain is made up in such a way that to understand something in the first column, it needs the second). To provide applications for the first column, other than pure aesthetic satisfaction (granting that you like the subject).

315

Mathematics	Physics and geometry
numbers	points on a line
derivative	slope of a line rate of change
$\dfrac{df}{dx} = Kf(x)$	exponential decay
integral	area work moments

Nevertheless, it is important to keep in mind that the derivative, as the limit of

$$\frac{f(x + h) - f(x)}{h},$$

and the integral, as a unique number between upper and lower sums, are not to be confused with a slope or an area respectively. It is simply our mind which interprets the mathematical notion in physical or geometric terms. Besides, we frequently assign several such interpretations to the same mathematical notion (viz. the integral being interpreted as an area, or as the work done by a force).

And by the way, the above remarks which are about physics and mathematics belong neither to physics nor to mathematics. They belong to philosophy.

Answers to Exercises

I am much indebted to D. Levine, W. Anscher and M. Brender for the answers to the exercises.

Chapter I, §2

1. $-3 < x < 3$ **2.** $-1 \le x \le 0$ **3.** $-\sqrt{3} \le x \le -1$ or $1 \le x \le \sqrt{3}$
4. $x > 2$ **5.** $-1 < x < 2$ **6.** $x < -1$ or $x > 1$ **7.** $-5 < x < 5$
8. $-1 \le x \le 0$ **9.** $x \ge 1$ or $x = 0$ **10.** $x \le -10$ or $x = 5$
11. $x \le -10$ or $x = 5$ **12.** $x \ge 1$ or $x = -\frac{1}{2}$ **13.** $x < -4$

Chapter I, §3

1. $\frac{4}{3}, -\frac{3}{2}$ **2.** $\dfrac{1}{(2x+1)}$ **3.** $0, 2, 108$ **4.** $2z - z^2, 2w - w^2$
5. $x \ne \sqrt{2}$ or $-\sqrt{2}$. $f(5) = \frac{1}{23}$ **6.** All x. $f(27) = 3$
7. (a) 1 (b) 1 (c) -1 (d) -1 **8.** (a) 1 (b) 4 (c) 0 (d) 0
9. (a) -2 (b) -6 (c) $x^2 + 4x - 2$ **10.** $x \ge 0, 2$

Chapter I, §4

1. 8 and 9 **2.** $\frac{1}{5}$ and -1 **3.** $\frac{1}{16}$ and 2 **4.** $\frac{1}{9}$ and $2^{1/3}$ **5.** $\frac{1}{16}$ and $\frac{1}{2}$
6. 9 and 8 **7.** $-\frac{1}{3}$ and -1 **8.** $\frac{1}{4}$ and $\frac{1}{4}$ **9.** 1 and $-\frac{1}{4}$ **10.** $-\frac{1}{512}$ and $\frac{1}{3}$

Chapter II, §1

3. x negative, y positive   **4.** x negative, y negative

Chapter II, §3

5. $y = -\frac{8}{3}x - \frac{5}{3}$ **6.** $y = -\frac{3}{2}x + 5$ **7.** $x = \sqrt{2}$
8. $y = \dfrac{9}{\sqrt{3}+3}x + 4 - \dfrac{9\sqrt{3}}{\sqrt{3}+3}$ **9.** $y = 4x - 3$ **10.** $y = -2x + 2$
11. $y = -\frac{1}{2}x + 3 + \dfrac{\sqrt{2}}{2}$ **12.** $y = \sqrt{3}\,x + 5 + \sqrt{3}$

Chapter II, §4

1. $\sqrt{97}$ **2.** $\sqrt{2}$ **3.** $\sqrt{52}$ **4.** $\sqrt{13}$ **5.** $\sqrt{5/4}$ **6.** $(4, -3)$ **7.** 5 and 5

A1

Chapter II, §7

5. $(x - 2)^2 + (y + 1)^2 = 25$ **6.** $x^2 + (y - 1)^2 = 9$

7. $(x + 1)^2 + y^2 = 3$ **8.** $y + \frac{25}{8} = 2(x + \frac{1}{4})^2$ **9.** $y - 1 = (x + 2)^2$

10. $y + 4 = (x - 1)^2$ **11.** $(x + 1)^2 + (y - 2)^2 = 2$

12. $(x - 2)^2 + (y - 1)^2 = 2$ **13.** $x + \frac{25}{8} = 2(y + \frac{1}{4})^2$

14. $x - 1 = (y + 2)^2$

Chapter III, §1

1. 4   **2.** -2 **3.** 2   **4.** $\frac{3}{4}$ **5.** $-\frac{1}{4}$ **6.** 0

Chapter III, §2

	Tangent line at $x = 2$
1. $2x$	$y = 4x - 3$
2. $3x^2$	$y = 12x - 16$
3. $6x^2$	$y = 24x - 32$
4. $6x$	$y = 12x - 12$
5. $2x$	$y = 4x - 9$
6. $4x + 1$	$y = 9x - 8$
7. $4x - 3$	$y = 5x - 8$
8. $\dfrac{3x^2}{2} + 2$	$y = 8x - 8$
9. $-\dfrac{1}{(x + 1)^2}$	$y = -\frac{1}{9}x + \frac{5}{9}$
10. $-\dfrac{2}{(x + 1)^2}$	$y = -\frac{2}{9}x + \frac{10}{9}$

11. The slopes are 4, 12, 24, 12, 4, 9, 5, 8, $-\frac{1}{9}$, $-\frac{2}{9}$. The tangent lines at the point $x = 2$ are indicated near the corresponding problem.

12. -1. Left derivative -1. No right derivative.

13. No. $f'(x)$ exists for all other values of x.

14. Left derivative 0. No right derivative. $f'(x) = 0$ if $x < 0$ and $f'(x) = 1$ if $x > 1$.

15. 0, 0, 0

Chapter III, §3

1. $4x + 3$ **2.** $-\dfrac{2}{(2x + 1)^2}$ **3.** $\dfrac{1}{(x + 1)^2}$ **4.** $2x + 1$ **5.** $-\dfrac{1}{(2x - 1)^2}$

6. $9x^2$ **7.** $4x^3$ **8.** $5x^4$ **9.** $6x^2$ **10.** $\dfrac{3x^2}{2} + 1$

Chapter III, §4

1. $x^4 + 4x^3h + 6x^2h^2 + 4xh^3 + h^4$ **2.** $4x^3$

3. (a) $\frac{2}{3}x^{-1/3}$ (b) $-\frac{3}{2}x^{-5/2}$ (c) $\frac{7}{6}x^{1/6}$ **4.** $y = 9x - 8$

5. $y = \frac{1}{3}x + \frac{4}{3}$, slope $\frac{1}{3}$ **6.** $y = \dfrac{-3}{29}x + \dfrac{7}{32}$, slope $\dfrac{-3}{29}$

7. $y = \dfrac{1}{2\sqrt{3}}x + \dfrac{\sqrt{3}}{2}$, slope $\dfrac{1}{2\sqrt{3}}$

8. (a) $\frac{1}{4}5^{-3/4}$ (b) $-\frac{1}{4}7^{-5/4}$ (c) $\sqrt{2}\,(10^{\sqrt{2}-1})$ (d) $\pi 7^{\pi-1}$

Chapter III, §5

1. $\frac{2}{3}x^{-2/3}$ **2.** $55x^{10}$ **3.** $-\frac{3}{8}x^{-7/4}$ **4.** $21x^2 + 8x$ **5.** $-25x^{-2} + 6x^{-1/2}$

6. $\frac{6}{5}x - 16x^7$ **7.** $(x^3 + x) + (3x^2 + 1)(x - 1)$

8. $(2x^2 - 1)4x^3 + 4x(x^4 + 1)$ **9.** $(x + 1)(2x + \frac{15}{2}x^{1/2}) + (x^2 + 5x^{3/2})$

10. $(2x - 5)(12x^3 + 5) + 2(3x^4 + 5x + 2)$

11. $(x^{-2/3} + x^2)\left(3x^2 - \dfrac{1}{x^2}\right) + (-\frac{2}{3}x^{-5/3} + 2x)\left(x^3 + \dfrac{1}{x}\right)$

12. $(2x + 3)(-2x^{-3} - x^{-2}) + 2(x^{-2} + x^{-1})$

13. $\dfrac{9}{(x + 5)^2}$ **14.** $\dfrac{(-2x^2 + 2)}{(x^2 + 3x + 1)^2}$

15. $\dfrac{(t + 1)(t - 1)(2t + 2) - (t^2 + 2t - 1)2t}{(t^2 - 1)^2}$

16. $\dfrac{(t^2 + t - 1)(-5/4)t^{-9/4} - t^{-5/4}(2t + 1)}{(t^2 + t - 1)^2}$

17. $\frac{5}{49}$. $y = \frac{5}{49}t + \frac{4}{49}$ **18.** $\frac{1}{2}$. $y = \frac{1}{2}t$

Chapter III, §6

1. $8(x + 1)^7$ **2.** $\frac{1}{2}(2x - 5)^{-1/2} \cdot 2$ **3.** $3(\sin x)^2 \cos x$ **4.** $5(\log x)^4 \dfrac{1}{x}$

5. $(\cos 2x)2$ **6.** $\dfrac{1}{x^2 + 1}2x$ **7.** $e^{\cos x}(-\sin x)$ **8.** $\dfrac{1}{e^x + \sin x}(e^x + \cos x)$

9. $\cos\left(\log x + \dfrac{1}{x}\right)\left(\dfrac{1}{x} - \dfrac{1}{x^2}\right)$ **10.** $\dfrac{\sin 2x - (x + 1)(\cos 2x)2}{(\sin 2x)^2}$

11. $3(2x^2 + 3)^2(4x)$ **12.** $-\sin(\sin 5x)(\cos 5x)5$ **13.** $\dfrac{1}{\cos 2x}(-\sin 2x)2$

14. $\cos((2x + 5)^2)2(2x + 5)2$ **15.** $\cos(\cos(x + 1))(-\sin(x + 1))$

16. $(\cos e^x)e^x$ **17.** $-\dfrac{1}{(3x - 1)^8}[4(3x - 1)^3] \cdot 3$ **18.** $-\dfrac{1}{(4x)^6} \cdot 3(4x)^2 \cdot 4$

19. $-\dfrac{1}{(\sin 2x)^4}2(\sin 2x)(\cos 2x) \cdot 2$ **20.** $-\dfrac{1}{(\cos 2x)^4}2(\cos 2x)(-\sin 2x)2$

21. $-\dfrac{1}{(\sin 3x)^2}\cos 3x \cdot 3$ **22.** $-\sin^2 x + \cos^2 x$ **23.** $(x^2 + 1)e^x + 2xe^x$

24. $(x^3 + 2x)\cos 3x \cdot 3 + (3x^2 + 2)\sin 3x$

25. $-\dfrac{1}{(\sin x + \cos x)^2}(\cos x - \sin x)$ **26.** $\dfrac{2e^x \cos 2x - (\sin 2x)e^x}{e^{2x}}$

27. $\dfrac{(x^2+3)/x - (\log x)(2x)}{(x^2+3)^2}$ **28.** $\dfrac{\cos 2x - (x+1)(-\sin 2x) \cdot 2}{\cos^2 2x}$

29. $(2x-3)(e^x+1) + 2(e^x+x)$ **30.** $(x^3-1)(e^{3x} \cdot 3 + 5) + 3x^2(e^{3x}+5x)$

31. $\dfrac{(x-1)3x^2 - (x^3+1)}{(x-1)^2}$ **32.** $\dfrac{(2x+3)2x - (x^2-1)2}{(2x+3)^2}$

33. $2(x^{4/3} - e^x) + (\frac{4}{3}x^{1/3} - e^x)(2x+1)$

34. $(\sin 3x)\frac{1}{4}x^{-3/4} + 3(\cos 3x)(x^{1/4} - 1)$ **35.** $[\cos (x^2 + 5x)](2x+5)$

36. $e^{3x^2+8}(6x)$ **37.** $\dfrac{-1}{[\log (x^4+1)]^2} \cdot \dfrac{1}{x^4+1} \cdot 4x^3$

38. $\dfrac{-1}{[\log (x^{1/2}+2x)]^2} \dfrac{1}{(x^{1/2}+2x)} (\frac{1}{2}x^{-1/2} + 2)$ **39.** $\dfrac{2e^x - 2xe^x}{e^{2x}}$.

Chapter III, §7

1. $18x$ **2.** $5(x^2+1)^4 \cdot 2 + 20(x^2+1)^3 4x^2$ **3.** 0 **4.** 5040 **5.** 0 **6.** 6

7. $-\cos x$ **9.** $-\sin x$

Chapter III, §8

1. (a) 1/6 **2.** 0 **4.** 0 **5.** 240 in³/sec **6.** 36π in³/sec

7. $2\pi r, \dfrac{\pi d}{2}, \dfrac{c}{2\pi}$ **8.** $-3/16$ units/sec

Supplementary Exercises

Chapter III, Sums, Products, and Quotients

1. $9x^2 - 4$ **3.** $2x + 1$ **5.** $\frac{5}{2}x^{3/2} - \frac{5}{2}x^{-7/2}$ **7.** $x^2 - 1 + (x+5)(2x)$

9. $(\frac{3}{2}x^{1/2} + 2x)(x^4 - 99) + (x^{3/2} + x^2)(4x^3)$

11. $(4x)\left(\dfrac{1}{x^2} + 4x + 8\right) + (2x^2 + 1)\left(\dfrac{-2}{x^3} + 4\right)$

13. $(x+2)(x+3) + (x+1)(x+3) + (x+1)(x+2)$

15. $3x^2(x^2+1)(x+1) + x^3(2x)(x+1) + (x^3)(x^2+1)$

17. $\dfrac{-2}{(2x+3)^2}$ **19.** $\dfrac{5(3x^2+4x)}{(x^3+2x^2)^2}$ **21.** $\dfrac{-2(x+1) + 2x}{(x+1)^2}$

23. $\dfrac{(x+1)(x-1)3(\frac{1}{2}x^{-1/2}) - 3x^{1/2}[(x-1) + (x+1)]}{(x+1)^2(x-1)^2}$

25. $\dfrac{(x^2+1)(x+7)(5x^4) - (x^5+1)((x^2+1) + (2x)(x+7))}{(x^2+1)^2(x+7)^2}$

27. $\dfrac{(1-x^2)(3x^2) - x^3(-2x)}{(1-x^2)^2}$ **29.** $\dfrac{(x^2+1)(2x-1) - (x^2-x)(2x)}{(x^2+1)^2}$

31. $\dfrac{(x^2+x-4)(2) - (2x+1)(2x+1)}{(x^2+x-4)^2}$

33. $\dfrac{(x^2 + 2)(4 - 3x^2) - (4x - x^3)(2x)}{(x^2 + 2)^2}$ **35.** $\dfrac{-5x - (1 - 5x)}{x^2}$

37. $\dfrac{(x + 1)(x - 2)(2x) - x^2((x - 2) + (x + 1))}{(x + 1)^2(x - 2)^2}$

39. $\dfrac{(4x^3 - x^5 + 1)(12x^3 + \frac{5}{4}x^{1/4}) - (3x^4 + x^{5/4})(12x^2 - 5x^4)}{(4x^3 - x^5 + 1)^2}$

41. $32y = 25x + 176$ **43.** $y = 19x - 12$ **45.** $y = 14x - 4$

47. $27y = -4x + 20$ **49.** $9y = -4x + 20$

51. Point of tangency: $(3, -3)$. Both curves intersect here and have the same slope.

53. Both curves have the same slope at this point.

55. $(-1, -13)$, $y = 16x + 3$; $(0, 7)$, $y = 16x + 7$; $(1, 19)$, $y = 16x + 3$

Chapter III, Chain rule

1. $2(2x + 1)2$ **3.** $7(5x + 3)^6 5$ **5.** $3(2x^2 + x - 5)^2(4x + 1)$

7. $\frac{1}{2}(3x + 1)^{-1/2}(3)$ **9.** $-2(x^2 + x - 1)^{-3}(2x + 1)$

11. $-\frac{5}{3}(x + 5)^{-8/3}$ **13.** $(x - 1)3(x - 5)^2 + (x - 5)^3$

15. $4(x^3 + x^2 - 2x - 1)^3(3x^2 + 2x - 2)$

17. $\dfrac{(x - 1)^{1/2}(\frac{3}{4})(x + 1)^{-1/4} - (x + 1)^{3/4}(\frac{1}{2})(x - 1)^{-1/2}}{x - 1}$

19. $\dfrac{(3x + 2)^9(\frac{5}{2})(2x^2 + x - 1)^{3/2}(4x + 1) - (2x^2 + x - 1)^{5/2}(9)(3x + 2)^8(3)}{(3x + 2)^{18}}$

21. $\frac{1}{2}(2x + 1)^{-1/2}(2)$ **23.** $\frac{1}{2}(x^2 + x + 5)^{-1/2}(2x + 1)$

25. $3x^2 \cos(x^3 + 1)$ **27.** $(e^{x^3+1})(3x^2)$ **29.** $(\cos(\cos x))(-\sin x)$

31. $(e^{\sin(x^3+1)})(3x^2 \cos(x^3 + 1))$

33. $[\cos((x + 1)(x^2 + 2))][(x + 1)(2x) + (x^2 + 2)]$

35. $(e^{(x+1)(x-3)})((x + 1) + (x - 3))$ **37.** $2 \cos(2x + 5)$

39. $\dfrac{2}{2x + 1}$ **41.** $\left(\cos \dfrac{x - 5}{2x + 4}\right)\left(\dfrac{(2x + 4) - (x - 5)2}{(2x + 4)^2}\right)$

43. $(e^{2x^2+3x+1})(4x + 3)$ **45.** $\dfrac{1}{2x + 1} \cos(\log(2x + 1))2$

47. $-(6x - 2)\sin(3x^2 - 2x + 1)$ **49.** $80(2x + 1)^{79}(2)$

51. $49(\log x)^{48}(x^{-1})$ **53.** $5(e^{2x+1} - x)^4(2e^{2x+1} - 1)$

55. $\frac{1}{2}(3\log(x^2 + 1) - x^3)^{-1/2}\left(\dfrac{3}{x^2 + 1}(2x) - 3x^2\right)$

57. $\dfrac{2\cos(3x)\cos(2x) - 3\sin 2x(-\sin 3x)}{(\cos 3x)^2}$

59. $\dfrac{(\sin x^3)(1/2x^2)4x - (\log 2x^2)(\cos x^3)3x^2}{(\sin x^3)^2}$

61. $\dfrac{(\cos 2x)(4x^3 + 1) - 2(x^4 + 1)(-\sin 2x)}{(\cos 2x)^2}$

63. $\dfrac{(\cos x)^3(4)(2x^2 + 1)^3(4x) - (2x^2 + 1)^4(3)(\cos x)^2(-\sin x)}{(\cos x)^6}$

65. $-3e^{-3x}$ **67.** $e^{-4x^2+x}(-8x + 1)$

69. $\dfrac{e^{-x}[2x/(x^2 + 2)] - (\log x^2 + 2)e^{-x}(-1)}{e^{-2x}}$

Chapter III, Rate of change

1. $(\frac{1}{2}, \frac{1}{4})$; $dx/dt = 3$, $dy/dt = 6$; $dx/dt = 1$, $dy/dt = 4$
3. 90 sq in/sec   **5.** 0.015 ft/min   **7.** $t = \frac{1}{4}$, acc $= 4$ **9.** $4/75\pi$ ft/min
11. $1/12\pi$ ft/min

Chapter IV, §1

1. $1/\sqrt{2}$ **2.** $\sqrt{3}/2$ **3.** $\dfrac{1}{2\sqrt{2}}(\sqrt{3} + 1)$ **4.** $\frac{1}{2}$ **5.** $-\sqrt{3}/2$ **6.** $-\frac{1}{2}$

7. $\sqrt{3}/2$ **8.** $-\dfrac{1}{\sqrt{2}}$ **9.** 1   **10.** $\sqrt{3}$ **11.** -1 **12.** -1

18. $\pi - a + 2\pi n$, where n is an integer.

Chapter IV, §3

1. $\dfrac{1}{2\sqrt{2}}(\sqrt{3} + 1)$ **3.** (a) $\dfrac{\sqrt{3} - 1}{2\sqrt{2}}$

Chapter IV, §4

1. $1 + \tan^2 x$ **2.** $\cos (3x) \cdot 3$ **3.** $-\sin (5x) \cdot 5$ **4.** $\cos (4x^2 + x)(8x + 1)$
5. $\sec^2 (x^3 - 5)(3x^2)$ **6.** $\sec^2 (x^4 - x^3)(4x^3 - 3x^2)$ **7.** $\sec^2 (\sin x) \cos x$
8. $\cos (\tan x)(1 + \tan^2 x)$ **9.** $-\sin (\tan x)(1 + \tan^2 x)$ **10.** -1

11. -1 **12.** $\sqrt{3}/2$ **13.** $-\dfrac{2}{\sqrt{2}}$ **14.** 2   **15.** $-2\sqrt{3}$

16. (a) $y = 1$ (c) $y = 1$ (e) $y = 1$ (g) $2y = -4x + 2 + \pi$
     (i) $12y = 3\sqrt{3}\,x + 6 - \sqrt{3}\,\pi$ (k) $y = 1$ **18.** $12.5\pi\sqrt{3}$ ft/min

Chapter IV, §5

1. 2   **2.** 3   **3.** $\frac{1}{3}$ **4.** 1   **5.** 1   **6.** 0   **7.** 0   **8.** 1   **9.** 2   **10.** $\frac{1}{2}$ **11.** $\frac{2}{3}$

Chapter V, §1

1. 1   **2.** $\frac{3}{4}$ **3.** $\frac{1}{6}$ **4.** 1   **5.** $\frac{3}{4}$ **6.** 0   **7.** ± 1

8. $\dfrac{\pi}{4} + 2n\pi$ and $\dfrac{5\pi}{4} + 2n\pi$, $n =$ integer.   **9.** $n\pi$, $n =$ integer

10. $\dfrac{\pi}{2} + n\pi$, n = integer   **11.** Base = $\sqrt{C/3}$, height = $\sqrt{C/12}$

12. Radius = $\sqrt{C/3\pi}$, height = $\sqrt{C/3\pi}$

13. Base = $\sqrt{C/6}$, height = $\sqrt{C/6}$; Radius = $\sqrt{C/6\pi}$, height = $2\sqrt{C/6\pi}$

Chapter V, §2

1. Maximum: 2; minimum: -1 3. maximum: -2; minimum: -1
5. No maximum; minimum: 2   7. Minimum at 1, maximum at 3
9. Minimum at $\frac{1}{3}$, maximum at 5
11. Relative and absolute maximum: $\pi/4$; relative and absolute minimum: $5\pi/4$
13. Relative and absolute maximum: $\pi/3$, $5\pi/3$; relative minima: 0, π, 2π; absolute minimum: π
15. Relative and absolute maxima: $\pi/6$, $5\pi/6$, $9\pi/6$; relative and absolute minima: $\pi/2$, $7\pi/6$, $11\pi/6$
17. Maximum at 0, π, 2π; minimum at $\pi/2$, $3\pi/2$ 19. $\pi/2$
21. Minimum at 0, $\pi/2$; maximum at $\pi/3$

Chapter V, §3

1. $(\frac{13}{3})^{1/2}$ 2. 0   3. $\sqrt{7/3}$ 4. 1

Chapter V, §4

1. Increasing for all x.
2. Increasing for $x \leq 2 - 1/\sqrt{3}$, and $x \geq 2 + 1/\sqrt{3}$.   Decreasing for $2 - 1/\sqrt{3} \leq x \leq 2 + 1/\sqrt{3}$.
3. Decreasing for $x \leq \frac{1}{2}$, increasing for $x \geq \frac{1}{2}$.
4. Decreasing for $\pi/4 \leq x \leq 5\pi/4$, increasing for $0 \leq x \leq \pi/4$ and $5\pi/4 \leq x \leq 2\pi$. In general, add $2n\pi$ to these intervals.
5. Decreasing for $\pi/4 \leq x \leq 3\pi/4$ and $5\pi/4 \leq x \leq 7\pi/4$, increasing for $0 \leq x \leq \pi/4$ and $3\pi/4 \leq x \leq 5\pi/4$ and $7\pi/4 \leq x \leq 2\pi$.
6. Decreasing $x \leq -\sqrt{3/2}$ and $0 \leq x \leq \sqrt{3/2}$. Increasing $-\sqrt{3/2} \leq x \leq 0$ and $\sqrt{3/2} \leq x$.
7. Increasing all x.
8. Decreasing $x \leq -\sqrt{2/3}$ and $x \geq \sqrt{2/3}$. Increasing $-\sqrt{2/3} \leq x \leq \sqrt{2/3}$.
9. Increasing all x.
10. Decreasing for $x \leq 0$. Increasing for $x \geq 0$.   11. All increasing.
13. (a) no maximum; minimum: 1   (b) minimum: 1; maximum: 4
    (c) $x < 1$ decreasing; $x > 1$ increasing
15. (a) maximum: -2; no minimum   (b) maximum: -1; minimum: 4
    (c) $x < -2$ increasing; $x > -2$ decreasing
17. (a) no maximum or minimum   (b) minimum: -1; maximum: -2, 1
    (c) $x < -1$, $x > 1$ decreasing; $-1 < x < 1$ increasing

19. (a) no maximum; minima: ± 1 (b) maximum: -2; minima: ± 1
(c) $x < -1, 0 < x < 1$ decreasing; $-1 < x < 0, x > 1$ increasing
21. (a) no maximum; minimum: 0   (b) maxima: ± 1; minimum: 0
(c) $x < 0$ decreasing; $x > 0$ increasing

Supplementary Exercises, Chapter V

1. $r\sqrt{2}$ by $\frac{1}{2}r\sqrt{2}$ where r is the radius of the semicircle.   **5.** $8\sqrt{2}$ by $4\sqrt{2}$
7. Minimum: use $24\pi/(4 + \pi)$ inches for circle; $96/(4 + \pi)$ inches for square.
Maximum: use whole wire for circle.
9. $(\sqrt{5}/2, \frac{1}{2}), (-\sqrt{5}/2, \frac{1}{2})$ **11.** $(5, 3), (-5, 3)$ **13.** $(-1, 0)$
15. $F = 2\sqrt{3}\, Q/9b^2$ **17.** $(2, 0)$ **19.** $13\sqrt{13}/2$ **21.** $4(1 + \sqrt[3]{4})^{3/2}$
25. $3y = -2x + 12$ **27.** $12.5\sqrt{2}$ **29.** $\pi/3$
31. $\dfrac{c}{1 + \sqrt[3]{a/b}}$ away from b **33.** radius $= 4$ ft; angle $= 2$ radians
35. $2(1 + \sqrt[3]{36})^{3/2}$

Chapter VI, §1

1. 0, 0   **2.** 0, 0   **3.** 0, 0   **4.** $\dfrac{1}{\pi}, \dfrac{1}{\pi}$ **5.** 0, 0   **6.** $\infty, -\infty$ **7.** $-\infty, \infty$
8. $-\frac{1}{2}, -\frac{1}{2}$ **9.** $-\infty, +\infty$ **10.** 0, 0   **11.** $\infty, -\infty$ **12.** $-\infty, \infty$
13. ∞, ∞ **14.** $-\infty, -\infty$ **15.** $\infty, -\infty$ **16.** $-\infty, \infty$ **17.** ∞, ∞
18. $-\infty, -\infty$

19.

$x \to \infty$	$a_n > 0$	$a_n < 0$
n odd	∞	$-\infty$
n even	∞	$-\infty$

$x \to -\infty$	$a_n > 0$	$a_n < 0$
n odd	$-\infty$	∞
n even	∞	$-\infty$

Chapter VI, §2

	c.p.	Increasing	Decreasing
1.	$3 \pm \sqrt{11}$	$x \leq 3 - \sqrt{11}$ and $x \geq 3 + \sqrt{11}$	$3 - \sqrt{11} \leq x < 3$ and $3 < x \leq 3 + \sqrt{11}$
2.	$3 \pm \sqrt{10}$	$3 - \sqrt{10} \leq x \leq 3 + \sqrt{10}$	$3 + \sqrt{10} \leq x$ and $x \leq 3 - \sqrt{10}$
3.	$-1 \pm \sqrt{2}$	$-1 - \sqrt{2} \leq x \leq -1 + \sqrt{2}$	$x \leq -1 - \sqrt{2}$ and $x \geq -1 + \sqrt{2}$
4.	$n\pi/2$	$0 \leq x \leq \pi/2$ and add $n\pi$	$\pi/2 \leq x \leq \pi$ and add $n\pi$
5.	$n\pi/2$	$\pi/2 \leq x \leq \pi$ and add $n\pi$	$0 \leq x \leq \pi/2$ and add $n\pi$
6.	None	$x < 0$ and $x > 0$	Never
7.	$n\pi$	$0 \leq x < \pi/2$ and add $n\pi$	$-\pi/2 < x \leq 0$ and add $n\pi$
8.	$\frac{1}{2}$	$x \geq \frac{1}{2}$	$x \leq \frac{1}{2}$
9.	$0, \frac{3}{2}$	$x \geq \frac{3}{2}$	$x \leq \frac{3}{2}$

	c.p.	Increasing	Decreasing
10.	0	$x \leq 0$	$\sqrt{2} < x$ and $0 \leq x < \sqrt{2}$
11.	None	$x < -\frac{1}{3}$	$x > -\frac{1}{3}$
12.	-1	$x \geq -1$	$x \leq -1$
13.	None	All x	Never
14.	-1	$x \geq -1$	$x \leq -1$
15.	None	All x	Never
16.	$-(\frac{1}{8})^{1/7}$	$x \geq -(\frac{1}{8})^{1/7}$	$x \leq -(\frac{1}{8})^{1/7}$

17. (a), (e) **18.** (c)

	Rel. Max.	Rel. Min.	Increasing	Decreasing
21.	2	-2	$-2 < x < 2$	$x < -2, x > 2$
23.	None	-2	$x > -2$	$x < -2$
25.	$-\sqrt{3}$	$\sqrt{3}$	$x < -\sqrt{3}, x > \sqrt{3}$	$-\sqrt{3} < x < 0, 0 < x < \sqrt{3}$
27.	$-1 + \sqrt{3}$	$-1 + \sqrt{3}$	$x < -1 - \sqrt{3}, x > \sqrt{3} - 1$	$-1 - \sqrt{3} < x < \sqrt{3} - 1$
29.	None	None	Nowhere	$x < 2, x > 2$
31.	None	None	Nowhere	$x < 5/3, x > 5/3$
33.	None	0	$x > 0$	$-1 < x < 0$
35.	None	None	Nowhere	$x < -\sqrt{5}, -\sqrt{5} < x < \sqrt{5}, x > \sqrt{5}$
37.	0	None	$x < -2, -2 < x < 0$	$0 < x < 2, x > 2$
39.	$\pm 3\sqrt{10}/5$	0	$-3 \leq x < -3\sqrt{10}/5$, $0 \leq x < 3\sqrt{10}/5$	$-3\sqrt{10}/5 < x \leq 0$, $3\sqrt{10}/5 < x \leq 3$
41.	None	-1	$-1 \leq x \leq 7$	$-2 \leq x \leq -1$
43.	$(\pi/4) + 2n\pi$	$(5\pi/4) + 2n\pi$	$5\pi/4 < x < 9\pi/4$ and add $2n\pi$	$\pi/4 < x < 5\pi/4$ and add $2n\pi$
45.	$(\pi/12) + n\pi$	$(7\pi/12) + n\pi$	$7\pi/12 < x < 13\pi/12$ and add $n\pi$	$\pi/12 < x < 7\pi/12$ and add $n\pi$
47.	$(\pi/3) + 2n\pi$	$(5\pi/3) + 2n\pi$	$5\pi/3 < x < 7\pi/3$ and add $2n\pi$	$\pi/3 < x < 5\pi/3$ and add $2n\pi$

49. Relative maxima: $3\pi/2$, arcsin $(\sqrt{3}/3)$, $\pi - $ arcsin $(\sqrt{3}/3)$ and add $2n\pi$. Relative minima: $\pi/2$, $\pi + $ arcsin $(\sqrt{3}/3)$, $2\pi - $ arcsin $(\sqrt{3}/3)$ and add $2n\pi$. Increasing and decreasing as expected, i.e. between each maximum and the next minimum it is decreasing and between each minimum and the next maximum it is increasing.

Chapter VI, §3

11. (a) Convex upward for $x > 0$. Convex downward for $x < 0$.
(c) Convex upward for $x > 1$, $-1 < x \leq 0$. Downward for $x < -1$ and $0 \leq x < 1$.

Chapter VI, §4

3. (a) $(\sqrt{2}, \pi/4)$ (b) $(\sqrt{2}, 5\pi/4)$ (c) $(6, \pi/3)$ (d) $(1, \pi)$
32. $y = x(\tan 2)$, $x \leq 0$ **34.** $(y - 1)^2 + x^2 = 1$
36. $(x^2 + x + y^2)^2 = x^2 + y^2$ **38.** $x = 1$ **40.** $y^2 = 2x + 1$
42. $y = 0$, $x \leq 0$ **43.** $y = x(\tan 3)$, $x \leq 0$ **46.** $y = x(\tan 0.3)$, $x \geq 0$

Chapter VII, §1

1. Yes; all real numbers **3.** Yes; all real numbers **5.** Yes; for $y < 1$
7. Yes; for $y \geq 1$ **9.** Yes; for $y \leq -1$ **11.** Yes; for $y \geq 2$
13. Yes; for $-1 \leq y \leq 1$

Chapter VII, §2 (Alternative answers depend on the choice of intervals.)

1. $\frac{1}{3}$ **2.** $\frac{1}{8}$ **3.** $\frac{1}{11}$ **4.** -1 or 1 **5.** 1 or -1

6. $-\frac{1}{2}$ or $-\frac{1}{10}$, or $\pm\dfrac{1}{2\sqrt{2}}$ **7.** $\frac{1}{4}$ **8.** -1 or $\frac{1}{2}\pm\frac{3}{10}\sqrt{5}$ **9.** $\frac{1}{24}$

10. $\dfrac{1}{10\sqrt{2}}$ or $\dfrac{-1}{10\sqrt{2}}$

Chapter VII, §3

2. $-1/\sqrt{1-x^2}$ **3.** $2/\sqrt{3},\sqrt{2},\pi/6,\pi/4$ **4.** $-2/\sqrt{3},-\sqrt{2},\pi/3,\pi/4$

5. Let $y=\sec x$ on interval $0<x<\pi/2$. Then $x=\operatorname{arcsec} y$ is defined

on $1<y$, and $dx/dy=\dfrac{1}{y\sqrt{y^2-1}}$.

6. $-\pi/2$ **7.** 0 **8.** $\pi/2$ **9.** $\pi/2$ **10.** $-\pi/4$

11. $\dfrac{2}{\sqrt{2-x^2}}\ (x\neq 0)$ **13.** $\dfrac{-1}{(\arcsin x)^2\sqrt{1-x^2}}$

Chapter VII, §4

1. $\pi/4,\pi/6,-\pi/4,\pi/3$ **2.** $\frac{1}{2},\frac{3}{4},\frac{1}{2},\frac{1}{4}$ **3.** $1/(1+y^2)$

4. (a) $-\pi/4$ (b) 0 (c) $-\pi/6$ (d) $\pi/6$ **5.** $\dfrac{3}{1+9x^2}$ **7.** 0

9. $\dfrac{2\cos 2x}{1+\sin^2 2x}$ **11.** $\dfrac{(\cos x)(\arcsin x)-(\sin x)/\sqrt{1-x^2}}{(\arcsin x)^2}$

13. $\dfrac{-1}{1+x^2}$ **15.** $\dfrac{9}{\sqrt{1-9x^2}}(1+\arcsin 3x)^2$

17. $4y=4\sqrt{2}\,x+\pi-4$ **19.** $12y=6x+4\pi-3\sqrt{3}$

21. $6y=4\sqrt{3}\,x+2\sqrt{3}-\pi$ **23.** 440 ft/sec **25.** 0.02 rad/sec

27. $\dfrac{d\theta}{dt}=\frac{1}{6}\sin\theta\tan\theta$ **29.** $\frac{1}{82}$ rad/sec

Chapter VIII, §1

1. (a) $y=\frac{1}{2}x+\log 2-1$ (b) $y=\frac{1}{5}x+\log 5-1$

  (c) $y=2x-\log 2-1$ **×** $2x + \log \frac{1}{2}, -1$

2. (a) $y=-x+\log 2-1$ (b) $y=\frac{4}{5}x+\log 5-\frac{8}{5}$

  (c) $y=-\frac{3}{5}x+\log 10-\frac{9}{5}$

3. (a) $\dfrac{\cos x}{\sin x}$ (b) $\cos\left(\log(2x+3)\right)\dfrac{1}{2x+3}\cdot 2$ (c) $\dfrac{1}{x^2+5}\cdot 2x$

  (d) $\dfrac{(\sin x)1/x-(\log 2x)\cos x}{\sin^2 x}$

4. $y=\frac{1}{4}x+\log 4-\frac{3}{4}$ **5.** $y=\dfrac{2x}{3}+\log 3-\frac{8}{3}$

11. $\dfrac{2}{2x+5}$ **13.** $\dfrac{1}{\sqrt{1-x^2}\,\arcsin x}$ **15.** $\dfrac{-1}{x(\log x)^2}$

17. $\tfrac{1}{3}(\log x)^{-2/3}+(\log x)^{1/3}$

Chapter VIII, §2

1. (a) $y=2e^2x-e^2$ (b) $y=2e^{-4}x+5e^{-4}$ (c) $y=2x+1$

2. (a) $y=\tfrac{1}{2}e^{-2}x+3e^{-2}$ (b) $y=\tfrac{1}{2}e^{1/2}x+\tfrac{1}{2}e^{1/2}$ (c) $y=\tfrac{1}{2}x+1$

3. $y=3e^2x-4e^2$

4. (a) $e^{\sin 3x}(\cos 3x)3$ (b) $\dfrac{1}{e^x+\sin x}(e^x+\cos x)$ (c) $\cos(e^{x+2})e^{x+2}$

(d) $4\cos(e^{4x-5})e^{4x-5}$

9. $y=\dfrac{x}{e}$ **11.** $y=(1+\log 2)x-2$ **13.** $y=\dfrac{-1}{e}x+2$

15. $y=2e^2x-e^2$ **17.** $y=6e^5x-25e^5$ **19.** $y=1$

27. $0\leqq x<1$; defined by $y\geqq 0$.

31. f is increasing in the interval; as x approaches 1, $f(x)$ approaches ∞, and as x approaches -1, $f(x)$ approaches $-\infty$.

Chapter VIII, §3

1. $10^x\log 10,\ 7^x\log 7$ **2.** $3^x\log 3,\ \pi^x\log\pi$ **3.** $x^x(1+\log x)$

4. $x^{(x^x)}[x^{x-1}+(\log x)x^x(1+\log x)]$ **5.** e **6.** Yes   **8.** $y=x$

9. $y=(\log 10)x+1,\ y=(\log 7)x+1$

10. $y=(9\log 3)x-18\log 3+9$ and $y=(\pi^2\log\pi)x-2\pi^2\log\pi+\pi^2$

Chapter VIII, §4

13. **14.** All derivatives are 0 at 0.   **17.** Limit is 0 in both cases.

22. (a) 1   (b) 1   (c) $1/e$ (d) 1

$5e^{-4}$

Chapter VIII, §5

1. $-\log 25$ **2.** $5e^{-4}$ **3.** $e^{-(\log 10)10^{-6}t}$ **4.** $20/e$ **5.** $-(\log 2)/K$

6. $(\log 3)/4$ **7.** $12\log 10/\log 2$ **8.** $\dfrac{-3\log 2}{\log 9-\log 10}$

Chapter IX, §1

1. $-(\cos 2x)/2$ **2.** $\dfrac{\sin 3x}{3}$ **3.** $\log(x+1),\ x>-1$

4. $\log(x+2),\ x>-2$

Chapter IX, §3

1. $\tfrac{624}{4}$ **2.** 2   **3.** 2   **4.** $\log 2$ **5.** $\log 3$ **6.** $\tfrac{2}{5}$ **7.** $e-1$

Chapter X, §1

1. $\tfrac{63}{6}$ **2.** 0   **3.** 0   **4.** 0

Chapter X, §2

1. x^4 **2.** $3x^5/5 - x^6/6$ **3.** $-2 \cos x + 3 \sin x$ **4.** $\frac{9}{5}x^{5/3} + 5 \sin x$
5. $5e^x + \log x$ **6.** 0 **7.** 0 **8.** $e^2 - e^{-1}$ **9.** $4 \cdot 28/3$ **11.** $\frac{1}{2}$ **12.** $\frac{1}{12}$
13. $70 - \frac{139}{2}$ **14.** $\frac{8}{3} + \frac{5}{12}$ **15.** $\sqrt{2} - 1$ **16.** $9/2$ **17.** $\frac{1}{3} - 1$ **18.** 0
19. $2 + \pi^2/2$ **20.** 4 **21.** 4 **22.** 1 **23.** 4 **24.** π^2 **25.** 4

Chapter X, §4

1. Yes **2.** No **3.** Yes **4.** No **5.** No **6.** Yes
7. $-\frac{1}{2}e^{-2B} + \frac{1}{2}e^{-4}$. Yes, $\frac{1}{2}e^{-4}$.

Chapter XI, §1

1. $e^{x^2}/2$ **2.** $-\frac{1}{4}e^{-x^4}$ **3.** $\frac{1}{6}(1 + x^3)^2$ **4.** $(\log x)^2/2$

5. $\dfrac{(\log x)^{-n+1}}{1 - n}$ if $n \neq 1$, and log (log x) if $n = 1$. **6.** $\log (x^2 + x + 1)$

7. $x - \log (x + 1)$ **8.** $\dfrac{\sin^2 x}{2}$ **9.** $\dfrac{\sin^3 x}{3}$ **10.** 0 **11.** $\frac{2}{5}$

12. $-\arctan (\cos x)$ **13.** $\frac{1}{2}(\arctan x)^2$ **14.** $2/15$ **15.** $-\frac{1}{4} \cos (\pi^2/2) + \frac{1}{4}$
16. $-\frac{1}{2}e^{-B^2} + \frac{1}{2}$. Yes, $\frac{1}{2}$ **17.** $-\frac{1}{3}e^{-B^3} + \frac{1}{3}$. Yes, $\frac{1}{3}$
18. $2\sqrt{1 + e^x} - \log (\sqrt{1 + e^x} + 1) + \log (\sqrt{1 + e^x} - 1)$
19. $x - \log (1 + e^x)$ **20.** $\arctan (e^x)$
21. $-\log (\sqrt{1 + e^x} + 1) + \log (\sqrt{1 + e^x} - 1)$

Chapter XI, §2

1. $x \arcsin x + \sqrt{1 - x^2}$ **2.** $x \arctan x - \frac{1}{2} \log (x^2 + 1)$

3. $\dfrac{e^{2x}}{13} (2 \sin 3x - 3 \cos 3x)$ **4.** $\frac{1}{10}e^{-4x} \sin 2x - \frac{2}{5}e^{-4x} \cos 2x$
5. $x(\log x)^2 - 2x \log x + 2x$ **6.** $(\log x)^3 x - 3\int (\log x)^2 \, dx$
7. $x^2 e^x - 2xe^x + 2e^x$ **8.** $-x^2 e^{-x} - 2xe^{-x} - 2e^{-x}$ **9.** $-x \cos x + \sin x$
10. $x \sin x + \cos x$ **11.** $-x^2 \cos x + 2\int x \cos x \, dx$
12. $x^2 \sin x - 2\int x \sin x \, dx$ **13.** $\frac{1}{2}[x^2 \sin x^2 + \cos x^2]$

14. $-\frac{1}{3}x^4(1 - x^2)^{3/2} - \dfrac{4}{3 \cdot 5}x^2(1 - x^2)^{5/2} - \dfrac{8}{3 \cdot 5 \cdot 7}(1 - x^2)^{7/2}$

15. $\frac{1}{3}x^3 \log x - \frac{1}{9}x^3$ **16.** $(\log x)\dfrac{x^4}{4} - \dfrac{x^4}{16}$ **17.** $(\log x)^2 \dfrac{x^3}{3} - \dfrac{2}{3}\int x^2 \log x \, dx$

18. $-\frac{1}{2}x^2 e^{-x^2} - \frac{1}{2}e^{-x^2}$ **19.** $\frac{1}{4}x^4 \left(\dfrac{1}{1 - x^4}\right) + \frac{1}{4} \log (1 - x^4)$ **20.** -4π

21. $-Be^{-B} - e^{-B} + 1$. Yes, 1 **22.** Yes **23.** Yes

24. $-\dfrac{1}{\log B} + \dfrac{1}{\log 2}$. Yes, $1/\log 2$. **25.** Yes, $1/3(\log 3)^3$

Chapter XI, §3

1. $-\frac{1}{4}\sin^3 x \cos x - \frac{3}{8}\sin x \cos x + \frac{3}{8}x$ **2.** $\frac{1}{3}\cos^2 x \sin x + \frac{2}{3}\sin x$

3. $\dfrac{\sin^3 x}{3} - \dfrac{\sin^5 x}{5}$ **4.** 3π **5.** 8π **6.** πab (If $a, b > 0$). **7.** πr^2

13. $-\log \cos x$ **14.** $\arcsin \dfrac{x}{3}$ **15.** $\arcsin \dfrac{x}{\sqrt{3}}$ **16.** $\frac{1}{2}\arcsin (\sqrt{2}\, x)$

17. $\dfrac{1}{b}\arcsin \dfrac{bx}{a}$

18. (a) $c_0 = a_n = 0$ all n, $b_n = -2/n$.

(b) $c_0 = 4\pi^2/3$, $a_n = 4/n^2$, $b_n = 0$ all n.

(c) $c_0 = \pi/2$, $a_n = 2(\cos n\pi - 1)/\pi n^2$, $b_n = 0$

19. (b) all a_n and $c_0 = 0$

Chapter XI, §4

1. $C_1 = -\frac{33}{100}$, $C_2 = -\frac{11}{100}$, $C_3 = -\frac{130}{100}$, $C_4 = -\frac{110}{100}$, $C_5 = \frac{11}{100}$

2. $\dfrac{x}{2(x^2 + 1)} + \frac{1}{2}\arctan x$

3. (a) $\frac{1}{5}[\log (x - 3) - \log (x + 2)]$ (b) $\log (x + 1) - \log (x + 2)$

4. $-\frac{1}{2}\log (x + 1) + 2 \log (x + 2) - \frac{3}{2}\log (x + 3)$

5. $-\log (x^2 + x) + 3 \log x$, **6.** $\log (x + 1) + \dfrac{1}{x + 1}$

7. $\dfrac{1}{2}\dfrac{-1}{x^2 + 9} + \dfrac{1}{18}\dfrac{x}{x^2 + 9} + \dfrac{1}{54}\arctan \dfrac{x}{3}$ **8.** $\dfrac{1}{8}\dfrac{x}{x^2 + 16} + \dfrac{1}{32}\arctan \dfrac{x}{4}$

9. $-\log (x + 1) + \log (x + 2) - \dfrac{2}{x + 2}$

10. $\dfrac{1}{4}\dfrac{x}{(x^2 + 1)^2} + \dfrac{3}{8}\dfrac{x}{(x^2 + 1)} + \dfrac{3}{8}\arctan x$

11. $-\frac{1}{8}\log (x - 1) + \frac{17}{8}\log (x + 7)$

12. $\frac{1}{2}\log \dfrac{x^2}{x^2 + x + 1} - \dfrac{1}{\sqrt{3}}\arctan \dfrac{2x + 1}{\sqrt{3}}$

13. $\frac{1}{4}\log \dfrac{(x + 1)^2}{x^2 + 1} + \dfrac{1}{2}\arctan x$

14. $\dfrac{1}{2}\left(\arctan x + \dfrac{x}{x^2 + 1}\right)$

Supplementary Exercises

Chapter XI, Substitution

1. $\frac{1}{4}\log (x^4 + 2)$ **3.** $\dfrac{\sin^5 x}{5}$ **5.** $\sqrt{x^2 - 1}$ **7.** $\dfrac{-1}{6(3x^2 + 5)}$ **9.** $\dfrac{-1}{2\sin^2 x}$

11. $\frac{5}{51}(x^3 + 1)^{12/5}(x^3 - \frac{5}{12})$ **13.** $\dfrac{-\cos 3x}{3}$ **15.** $-\cos e^x$ **17.** $\log (\log x)$

19. $\log(e^x + 1)$ **21.** $\frac{1}{4}$ **23.** $\dfrac{4\sqrt{2}}{3} - \dfrac{2}{3}$

25. $\dfrac{\pi}{4}$ **27.** $\dfrac{\pi^2}{72}$ **29.** $e - \dfrac{1}{e}$

31. $-2e^{-\sqrt{x}}(x^{3/2} + 3x + 6x^{1/2} + 6)$

Chapter XI, By parts

1. $\frac{1}{2}(x^2 \arctan x + \arctan x - x)$

3. $\frac{1}{4}(2x^2 \arccos x - \arccos x - x\sqrt{1 - x^2})$

5. $1 - \dfrac{\pi}{2}$ **7.** $\dfrac{\pi}{32}$ **9.** $\dfrac{2}{e}$

Chapter XI, Trigonometric integrals

1. $\log \sin x - \dfrac{\sin^2 x}{2}$ **3.** $-\cos e^x$ **5.** $\dfrac{\pi}{4}$ **7.** $\dfrac{\pi}{4}$ **9.** $\dfrac{\pi}{16}$

11. $\frac{1}{3}\log\dfrac{\sqrt{x^2 + 9} - 3}{x}$ **13.** $\dfrac{\pi}{2}$ **15.** $\dfrac{-1}{3}(x^2 + 32)(16 - x^2)^{1/2}$

17. $\dfrac{-1}{a}\log\left[\dfrac{a + \sqrt{a^2 - x^2}}{x}\right]$ **19.** $\dfrac{-1}{a}\log\left[\dfrac{a + \sqrt{a^2 + x^2}}{x}\right]$

21. $\dfrac{x}{\sqrt{x^2 + 1}}$ **23.** $\dfrac{x}{\sqrt{a^2 - x^2}} - \arcsin\dfrac{x}{a}$ **25.** $\dfrac{\pi + 2}{512}$

Miscellaneous Exercises

3. -1 **4.** $n!$ **5.** $-1/2$

Chapter XII, §1

2. (a) $4/e^2$ (b) $2^2 5^5 e^{-4}/3^3$

Chapter XIII, §1

2. $2\pi r$ **3.** $\sqrt{2}\,(e - e)$ **4.** (a) $\frac{3}{4}$ (b) 3

5. $\sqrt{1 + e^2} - \sqrt{2} + \frac{1}{2}\log\dfrac{\sqrt{1 + e^2} - 1}{\sqrt{1 + e^2} + 1} + \frac{1}{2}\log\dfrac{\sqrt{2} + 1}{\sqrt{2} - 1}$

6. $\frac{1}{27}(31^{3/2} - 13^{3/2})$ **7.** $e - \dfrac{1}{e}$ **8.** 4

9. π **10.** $2\sqrt{3}$ **11.** 2π

13. $\sqrt{2}\,(e^2 - e)$ **14.** $\sqrt{2}\,(e^{\theta_2} - e^{\theta_1})$

Chapter XIII, §2

1. 6π **2.** a^2 (taking values of θ such that $\sin 2\theta \geqq 0$)   **3.** πa^2 **4.** $\dfrac{\pi}{12}$

5. $3\pi/2$ **6.** $3\pi/2$ **7.** $9\pi/2$ **8.** $\pi/3$

Chapter XIII, §3

1. $\frac{4}{3}\pi r^3$ **2.** π **3.** $\frac{\pi^2}{8} - \frac{\pi}{4}$ **4.** $\frac{\pi^2}{8} + \frac{\pi}{4}$ **5.** $\frac{2 \cdot 5^4 \pi}{3}$ **6.** $\pi(e - 2)$ **7.** πe^2

8. $\pi[2(\log 2)^2 - 4\log 2 + 2]$ **9.** 16π **10.** $\frac{\pi}{2}\left[\frac{1}{e^2} - \frac{1}{e^{2B}}\right]$, yes, $\frac{\pi}{2e^2}$

11. $\pi r^2 h/3$

Chapter XIII, §6

1. $c = 1$, x, $1/2$ **2.** $c = 2$, x^2, $1/2$ **4.** $c = \pi/2$, $\frac{1}{2}(1 - \cos \pi x)$, $1/2$
7. $c = 1$, $ex - e^x + 1$, $(e/2) - e^{1/2} + 1$
8. $c = 1/4$, $F(\pi/2) - F(0) = 1/4$.

$$F(x) = \begin{cases} \frac{1}{4}|\sin x| & -\pi \leq x \leq -\pi/2 \\ \frac{1}{4}(2 + \sin x) & -\pi/2 \leq x \leq \pi/2 \\ \frac{1}{4}(4 - \sin x) & \pi/2 \leq x \leq \pi \end{cases}$$

12. $c = 1/\pi$, $F(x) = 0$ if $-\pi \leq x \leq 0$, and $F(x) = (1/\pi)(x - \sin x)$ if $0 \leq x \leq \pi$. $F(\pi/2) - F(0) = \frac{1}{2} - (1/\pi)$.

Supplementary Exercises

Chapter XIII, Length of curves

1. $\frac{8}{27}(10^{3/2} - 1)$
3. $\sqrt{e^4 + 1} + 2 - \sqrt{2} + \log(1 + \sqrt{2}) - \log(1 + \sqrt{e^4 + 1})$
5. $2\sqrt{5} + \log(\sqrt{5} + 2)$ **7.** $2\sqrt{3}$ **9.** $\log 7 - \frac{3}{4}$ **11.** $\log(2 + \sqrt{3})$

13. $4a$ **15.** $\frac{\sqrt{17}}{4}(e^{-4} - e^{-8})$ **17.** $2\sqrt{5} - \frac{\sqrt{17}}{2} + 2\log\left[\frac{8 + 2\sqrt{17}}{1 + \sqrt{5}}\right]$

19. 4

Chapter XIII, Area

1. 25π **3.** π **5.** $\frac{3\pi}{8}$ **7.** $2\pi + \frac{3\sqrt{3}}{2}$ **9.** $\frac{\pi}{4}$ **11.** $10\frac{2}{3}$ **13.** $\frac{4}{3}$ **15.** $\frac{5\sqrt{5}}{6}$

Chapter XIII, Volumes of revolution

1. $\frac{\pi r^2 h}{3}$ **3.** 12π **5.** $\frac{2}{3}\pi$ **7.** $\frac{\pi}{3}$ **9.** $\frac{\pi}{2}(e^{-2} - e^{-10})$ **11.** $\pi\left(\sqrt{3} - \frac{\pi}{3}\right)$

13. $\frac{\pi}{3}\left(1 - \frac{1}{B^3}\right)$; as B becomes very large, the volume approaches $\frac{\pi}{3}$.

15. $\pi \log\left(\frac{1}{a}\right)$; as a approaches 0, the volume increases without limit.

17. $\pi\left[\frac{\sqrt{2}}{2} - \cos a - \log(\sqrt{2} + 1) + \log(\csc a + \cot a)\right]$; as a approaches 0, the volume increases without limit.

Chapter XIII, Work

1. 5 lb/in; 80 in-lb   **3.** $c\left[\dfrac{1}{r_1} - \dfrac{1}{r}\right]$

5. $\dfrac{99c}{200}$ where c is the constant of proportionality   **7.** 1944 ft-lb

Chapter XIV, §3

1. $1 - \dfrac{x^2}{2!} + \dfrac{x^4}{4!}$ **2.** $|R_n| \leq \dfrac{|x|^n}{n!}$ **3.** $1 - \dfrac{0.01}{2} = .995$ **4.** $|R_3| \leq \tfrac{1}{6}10^{-3}$

5. $|R_4| \leq \tfrac{2}{3}10^{-4}$ **6.** $\tan x = x + \dfrac{x^3}{3}$

7. $|R_4| \leq 10^{-4}$ by crude estimates

8. $\sin\left(\dfrac{\pi}{6} + \dfrac{\pi}{180}\right) = \dfrac{1}{2} + \dfrac{\sqrt{3}}{2} \cdot \dfrac{\pi}{180} = 0.515$ **9.** $x^2 - \tfrac{1}{8}x^4$

10. $1 - \dfrac{3x^2}{2} + \dfrac{7}{8}x^4$ **11.** $1 + \dfrac{x^2}{2} + \dfrac{5}{24}x^4$ **12.** x^3

Chapter XIV, §4

1. $1 - x^2 + \dfrac{x^4}{2}$ **2.** $|R_3| \leq 1/24$ **3.** $|R_4| \leq 10^{-9}$ **4.** $|R_3| \leq \tfrac{1}{3}10^{-6}$

5. $1 - x + \dfrac{x^2}{2!} - \dfrac{x^3}{3!} + \dfrac{x^4}{4!} - \dfrac{x^5}{5!}$

6. Use $|R_7| \leq \tfrac{1}{5040}$ **7.** All equal to 0.

Chapter XIV, §5

1. (a) $\log 1.2 = 0.2 - \dfrac{0.04}{2} + \dfrac{0.008}{3}$ with an error R_3 such that

$$|R_3| \leq 4 \times 10^{-4}.$$

(e) $\log\left(1 - \tfrac{1}{25}\right) = -\tfrac{1}{25}$ with an error R_2 such that $|R_2| \leq 10^{-3}$.

Chapter XIV, §6

5. 1   **6.** 1   **7.** 1   **8.** 1   **9.** 1   **10.** 2   **11.** $\tfrac{1}{2}$ **12.** 0   **13.** $-\tfrac{1}{2}$ **14.** 1
15. 1   **16.** 1

Chapter XIV, §7

1. $5 + \tfrac{1}{75}$ **2.** $10 - \tfrac{3}{20} - \tfrac{9}{8000}$ **3.** $|R_2| \leq 2 \times 10^{-2}$ **4.** (a) $|R_2| \leq 0.008$
5. (a) $|R_2| \leq 10^{-5}$ (b) $|R_2| \leq 0.04$

Supplementary Exercises, Chapter XIV

1. $1 - x + x^2 - \tfrac{5}{6}x^3$ **3.** $1 + x^2$ **5.** $x + \dfrac{x^3}{3}$ **7.** $-1 + x + \dfrac{x^2}{2} - \dfrac{x^3}{6}$

9. $x + x^2 + \dfrac{x^3}{3}$ **11.** $2 + x^2$ **13.** $\dfrac{1}{2} - \dfrac{x^2}{4}$ **15.** (a) $x - \dfrac{2x^3}{3}$

To see this, note that up to terms of degree 4, we have

$$\sin x = x - \frac{x^3}{3!} + O(x^4)$$

$$\cos x = 1 - \frac{x^2}{2!} + O(x^4).$$

Thus

$$(\sin x)(\cos x) = \left(x - \frac{x^3}{6}\right)\left(1 - \frac{x^2}{2}\right) + O(x^4),$$

and in multiplying out the polynomial, we can leave off the term of degree 5.

(f) $1 - x - \dfrac{x^2}{2} + \dfrac{x^3}{2}$.

17. 0.1353 **19.** 2 **21.** 1 **23.** -1 **25.** 1
27. $-\frac{1}{6}$ **29.** $\frac{1}{2}$ **31.** $-\frac{1}{8}$ **33.** (a) 0 (b) 0 (c) 0
35. $-\frac{1}{2}$ **37.** $\dfrac{1}{5!}$ **39.** -1 **41.** $\dfrac{1}{4!}$ **43.** 0 **45.** -1

46. (a) For $0 \leq x \leq 1$, we have

$$\sin x = x - \frac{x^3}{3!} + \frac{x^5}{5!} + R_7(x),$$

where $|R_7(x)| \leq x^7/7!$ Hence

$$\frac{\sin x}{x} = 1 - \frac{x^2}{3!} + \frac{x^4}{5!} + R_7(x)/x,$$

and

$$\int_0^1 \frac{\sin x}{x}\, dx = \left[x - \frac{x^3}{3!3} + \frac{x^5}{5!5}\right]_0^1 + \int_0^1 R_7(x)/x\, dx$$

$$= 1 - \frac{1}{3!3} + \frac{1}{5!5} = 0.946$$

with an error bounded by

$$\int_0^1 \frac{x^6}{7!}\, dx \leq \frac{1}{7!7} \leq \frac{1}{35{,}000}\ .$$

Chapter XV, §2

3. No **4.** Yes **5.** No **6.** No **7.** No **8.** Yes **9.** Yes

Chapter XV, §3

1. Yes **3.** No **5.** No **7.** No **9.** No **11.** No **13.** No **15.** Yes
17. Yes

Chapter XV, §4

3. Yes   **4.** Yes   **5.** Yes   **6.** Yes   **7.** Yes   **8.** Yes   **9.** Yes   **10.** Yes

Chapter XV, §5

1. Yes   **2.** Yes   **3.** Yes   **4.** Yes   **5.** Yes   **6.** Yes   **7.** Yes   **8.** No
9. Yes   **10.** Yes   **11.** Converges, but not absolutely
13. Does not converge; does not converge absolutely
15. Converges, but not absolutely   **17.** Converges, but not absolutely
19. Converges, but not absolutely

Chapter XV, §6

1. 0   **3.** 1   **5.** 1   **7.** 1   **9.** 2   **11.** 1   **13.** $\frac{1}{2}$ **15.** $\frac{1}{4}$ **16.** $1/e$
17. 27   **18.** $4/e^2$ **19.** 0   **20.** 2   **21.** 2   **22.** 3   **23.** 1   **24.** ∞
25. 1   **26.** ∞ **27.** 1   **28.** ∞ **29.** e **30.** ∞

Chapter XVI, §1

1. (a) $-\dfrac{1}{10} - \dfrac{3}{10}i$ (b) 2   (c) $-1 + 3i$ (d) $-1 + 3i$

   (e) $6\pi + (7 + \pi^2)i$ (f) $-2\pi + \pi i$ (g) $-3\sqrt{2} + \sqrt{2}\,\pi i$

   (h) $-8 - 6i$

2. (a) $\dfrac{1}{2} - \dfrac{i}{2}$ (b) $\dfrac{3}{10} - \dfrac{i}{10}$ (c) $\dfrac{3}{5} + \dfrac{4}{5}i$ (d) $\dfrac{2}{5} + \dfrac{1}{5}i$

   (e) $1 - i$ (f) $\dfrac{1}{2} + \dfrac{i}{2}$ (g) $-\dfrac{1}{5} + \dfrac{3}{5}i$ (h) $-\dfrac{1}{2} - \dfrac{i}{2}$

3. $1, \alpha$

Chapter XVI, §2

1. (a) $\sqrt{2}\,e^{i\pi/4}$ (b) $\sqrt{3}\,e^{i(\arctan \sqrt{2})}$ (c) $3e^{i\pi}$ (d) $4e^{i\pi/2}$

   (e) $\sqrt{3}\,e^{-i(\arctan \sqrt{2})}$ (f) $5e^{-i\pi/2}$ (g) $7e^{i\pi}$ (h) $\sqrt{2}\,e^{i5\pi/4}$

2. (a) -1 (b) $-\dfrac{1}{2} + \dfrac{\sqrt{3}}{2}i$ (c) $\dfrac{3}{\sqrt{2}} + \dfrac{3}{\sqrt{2}}i$ (d) $\dfrac{\pi}{2} - \dfrac{\sqrt{3}}{2}\,\pi i$

   (e) $\dfrac{1}{2} + \dfrac{\sqrt{3}}{2}i$ (f) $-i$ (g) -1 (h) $-\dfrac{1}{\sqrt{2}} + \dfrac{1}{\sqrt{2}}i$

4. If $\alpha = re^{i\theta}$, then the n-th roots are

$$r^{1/n}e^{i(\theta + 2\pi k)/n}, \qquad 0 \leqq k \leqq n - 1$$

6. $\sqrt{\dfrac{a + \sqrt{a^2 + b^2}}{2}} + \sqrt{\dfrac{-a + \sqrt{a^2 + b^2}}{2}}\,i$

7. All u such that $u = z + 2n\pi i$, n integer
8. All $z = 2n\pi i$ **11.** (c) 0   **13.** (a) $1 - 3i$ (b) $-6 - 4i$ **14.** Yes

Index

BCDE79876543210

p. 83 ; 17 + 18

P. 92 ;   11, 12, 13.

p 104

have trouble with improper integrals.